THE LORE OF SHIPS

BARNES
& NOBLE
BOOKS
NEW YORK

This edition published by Barnes & Noble, Inc.,
by arrangement with Nordbok International.
1998 Barnes & Noble Books
M10 9 8 7 6 5 4 3 2 1

Printed and bound in Spain 1998

ISBN 0760707081

THE LORE OF SHIPS has been produced through comprehensive international cooperation with nautical experts from many parts of the world. When this work first appeared in 1966 it was an immediate success due to its way of presenting information, and the combination of pictures with texts became a model for publishing facts in book form. It was soon accepted as a standard reference volume in nautical literature, and few in the business either nationally or globally do not know of THE LORE OF SHIPS today.

In 1975 a thorough revision was made, as the field had changed greatly in the previous decade and developments were proceeding rapidly. By then the book had sold over 300,000 copies and many welcomed the improved edition.

Now that the latest revision is complete, little remains of the original work. The historical sections are mostly unaltered, as are all illustrations of old vessels – but the technical aspects have been fully reconsidered and updated. Modern communications technology has created a revolution in seafaring, for example through satellite navigation. Nonetheless it is still of wide interest to know about, and to use, the old sailor's sextant.

Nordbok extends warm thanks to all collaborators in the work with this current edition, notably:
Göran Sundström, former director of the Maritime Museum in Gothenburg.
Captain Rolf Petrén Nilsson, contributor to "The Hull".
Lars-Erik Larsson, ship consultant, contributor to "The Hull".
Monika Andersson, marine engineer, contributor to "Propulsion".
Captain Bertil Johansson, contributor to "Fishing".
Commander Göran Romare, contributor to "Modern Yachting".
Commodore Lars Norrsell, contributor to "Gunnery".
Commander Bengt Ståhl, contributor to "Navigation and Ship-Handling".

Nordbok project editor: Kerstin Orpana Strand
Illustrations: Ulf Söderqvist
Cover and layout: Munir Lotia
Translation: Jon van Leuven

We hope that THE LORE OF SHIPS in this new edition will, as in the past, give readers an unforgettable voyage in space and time through the world of seafaring.

Gothenburg, August 1997
Nordbok International AB
Gunnar Stenmar

THE LORE OF SHIPS

PREFACE

Water has lured the heart of man all of his days — whether it was the silvery line of a river, the gilded sparkle of a lake, or the phosphorescing green glint in an ocean. Angry or calm, fresh or salt, helpful — in giving man his food — or cruel — in bringing him an enemy — the sea makes its presence always known to humans.

Man has depended on it for food, for sport, for transportation. From the moment an ancient man first used the water — perhaps floating down a river holding to a log — when he developed primitive dugout canoes, rafts, barges and sailing ships, liners and tankers, and atomic submarines and surface ships, man has needed the sea. And during this slow, and often painful, evolution, man has tried to conquer the vastness of the oceans. The Lore of Ships illustrates man's fascination with the sea and gives him a chance to satisfy — at least partly — his love of ships and shipping. It is an illustrated book which shows, by means of simplified illustration and detailed drawing, the most important parts of the construction, equipment, and development of all kinds of ships. An explanatory, numbered text allows the reader to follow the diagrams of rigging, sail, engines, spars, fishing, flags — even the weapons used aboard ships through the ages. Each of the chapters begins with a short introduction to the developments that took place in the various subdivisions of nautical history. For example, the first chapter, called "The Hull," explains each part of the evolution of this structure, from its initial appearance covered with animal skin or tree bark to the refined and sophisticated hulls of today's sleek atomic ships. Illustrated details — the basic structure, rudders, steering gears, anchors, and many others — make it easy for the reader to ground himself thoroughly in the lore of the hull.

The technical editors of The Lore of Ships include a curator of a maritime museum, a naval architect, engineers, sea captains, and many more. The book was produced under the expert guidance of captain Sam Svensson, internationally known maritime expert. Dictionary, survey, illustrated book — The Lore of Ships is most of all for the enjoyment of those who would go down to the sea in ships.

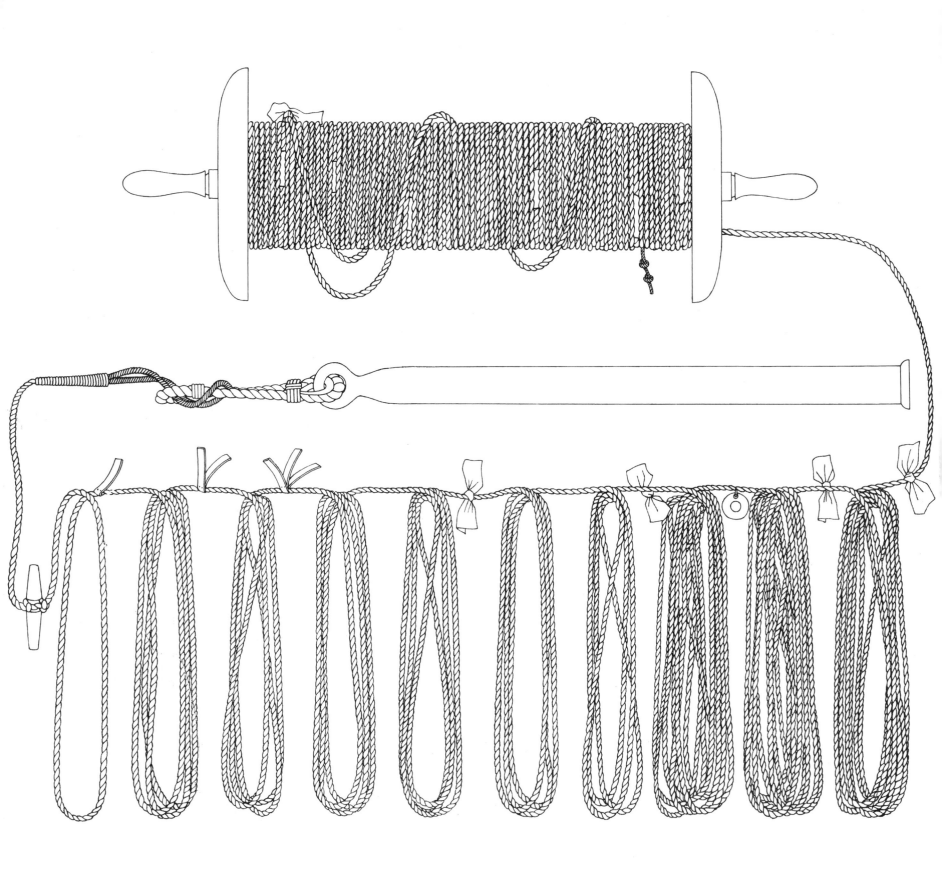

Contents

nd here on the jib-boom I could look at the ship as at
eparate vessel — and there rose up from the water, sup
orted only by the small black hull, a pyramid of canvas
preading out far beyond the hull, and towering up almos
s it seemed in the indistinct night-air, to the clouds. Th
ea was as still as an inland lake; the light trade-wind wa
ently and steadily breathing from astern; the dark blu
ky was studded with the tropical stars: there was no soun
ut the rippling of the water under the stem: and the sail
ere spread out, wide and high; — the two lower studding
ails stretching, on each side, far beyond the deck; the top
ast studding-sails, like wings to the topsails; the top-gal
nt studding-sails spreading fearlessly out above them; sti
igher, the two royal studding-sails, looking like two kite
lying from the same string; and, highest of all, the littl
kysail, the apex of the pyramid, seeming actually to touc
he stars, and to be out of reach of human hand. So quie
oo, was the sea, and so steady the breeze, that if thes
ails had been sculptured marble, they could not hav
een more motionless. Not a ripple upon the surface o
he canvas; not a quivering of the extreme edges of th
ail — so perfectly were they distended by the breeze

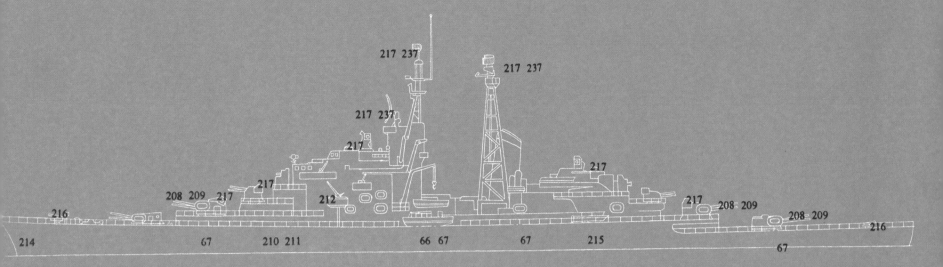

217 237 · 217 237 · 217 237 · 217 · 208 209 217 · 217 · 212 · 217 · 217 · 208 209 · 208 209 · 216 · 216

214 · 67 · 210 211 · 66 67 · 67 · 215 · 67

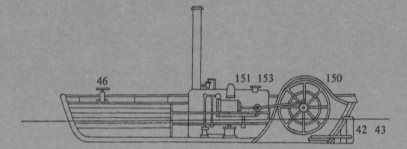

46 · 151 153 · 150 · 42 43

PICTORIAL CONTENTS

THE ILLUSTRATIONS ON THESE PAGES IDEN-
TIFY DETAILS FOR READERS WHO DO NOT
KNOW THE NAMES OF CERTAIN PARTS OF THE
SHIP. NUMBERS REFER TO THE PAGES WHERE
THE DETAILS CAN BE FOUND. IT MUST BE KEPT
IN MIND THAT THIS IS A GENERAL SURVEY
AND NOT EVERY ITEM IS INCLUDED.

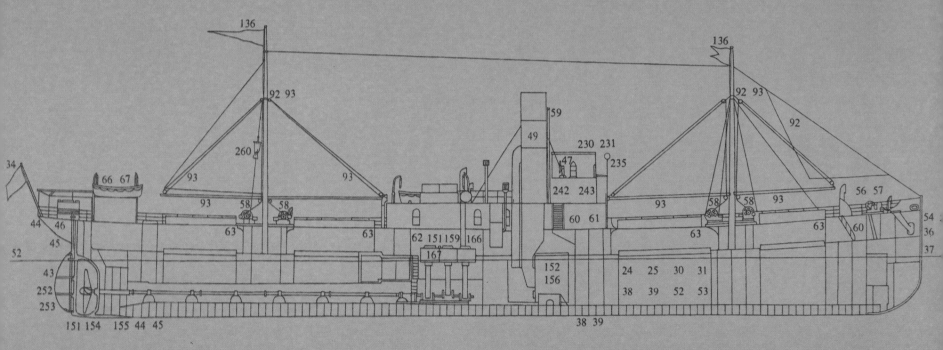

136 · 136 · 92 93 · 92 93 · 92 · 59 · 260 · 49 · 230 231 · 235 · 34 · 47 · 56 57 · 66 67 · 93 · 93 · 242 243 · 93 · 54 · 93 · 58 · 58 · 93 · 58 · 58 · 93 · 36 · 44 46 · 60 61 · 60 · 37 · 45 · 63 · 63 · 63 · 63 · 52 · 62 151159 166 · 24 25 30 31 · 43 · 167 · 152 · 38 39 52 53 · 252 · 156 · 253 · 151 154 · 155 44 45 · 38 39

The text on page 10 is a quotation from one of the classics of nautical literature, Two Years Before The Mast by Richard Henry Dana, who went to sea because his poor health had compelled him to interrupt his law studies. His description of his experience at sea is contained in one of the finest and most authentic books ever written about life on shipboard. The book was first published in 1834.

INTRODUCTION

BY SAM SVENSSON

From ancient times sailing the seas has been a unique profession, with techniques and methods which have always puzzled the landlubber. One thousand years before Christ, Solomon said that the way of a ship in the midst of the sea was too wonderful for him to understand.

In our time there have been radical technical developments. On the seas, ships as well as the life of the sailor has been changed to such a degree that no similarity whatsoever with the olden days exists. This may be why general interest in old nautical things and in the sailing ship in particular has grown to such an extent. People all over the world now want accurate data about the construction, equipment, and handling of old ships.

Long ago, ships were always built of wood, except in the case of even more primitive materials such as reed, skin, and bark; but these materials were only used for the most primitive sailing in narrow seas. Since ancient times ships have been built according to two methods: carvel and clinker. The first method was developed in the eastern Mediterranean countries, where Egyptians, Phoenicians, and others built ships with outside planking ingeniously joined by being placed edge to edge. This art came into general use in Southern Europe, and during the Middle Ages it spread along the coast of Western Europe, reaching the Baltic during the latter part of the 15th century. It then became the dominant way of shipbuilding, and after the middle of the 16th century all large vessels were carvel-built.

During the latter half of the 17th century, however, when shipbuilding had become a science and ships could, theoretically, be constructed in advance, larger and sturdier ships were being built. The pictures on pages 32 and 40 show constructional details of a large 18th-century ship. During the second half of the 19th century, when iron and steel were being used more generally for shipbuilding, fewer wooden ships were being constructed. Yet, these wooden ships were still used chiefly in the United States, where large wooden merchant sailing vessels were built up to the time of the First World War. The four-masted bark *Roanoke*—3,439 gross tons, built in

1892—and the six-masted schooner, *Wyoming*—3,730 tons, built in 1909—indicate the size limits of wood used in constructing ships. In many other places, perhaps mostly in the Eastern Mediterranean and in the Near East, but also in the Baltic, small sailing vessels were built of wood as late as the early years of the 20th century. In addition to carvel-built wooden ships, clinker-built vessels were also being constructed. This method originated in the Baltic where, even during the Viking Age, large clinker-built ships sailed to Iceland and Greenland. In the Middle Ages the clinker-building method was predominant in Northern Europe, and many large ships were constructed. Perhaps one of the largest was Henry IV's ship *Grace Dieu,* built in 1418; she was almost fifty meters long and about twelve meters wide. She had a complicated treble-clinker planking. According to the clinker method, the planking was built first and the frames were inserted afterward. We know this because the wreck of the *Grace Dieu* was discovered near Southampton, and showed that the rivets of the skin were clinched underneath the frames.

Experimental ships of iron were built during the first half of the 19th century, until, gradually, iron came into more general use. After 1850, England had several shipyards which built only iron vessels. The introduction of the steam engine for propulsion also encouraged the use of iron as a shipbuilding material. The first iron ships were built according to the same principles as those used for wooden vessels, but as builders grew more experienced, special methods were adopted for the structure of iron ships. One early change was to provide the iron steamship with a double bottom and internal keel, instead of the former bar keel used in sailing vessels. The keelson was now placed on top of the floors. Longitudinal framing, which slowly came into use around 1900, also deviated from the kind of standard shipbuilding that had been used for a thousand years.

Electric welding, which was used experimentally on a large scale for German pocket battleships built between the two World Wars, has now completely revolutionized all shipbuilding techniques. Many large ships are now built in sections according to highly specialized methods on the principle of the assembly line. As yet we cannot

determine the extent of this development. The most up-to-date shipyards have the facilities to build and equip a ship from the first steps to the point where it is ready for the sea.

The steam engine and later the diesel engine have only been in existence for a very short time in the whole history of navigation. During most of this time, masts and sails were the only means of propulsion on long voyages. For ages, rigging consisted of one mast and one sail only, and it was not until the end of the Middle Ages that mechanical progress made it possible to construct better and more functional rigging. These developments continued for several centuries and reached their high point after the middle of the 19th century, when, due to competition from the steamship, shipyards turned out perfectly sparred and rigged sailing ships.

There have been many important phases in the history of rigging: such as setting a topsail above the original single square sail, using fidded topmasts that could be sent down, the footrope and the jackstay, which together revolutionized the work of handling sails, the introduction of wire, first for the standing rigging and then for the running gear, and, finally, mechanical aids for handling sails in large ships, such as patent sheaves and brace-and-halliard winches. The introduction of the auxiliary engine with a propeller has, on the other hand, nothing to do with the improvement in sailing vessels.

Flags are not only decorative but also useful. Originally, flags come from field banners carried in ancient battles. In comparison with the flags of ancient kings and military commanders, our national flags are of very recent date. The oldest national flag now in use is the Danish flag, according to a legend of 1219, and was probably followed by the Swedish and Dutch flags. Among the flags of world powers, America has the oldest, dating in its present general form of stars and stripes from 1777. The French tricolor is dated 1794; the English flag in its present form is from 1801.

Page 136 shows the flags used by some of the old sailing ship companies. Perhaps Hansan's red-and-white flag of the Middle Ages should come as number one on this list. On page 137 are flags that were used later by steamship companies all over the world.

Once the oar had been invented, there were very early attempts to find some mechanical aid which could move ships in a calm or drive them against a headwind. There was no mechanical power. Thus, it was not until the steam engine was invented and perfected to some degree that steam navigation got under way. The first ships of this type were used for river traffic in the United States, and also for coastal traffic around the British Isles.

Steady improvements in the design of the steam engine contributed to the more widespread use of steam navigation. The engine was given several cylinders and was fitted with a condenser. The boilers had forced draft, superheaters, and oil fueling. Finally, the reciprocal steam engine was replaced by a steam turbine, which is frequently used today in very large ships.

In the years just preceding the First World War, attempts were made to use diesel motors as marine engines. Right from the start they appeared to have certain advantages: they had less weight and required less space for both the engine and the bunker. As the reliability of the diesel increased, more motor-driven ships were used throughout the world. In this respect the Scandinavian countries have been in the lead; for example, Sweden's merchant navy consists almost exclusively of motor-driven ships.

Deep-sea fishing is fun, but it is also an important means of getting food. Of old, deep-sea fishing was always carried out in fishing craft fitted with sails. Well-known examples of such craft are the English fishing smacks on the North Sea banks and the American schooners on the Newfoundland coast. Today, both large and small fishing boats are motor-driven, the catch is well taken care of, and there are some factory ships where the catch is cleaned and prepared and then canned or deep-frozen right on board. The most important methods of fishing are line fishing and fishing where a large net is dragged along the sea bed. Now, floating trawls are also used to catch fish on the surface. These trawls are towed by two

boats, and the method is more effective than the ordinary drift net. Modern fishing vessels are equipped with echo sounders for locating shoals of fish.

Sailing as a sport has an old heritage. Caligula had pleasure boats in Lake Nemi, and the Doge of Venice had a luxurious galley which he used every year in the ceremony of marrying himself to the sea. In ancient times pleasure sailing was a sport reserved for kings and men of rank only. During the 19th century, it began to occupy more industrialists and businessmen, and, gradually, sailing as a sport has reached the widespread popularity of our own time. Today, there are yacht clubs in all countries where there is access to navigable waters. In order to standardize rules for yachting competitions a great many so-called one-design boats which are built according to accurate measurements and regulations so that they will be exactly alike; thus it will be mostly the skill of the helmsman that decides the race. Pages 192 and 193 show many such internationally registered one-design boats. Yacht-racing courses are also decided according to an international standard. Figure C on page 194 shows the fixed track used for all Olympic sailing contests.

As long as man has sailed the ocean, he has struggled for supremacy on the sea. Even in ancient times, a variety of ships were built specifically for war or trade; nevertheless, merchant ships have been used in war and warships in commerce down through the years. As the nations were industrialized, diversity according to function became more noticeable. While today's merchant ships and warships differ in design, there are also various differences in a single category. Warships for both offensive and defensive combat are steadily being altered and improved. Mines, torpedoes, pom-pom guns, and tracer projectiles are standard equipment. Radar and data-processing machines are employed by naval forces; and submarines are fitted with underwater missiles.

It might be said that navigation is the sailor's theory and seamanship his practice. The sounding lead is the sailor's oldest instrument; recognition of the coastline his only way of piloting. In deep waters and when land was out of sight this simple method of navigation was useless. Before the compass was invented, the sailor had to find his way by

observations that would indicate a definite direction: the movement of the sun and stars, the direction of the wind and how the clouds were drifting, changes in ocean swell, the flight of birds and how the fish swam. On a long voyage not even the compass was a suffcient guide, so that such trips could not be undertaken until astronomic navigation had been discovered. Even then, for hundreds of years the only means by which a sailor could measure the sun's meridian height was with a simple instrument which determined latitude. The ability to make longitudinal calculations came at a much later date. For that purpose the navigator required Hadley's octant or a sextant, as well as a chronometer and complete nautical tables, or if there were no chronometer, he had to be able to calculate the longitude by means of lunar distances. As in other fields, electronics now does most of the work formerly done by astronomic navigation.

Previously, seamanship could be defined as the care and handling of sailing ships. Page 250 illustrates a portion of this almost forgotten art: how a brig can be put to sea against the wind by backing and filling downriver. Today, a vessel is guided by means of the rudder and the screw. To maneuver a large power-driven vessel properly differs vastly from the skillful handling of a large sailing ship. The art of guiding a power-driven vessel has been mastered by many of today's seamen, but skill in sailing is rarely to be found. *The Lore of ships* has tried to recover some small part of this forgotten art.

The first chapter of
The Lore of Ships
deals with the hull and
some of its more
important details. The
next page shows a
sketch of Columbus'
ship, the SANTA MARIA.

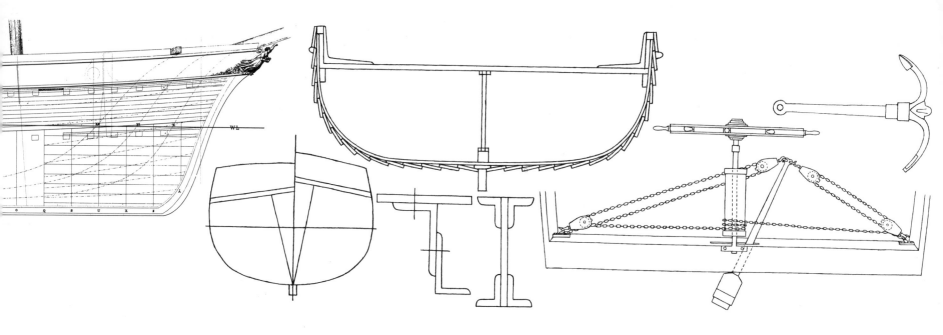

THE HULL

BY WILLIAM A. BAKER

Throughout history, the many shapes of hulls have been dictated by the methods of construction and propulsion, conditions of use and fashion, and sheer whim. Primitive craft ranged from round shapes – woven baskets, skin-covered framework, and even pottery – to the long and narrow forms of reed bundles and hewn logs. Very early, the Egyptians built flat-bottomed wooden vessels, resembling their rush boats, by "sewing" planks together. Other ancient peoples learned to improve the hollow-log rowboat, making it wider and higher with one or more wooden planks on each side. Ship hulls were modelled after such canoes for centuries.

Those two types, the bulky "round" cargo carrier and the fast "long" ship, have undergone a parallel development. Shipbuilding history is mainly concerned with rowed and sailed wooden vessels, as mechanically propelled metal ships have existed only recently, during a mere 2% of the age of seafaring.

Two basic techniques have been used to build wooden ships: the "shell" method and the "skeleton" ("frame") method. Combinations of these are documented back to the 7th century A.D. With the shell method, planks are fastened together before adding the inner supports, or frame, which must be shaped to fit the joined planks. With the skeleton method, a framework (carcass) is erected and the planks are attached to cover it; here the planking follows the framework's shape. The former, and older, technique has gradually given way to the latter, probably because this is stronger and allows the hull to be shaped more securely. The first reference to the frame technique is seemingly an early 14th-century painting of Italian shipbuilders at work.

Ship design was initially influenced by the kinds of tools available. North European builders used an adze to shape one plank from each half of a felled tree. These planks were overlapped at the edges and fastened by lacings, or later by metal rivets – the "clinker" planking of our day. Then the frame was inserted and lashed to lugs that had been left on the planks when shaped.

Experts do not agree on the origin of the Viking ship. Some trace its origin to the built-up log canoe; others think that it developed from skin boats, when thin planks replaced the

sewn skins on a flexible framework. The famous Gokstad ship, about 900 A.D. (page 26), is a late example of tied-on planking. Only the lower eight planks are lashed to the frame with ropes; the remainder are nailed.

Ancient Egyptian shipbuilders were plagued by a shortage of suitable wood. Where a modern builder glues small wood pieces into the required shapes and sizes, the Egyptian had to develop ingenious dowels and keys to hold together his short planks of acacia wood. His ship was essentially identical at both ends, with arc-shaped midsections. It had only a thicker plank strake instead of a structural keel. Heavy rope trusses, fitted from bow to stern, assisted in keeping these weak ships from sagging at the ends. Similar vessels existed early in Northern Europe, but their lengthwise planking and edge-set keel provided enough strength without special trussing.

Sources indicate that Phoenician, Greek and Roman ships were also basically double-enders and that their builders, who used the shell technique, had a sound knowledge of structure. Reports of numerous Roman warships built during very short periods – 220 in three months of the year 254 – imply that templates of some kind were employed for mass production. Roman vessels were of three types: chubby sailing merchantmen, stout war galleys with rams on their prows, and light speedy galleys for personal transport.

From Roman times to about 1200 A.D., there was little change in South European ships. Merchant hulls remained the same as the Roman double-ender with a rather full stern and steering oars, but as a rule with lower ends. Deck beams, secured to a heavy wale, protruded through the carvel (smooth edge-to-edge) planking, and "castles", separate from the hull, were fixed prominently on bow and stern – the square work of house carpenters contrasting with the curved work of the shipwrights. An important change, which was to influence hull design, occurred when the Roman square rig was replaced by the two- or three-masted lateen rig.

From 1095, the time of the First Crusade, the features of Northern and Southern "round" ships began to be mingled. Superstructures were added in the North, along with other details, while Southern shipbuilders adopted the stern rudder and returned to the square rig. The standard type which

resulted, commonly called the cog, was used from the Mediterranean to the Baltic until the early 1400s. The cog's hull was still basically double-ended. Its stem was raked forward and usually strongly curved; the slightly raked sternpost was straight in order to take the rudder. The forecastle was triangular in plan, projecting over the bow, but its after end was partially faired into the hull. The after castle remained an angular house.

Northern cogs were clinker-built, with decks supported generally inside the hull, whereas Southern cogs had carvel planking. In both versions, the ship's sides were bound together by deck beams going out through the planking, and the rig was a single mast with a square sail. The latter was apparently first altered by adding a mizzen sail to improve the steering balance. How Northern cogs looked was nicely illustrated by the discovery in 1962 of a well-preserved 14th-century cog in the Weser River at Bremen.

Western ship historians, who chiefly focus on the Mediterranean, tend to ignore Chinese seafaring – the foremost in the world between 700 and 1500 A.D., especially across the oceans. During the 14th and 15th centuries, voyages to the African coast were made by Chinese ships over 70 meters long, with four masts and hundreds of crewmen. The Chinese probably sailed westward around the Cape of Good Hope and into the South Atlantic before 1459, nearly 20 years before the Portuguese rounded the cape toward the Orient.

Although the origins of Chinese vessels are unknown, it is assumed that shipbuilding techniques were brought to China by colonists from the West. Even today, boats on the Yangtze River closely resemble Egyptian ones of 1600 B.C. A Chinese treatise in 1119 compared the shape of large ship hulls to that of rectangular grain-measures with sloping sides, and described a plaited sail that swung round its mast like a door on hinges. Marco Polo's account of Chinese vessels in the late 1200s is familiar, but some reports about them had doubtless reached Europe earlier through Arab traders. Chinese designers were far more advanced than their Western counterparts. They used watertight bulkheads and balance rudders as early as 100 B.C., and lee boards in the mid-700s. However, at the end of the 15th century, official Chinese marine activities were reduced to the minimum necessary for protecting coastal traffic. Several types of ship that were developed in China by that time have seemingly stayed the same ever since, while others have changed due to foreign influence.

European seagoing ships grew larger during the 15th century, and Northern builders began to realize that there was a limit to the size of effective clinker-built ships. The biggest vessel of this kind, "Grace Dieu", was launched in England in 1418 and proved a failure; she sailed only from Southampton to an estuary where she was struck by lightning and burned in 1439. Projecting beams, difficult to keep watertight, were abandoned in Southern ships. In general, the European ship combined a number of features: smooth planking on heavy framing and inside-supported decks. It is almost impossible to describe all the types of such ships fully, but some were the galleass and galliot, deriving from oared craft, and the caravel, galleon and carrack – pure sailing vessels.

During the 15th and 16th centuries, the appearance of the European ship's hull above water changed considerably. Castles remained large but lost their angular look and were merged into the main hull. Around 1550 large ships adopted a square stern that gave better support to the superstructure. About the same time, the forecastle lost its triangular shape and formed a beakhead below the bowsprit. The galleon, relatively low and elongated, was the major ship type for the next 75-100 years.

Methods of framing were greatly altered in the 17th century. Until then, each single frame was normally made from several naturally curved pieces of wood, scarfed together. But such joints were weak. The lowest pieces were nearly square and were spaced along the keel, separated by about their own thickness. The frame's parts were held in place by the inner and outer planking. In the early 18th century, builders began to make the frame as a homogeneous unit with fixed, overlapping joints. This is essentially the pattern of framing still used in large wooden ships.

The roughly semicircular shape of the original log canoes and the oldest vessels gave poor stability. Shipbuilders learned to increase stability by making the round hull flat-bottomed, and this principle was applied to the midsection of all vessels until the early 18th century. The Viking ship's unique V-shaped section was only a local feature in Scandinavia.

The oldest preserved treatises and plans of shipbuilding date from the early 1400s. Written in Italian, they described Mediterranean methods with a long tradition of hull design using arcs of circles. Later works from other countries are more thorough and show that ship proportions and parts were defined in terms of keel length or breadth. Vessels for fast sailing differed in relation to length to breadth, rather than in the shape of the sections. What were perhaps the first systematic experiments in ship hydrodynamics took place in England about 1670. Among other scientific studies, the first treatise on stability was published in France in 1746. Yet during this period there was little real progress in improving the form of ships.

In the 18th century many legal and extra-legal businesses required the use of small fast-sailing vessels, notably those built in Bermuda and the Chesapeake Bay area. Thus "Virginia-built" and "Virginia model" became almost synonymous with speed. Later on, this type was known as the Baltimore clipper. Its design returned to the Viking ship's V-shaped bottom, a "rising floor" which was gradually adopted for large ships wherever speed had more importance than carrying capacity.

The Baltimore clipper was also adapted for the East India and China trade, where sailing ability in light winds mattered more than space for bulky cargos. The large, extreme clipper lasted as a type from about 1845 to 1860, and was developed out of a rising fashion for speed and publicity. Successful clippers were built with both flat and rising floors, but few had the hollow water lines popularly associated with this type, the average being more like those shown on pages 22-23. The speeds of clipper ships owed much to the driving made possible by their size. Yet economic necessity finally forced a return to the best of the transatlantic packet ships, which were nearly as fast and could carry more cargo.

Around 1600 elaborate stern and quarter galleries, side carvings, and sizeable figureheads were introduced to decorate large merchantmen and warships. By 1800 these were reduced to some stern windows, small quarter galleries, and relatively simple head structures. During the same two centuries, superstructures shrank until even the forecastle and poop were hidden by a continuous sheer line.

The advent of steam propulsion brought new problems to the shipbuilder: the weight of machinery and the strains induced by paddle-wheels or screw propellers. Until around 1870 ocean-going steamships followed the form and construction of the sailing ship; and they continued to carry large sailing rigs until steam propulsion became more reliable.

By the mid-19th century, further hydrodynamic experiments, as well as experience with steam, had revealed that fine lines were necessary for speed. A sailing ship could increase sail in order to overcome poor lines, but early steam machinery had limited power. Although iron parts had been used on wooden ships as far back as 1675, commercial iron shipbuilding did not start until the 1830s. Early practice was to have an iron part similar to every wooden part, as shown on page 30. Many shipowners were prejudiced against iron, so its full adoption was preceded by the phase of the composite ship, with wood planking and decking on iron frames.

As builders gained experience, they found that the longitudinal material could be distributed better. Wooden ships had reflected the theory that the keel was the backbone and provided most of the strength. But it was soon realized that a metal ship should be built with as much strength in the deck as in the bottom. This, of course, is modern shipbuilding practice. Steel began to replace iron around 1870 and is now the leading material in all large ships.

Today, special nickel-steel alloys are used to build storage tanks on ships that carry liquid gas. Lightweight metals, chiefly aluminum, make up large ship superstructures and smaller hulls. The use of iron and steel in shipbuilding has provided designers and builders with vast possibilities. Almost any conceivable shape can be obtained, and the introduction of electric welding in the 1930s eliminated many of the joint problems associated with riveting. Large sections of ships, prefabricated in special workshops and wharfs, are now assembled on the building ways with the help of cranes.

Modern ship forms are the result of countless tests in both model size and full scale. Today a model is usually tested for each new design. The growing size of bulk carriers for ore and oil has enabled them to be built with a nearly square hull shape, since the relation between ship length and top speed becomes irrelevant at such sizes. Several recent bulk carriers have replaced the once-universal bulb bow with the cylinder bow, a vertical half-cylinder about half as wide as the ship.

Mixed cargos in ships have mostly given way to unit loading. Previously goods were loaded by the sack, or pallet, into the ship. Nowadays the cargo is collected in, or on, carriers such as containers and platforms, which are then lifted into a container ship. Smaller vessels of this kind are called feeder ships. These transfer goods from minor harbors to the central ones, where they are loaded onto big liners for global transport. The largest container ships have a cargo capacity amounting to over 6,000 containers of the standard length 20 feet.

A "ro/ro" (roll on/roll off) ship is another type with unit-loaded goods. The carriers are pulled onto and off it via ramps. Instead of holds, the ship has several cargo decks, connected internally by ramps or elevators. For short-distance transport, trailer trucks are common carriers. Trailers sometimes are pulled aboard by their own tractors, whose drivers often stay on the ship. But frequently a trailer is driven only to the harbor by a tractor, then left and pulled aboard by a harbor truck, to be met by a new tractor at the destination harbor.

Special vessels include diverse types of half-immersed and fully immersed ships, with most or all of the hull under the waterline. Examples of the former are oil-drilling ships. High-speed vessels are becoming ever more important, particularly for personal transport. New concepts of cargo transport, or combinations of freight and personal transport, are in various stages of development. Multi-hull ships, catamarans and trimarans, have found applications where great width and stability are needed – their main material being aluminum due to its light weight. Hydrofoil boats are used all over the world for rapid passenger transport and naval vessels. Hovercrafts serve as both ferries and freighters.

Synthetic resin materials and glassfibre-reinforced plastics are further kinds of materials which, today, are customarily used to build pleasure boats, small commercial vessels, and certain warships such as minesweepers.

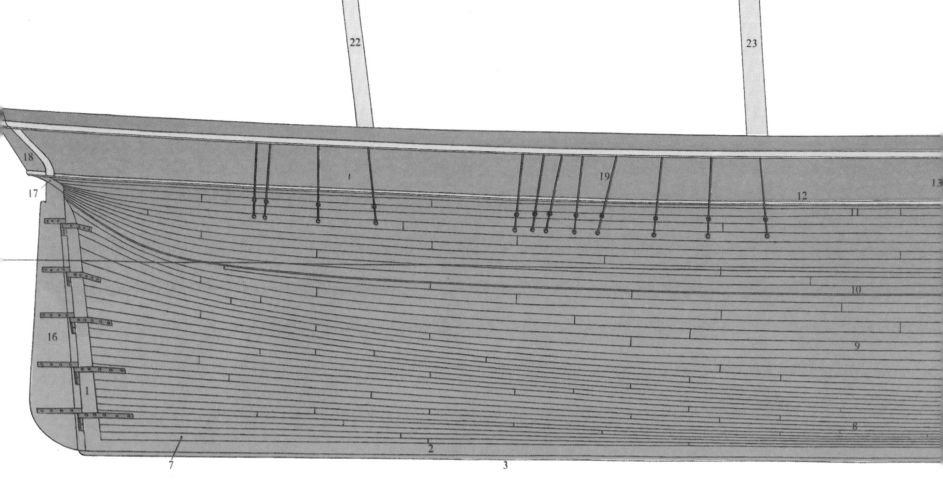

PROFILE OF A WOODEN SAILING SHIP, 1864.

This semi-clipper ship was constructed in 1862 by Niels Kierkegaard, naval architect and Master Shipwright at the Old Shipyard in Gothenburg. In 1864 he published a handbook on naval architecture which contained drawings of eighteen different ships, including this one. His example was followed by shipbuilders all over Scandinavia. The ship shown here has concave bows with narrow waterlines and a lean run under the transom counter and surmounting square stern. She was rigged as a bark, as indicated by the three shrouds and single backstay in the mizzen rigging and shown by the chain plates. All the chain plates are bolted flat to the side of the ship without any channels. They go through the main rail, so the deadeyes will be located inside the topgallant bulwark. The fore and main rigging has four lower shrouds, two topmast backstays, one topgallant backstay, and one royal backstay, as indicated by the chain plates. This same ship is shown on the next two pages.

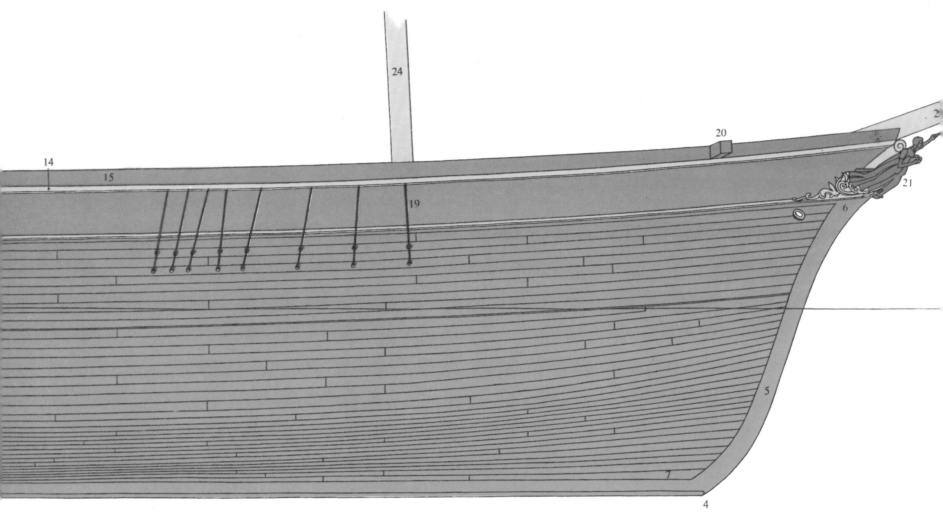

PROFILE OF A WOODEN SAILING SHIP, 1864

1 Sternpost	6 Headpiece	11 Sheer strake	16 Rudder	21 Figurehead
2 Keel	7 Garboard strake	12 Covering board	17 Counter	22 Mizzenmast
3 False keel or shoe	8 Bottom planking	13 Bulwark	18 Stern	23 Mainmast
4 Fore foot, gripe	9 Side planking	14 Rough-tree rail	19 Chain plates	24 Foremast
5 Stem	10 Wale	15 Topgallant bulwark	20 Cathead	25 Bowsprit

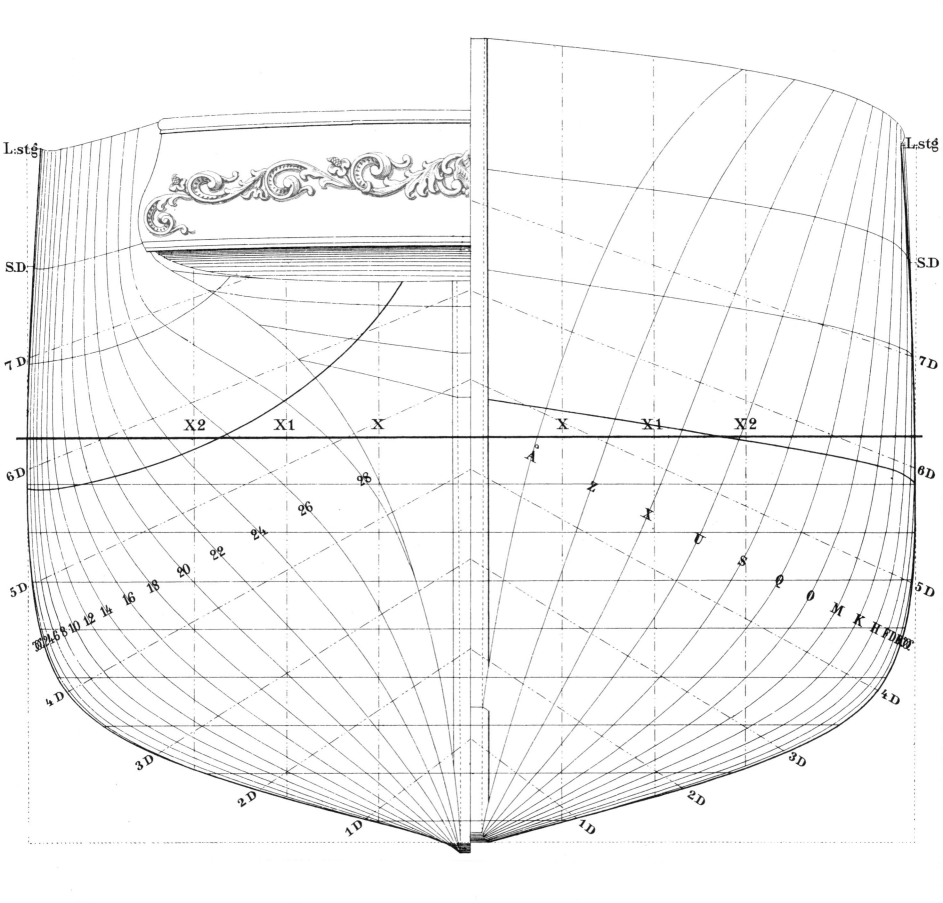

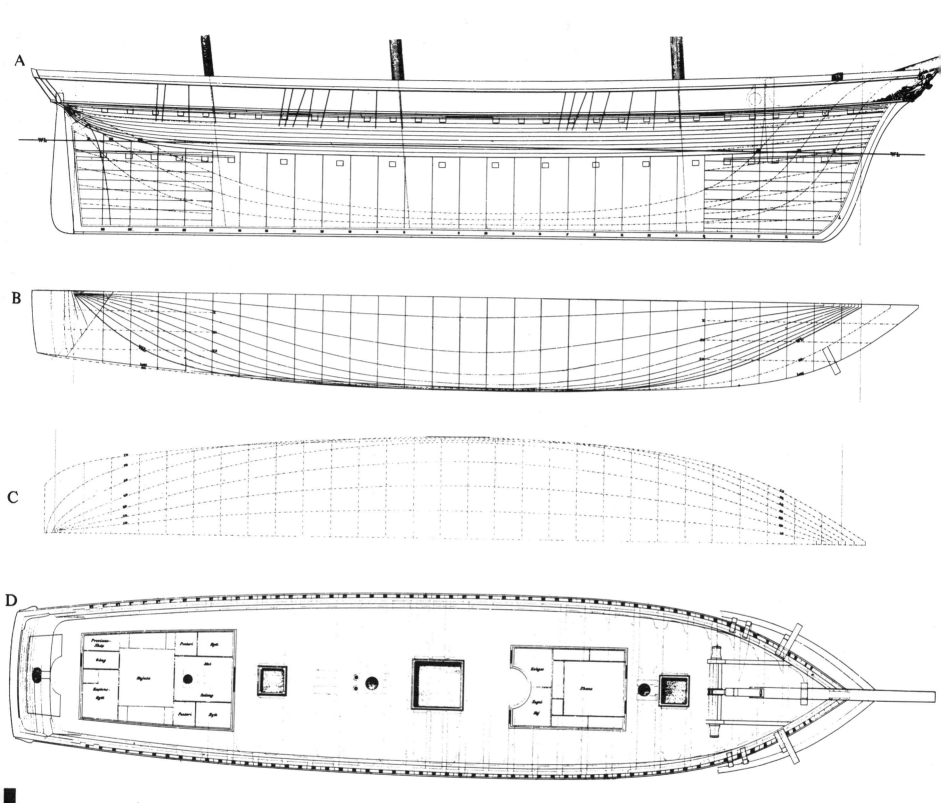

LINES OF A WOODEN SAILING SHIP OF 500 TONS DWT, 1864

The shape of the hull is determined by three sets of planes drawn at right angles to each other. Horizontal planes are called water lines, where they intersect the hull. They are shown as straight lines in A and as curves in B. WL indicates the load water line. Vertical planes going fore and aft and parallel to the longitudinal middle-line plane are called buttocks. Their intersections with the ship's hull are shown in A as curved lines, marked X, XI, and X2. Vertical planes going across the hull show the curves of the sides of the ship's transverse frame lines. Their shape is given in the body plan on page 22, which shows an end view of the hull. The frame lines are numbered in the afterbody and lettered in the forebody. The body plan also gives the diagonal lines extending from the middle-line plane. The diagonal intersections with the surface of the hull are drawn on page 23 in C. 23. D above gives the deck plan: three hatches, a fo'c'sle for 10 sailors, galley, and sail locker in the deckhouse, while the cabinhouse holds the captain's cabin, the mates' rooms, saloon, messroom, and pantries. The little house furthest aft holds the lamp locker and the officers' lavatory.

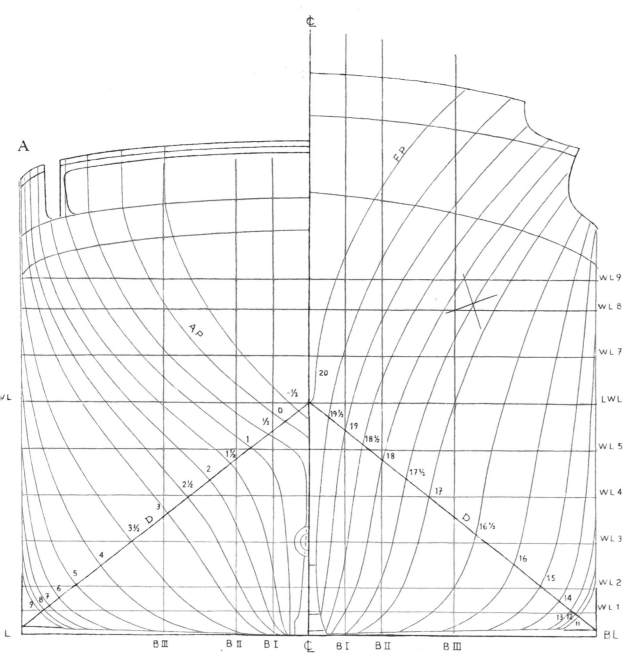

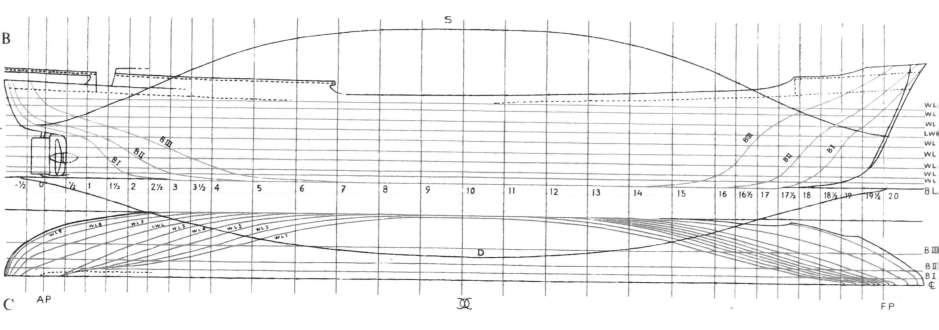

THE LINES OF A SHIP

A *Body Plan*
B *Sheer Plan*
C *Half Breadth Plan*

The shape of a ship is fully determined by three different systems of planes intersecting the molded surface of a ship's hull and drawn at right angles to each other.

Vertical sections going athwartship give the shape of the frames, as shown in red on the body plan. They are numbered from the sternpost forward. The distance between the first and last gives the length of the ship on her load water line, which equals the length between perpendiculars.

Sections drawn horizontally are called water lines, and are seen in brown on the half breadth plan, C. They are numbered from the bottom of the ship, which is the Base Line. One water line corresponds with the calculated Load Water Line, which is water line number six in this drawing. Vertical sections going fore and aft parallel with the middle line are called buttocks. They are shown in their true form as light brown lines on the sheer plan. They are marked in Roman numerals.

Besides all these lines, the shape of the hull is controlled by diagonal sec-tions; only one is shown on the body plan. Such diagonal planes intersect the shell plating nearly at right angles, and, thus indicate any unfairness that may exist in the molded shape of the hull. The laid off diagonals are shown below the base line in the sheer plan.

The drawing gives one more curve, marked S, using the load water line in the sheer plan as a datum. This curve represents the displacement of the ship. The area of each section below the load water line is represented by a proportional vertical line set off at the corresponding station. Thus the area within the curved line represents the volume of the submerged part of the ship's hull, i.e., her displacement. On the drawings are:

AP	After perpendicular
BL	Base line
CL	Center line
FP	Forward perpendicular
LWL	Load water line
D	Diagonal
S	Curve of areas (displacement curve)
0—20	Numbers of sections
WL 1— WL 9	Water lines
BI—B III	Buttock lines

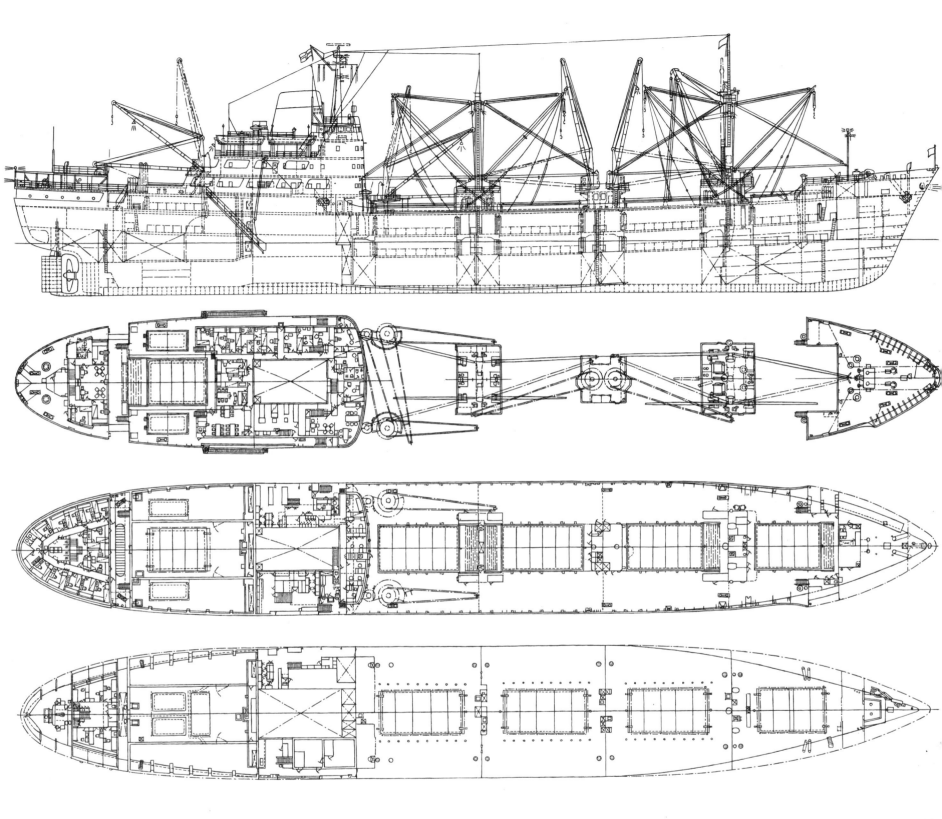

Shelter-decked ship of 8,200 tons dwt, built by Götaverken, 1961. Class: Lloyd's Register + 100 A 1. Ice class: 3

Dimensions

Length over all: 471'—7⅝"
Length between p.p. as per class: 430'—3"
Breadth molded: 65'—0"

Depth molded to shelter deck, 39'—0"
Depth molded to main deck, 29'—0"
Draft on summer freeboard: 26'—1½"

Machinery:

One six-cylinder, supercharged diesel engine
Two cycle single-acting: 8,950 IHP
Diameter of cylinder: 29.92"

Length of stroke: 59.06"
Revolutions per minute: 112
Diameter of propeller: 16'—10¾"
Pitch of propeller variable: 17'—2½"

The top drawing gives the general appearance of the ship, with principal layout details of the hull. The ship is of the shelter-deck type with fo'c'sle, bridge, and poop. The bridge is separated from the poop by only a narrow well, where the tonnage opening is placed. The ship has five cargo holds, and the number 5 hold is divided into several rooms for chilled cargo. For handling cargo there are four booms and a heavy lift boom at the foremast, two deck cranes between hatches 2 and 3, two samson posts with four booms between hatches 3 and 4, two deck cranes in front of the bridge, and another two cranes for number 5 hold.

Below the profile are three plans of the different decks. The first gives the fo'c'sle head, top of deckhouses, bridge deck, and poop deck. The middle plan shows the shelter deck with the space below the fo'c'sle head, bridge deck, and poop deck. The third plan is the main deck.

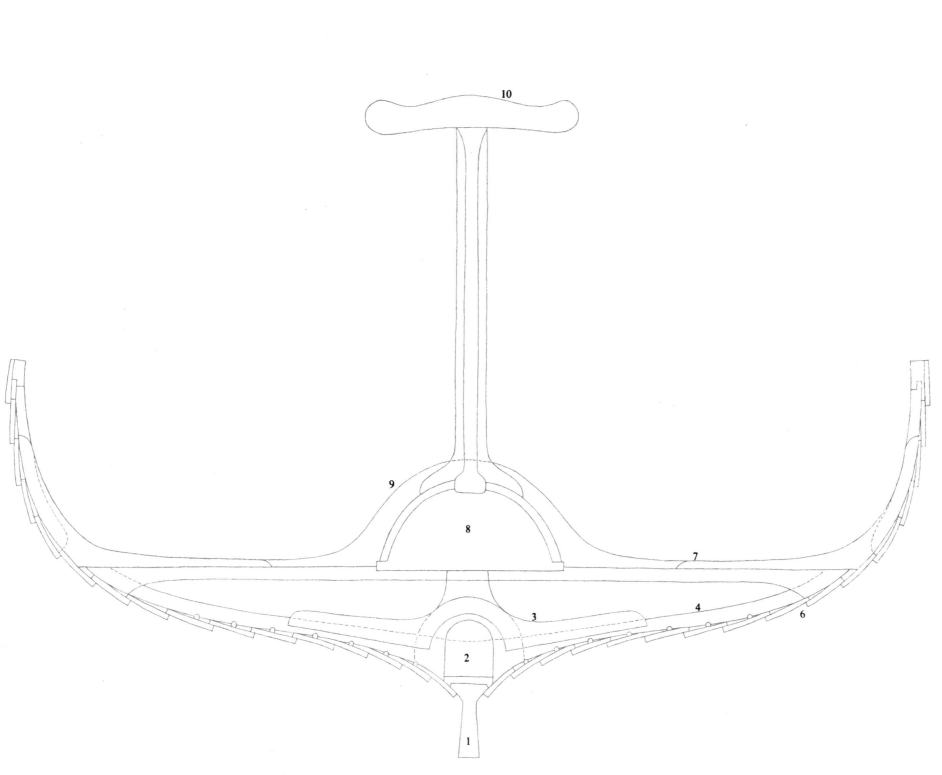

MIDSHIP SECTION OF A VIKING SHIP, MIDDLE OF 9TH CENTURY

(After the Gokstad ship). The ship is clinker-built from oak, with 16 boards on each side, and has a large keelson, and a deep keel for sailing. The lower eight boards are tied to the ribs through cleats that are left on each board-plank. The rest of the boards are nailed. The ship is undecked, but has a flat floor, on top of which a *very heavy mast partner runs over six of the beams. The high gallows make it possible to erect a large tent on board. There are no rowing-benches. The oarsmen probably sat on loose benches or sea-chests.*

1 Keel
2 Keelson
3 Floors
4 Futtocks
5 Toptimber
6 Clinker-built skin
7 Flooring
8 Mast partners
9 Riders to keep mast partners in place
10 Gallows

Page 27: MIDSHIP SECTION OF TWO DIFFERENT SHIPS, SECOND HALF OF THE 19TH CENTURY

A *Wooden ship*
1 Keel
2 Garboard strake
3 Bottom planking
4 Bends or wales
5 Topside planking
6 Sheer strake
7 Floor
8 2nd futtock
9 4th futtock
10 Long toptimber
11 Limbers, water course
12 Keelson

13 Limber board
14 Limber strake
15 Floor ceiling
16 Thick strakes of ceiling
17 Air courses
18 Lower deck hanging knee
19 Lower deck shelf
20 Lower deck clamp
21 Hold stanchion

22 Lower deck beam
23 Lower deck, lower deck planking
24 Lower deck waterway
25 Lower deck spirketing
26 Tween deck ceiling
27 Upper deck hanging knee
28 Upper deck shelf
29 Upper deck clamp
30 Tween deck stanchion

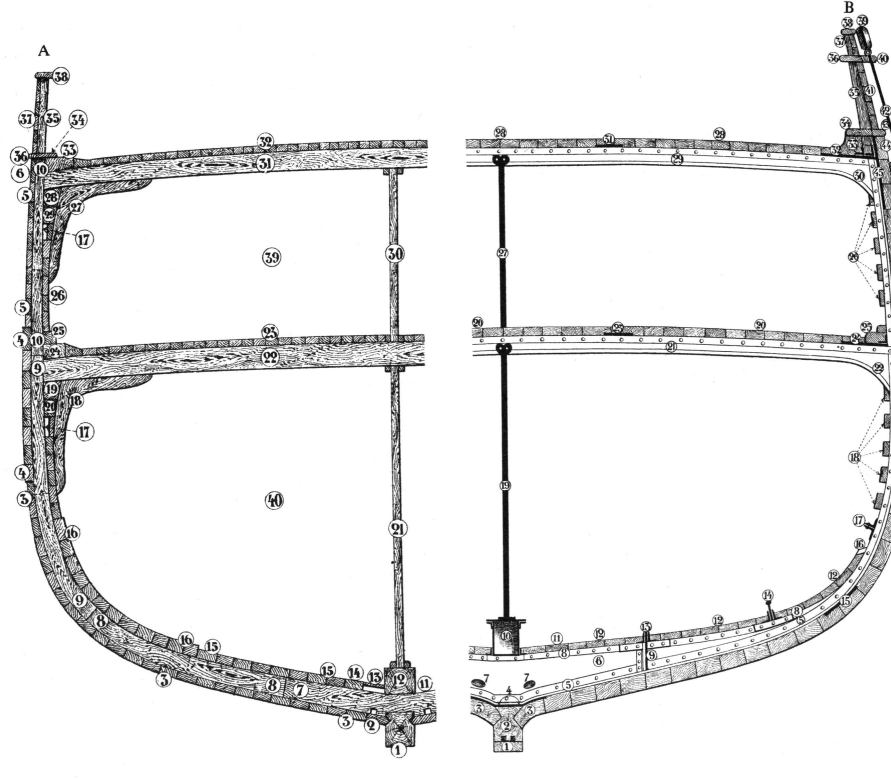

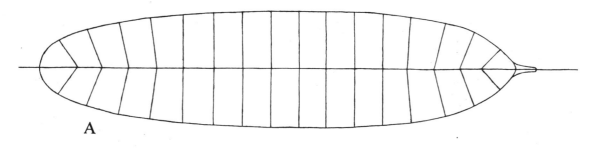

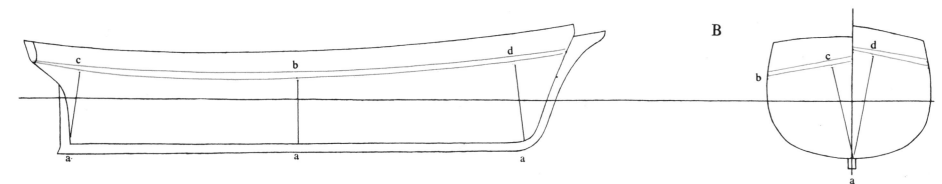

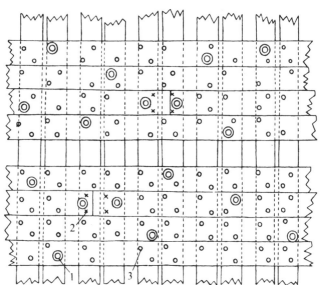

SOME CONSTRUCTION DETAILS OF WOODEN SHIPS, 19TH CENTURY

A *The timbers were plac-
ed at right angles to
the keel, except at the
ends, both fore and aft,
where they were placed
at right angles to the
ship's side. These frames
were called cant tim-
bers.*

B *To make the plank
strakes run fair, fore
and aft, the midship
bend (ab) was divided
into the same number
of planks as the frames
(ac) and as at the ends
of the ship (ad)*

C *At the ends of the ship,
if the planks were too
wide, stealers (a) were
put in between them; if
too narrow, they were
formed as joggle planks
(b)*

D *Below the water line
tree nails (trunnels) and
bolts were used to fast-
en the planking to the
frames in addition to
two bolts and one tree nail
in each plank butt*

1 Tree nail
2 Bolt
3 Nail

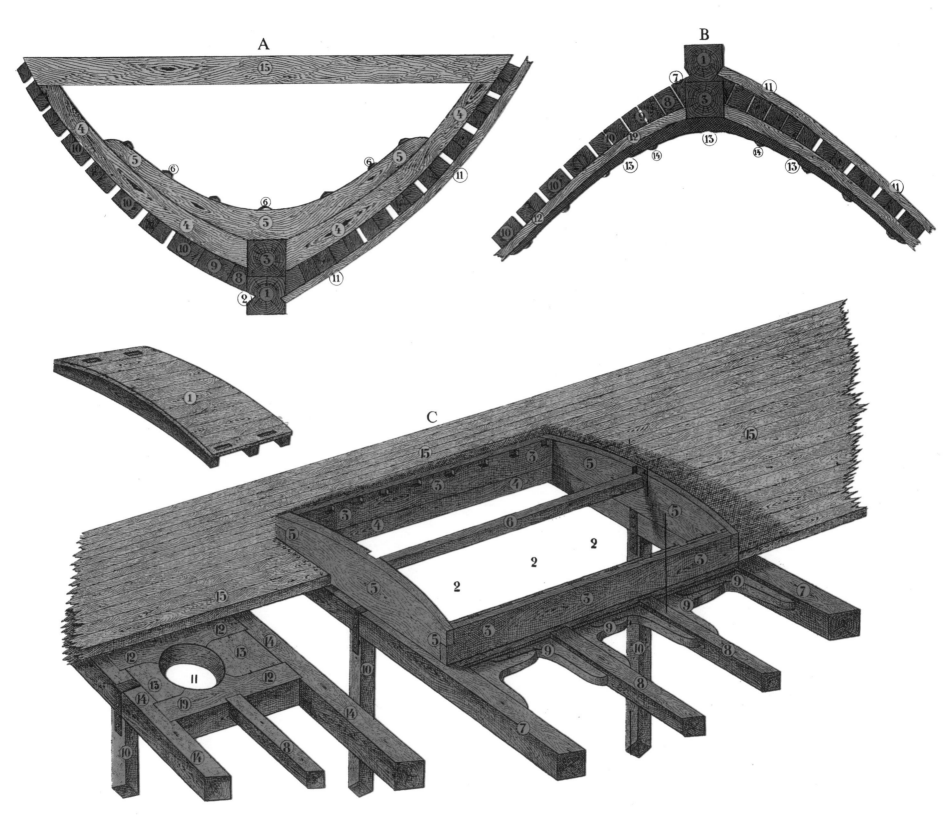

DETAILS OF A WOODEN VESSEL (FROM PAASCH)

A, B
*Horizontal section of
bow*
1 Stem
2 Stem rabbet
3 Apron

4 Eking
5 Deck hook
6 Deck hook bolts
7 Stem piece
8 Knight head
9 Hawse timbers
10 Fore cant timbers

11 Outside plank
12 Ceiling plank
13 Breast hook
14 Breast hook bolts
15 Deck beam

C *Deck and hatchway*
1 Hatch cover
2 Hatchway
3 Hatchway coamings
4 Hatchway carling

5 Head ledges
6 Fore and after
7 Hatch end beams
8 Half beams
9 Lodging knees
10 Deck stanchions
11 Mast hole

12 Mast carlings
13 Chocks
*(12 and 13 forming
mast partners)*
14 Mast beams
15 Deck planking

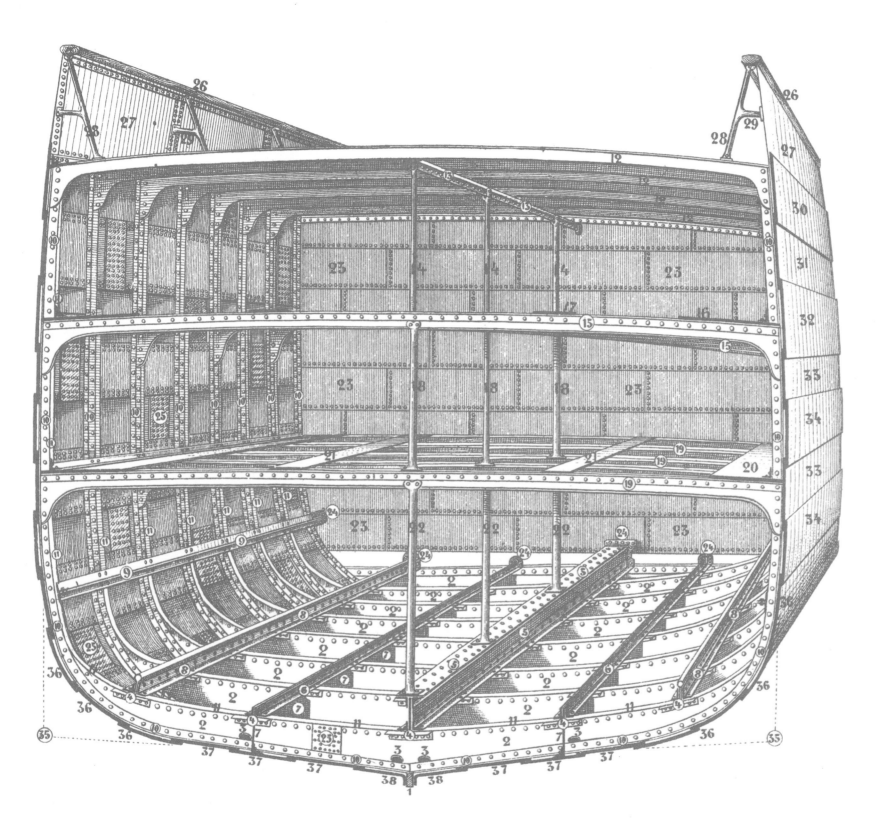

INSIDE VIEW OF A RIVETED IRON OR STEEL SHIP WITH SINGLE BOTTOM

 1 Keel
 2 Floors
 3 Limber holes
 4 Clips
 5 Center line keelson
 6 Side keelson
 7 Intercostal keelson, side intercostal keelson
 8 Bilge keelson
 9 Bilge stringer
10 Frames
11 Reverse frames
12 Upper deck beams
13 Center line deck stringer or girder
14 Upper deck pillars or stanchions
15 Main deck beams
16 Main deck stringer plate
17 Main deck tie plate
18 Main deck pillars or stanchions
19 Lower deck beams
20 Lower deck stringer plate
21 Lower deck tie plate
22 Hold pillars or stanchions
23 Bulkhead
24 Collars
25 Butt straps
26 Main rail cap or bulwark cap
27 Bulwark plating
28 Bulwark stays
29 Spurs (of bulwark stays)
30 Upper sheer strake
31 Topside strake
32 Main sheer strake
33 Side plating (inside strakes)
34 Side plating (outside strakes)
35 Bilge
36 Bilge strakes
37 Bottom plating
38 Garboard strakes

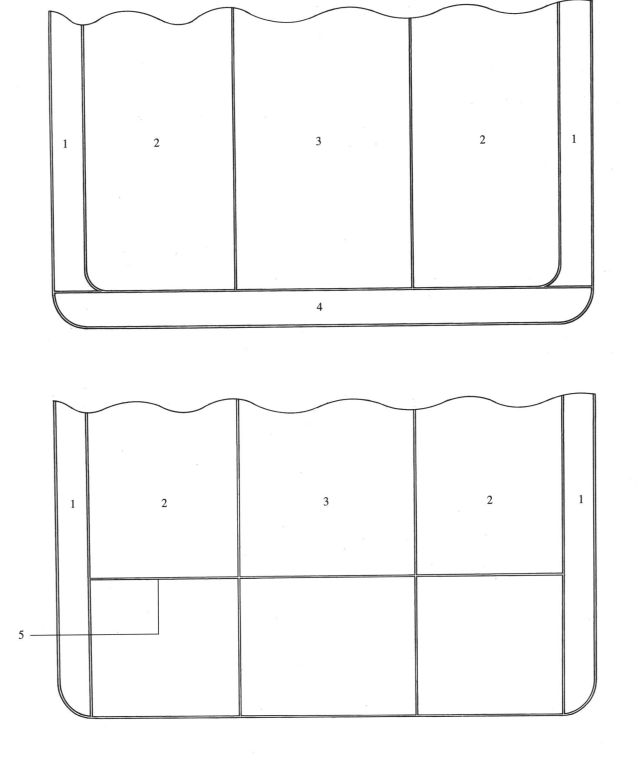

DOUBLE HULL AND BOTTOM

According to the MARPOL Convention, all vessels delivered from July 6, 1996 onward must be built with good protection from oil leakage in event of collisions or grounding. All ships of dead weight 600–5,000 tons must have a double bottom. Ships of dead weight 5,000 tons or more, in addition to a double bottom or equivalent protection, must have a double hull.

1 Double hull. The space in between is used only for water ballast
2 Side tank (for load)
3 Center tank (for load)
4 Double bottom. Space only for water ballast
5 The double bottom can be replaced by decks dividing the load tanks, so that the hydrostatic pressure of the load in their lower parts is less than the water pressure outside the hull. Thus if the hull is ruptured by grounding, water will be forced in and the oil is pushed up in the load pipes instead of running out into the sea

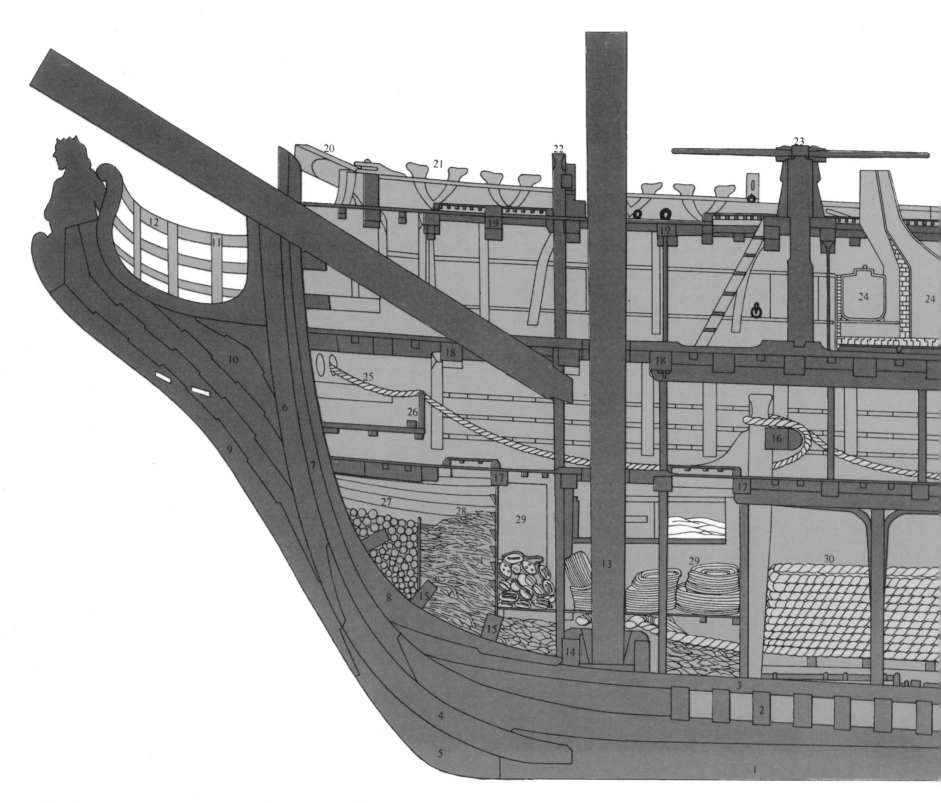

LONGITUDINAL SECTION OF THE FOREBODY OF A 40-GUN FRIGATE, 1768

1	Keel	6	Stem	11	Head timbers	16	Bitts	21	Kevels	26	Mangerboard
2	Floors	7	Apron	12	Head rails	17	Orlop deck beams	22	Topsail sheet bitt	27	Shotlocker
3	Keelson	8	Stemson	13	Foremast	18	Gun deck beams	23	Jeer capstan	28	Galley wood
4	Forefoot	9	Bobstay piece	14	Mast step	19	Upper deck beams	24	Galley	29	Bosun's stores
5	Gripe	10	Filling chocks	15	Breast hooks	20	Cathead	25	Cable	30	Cable tier

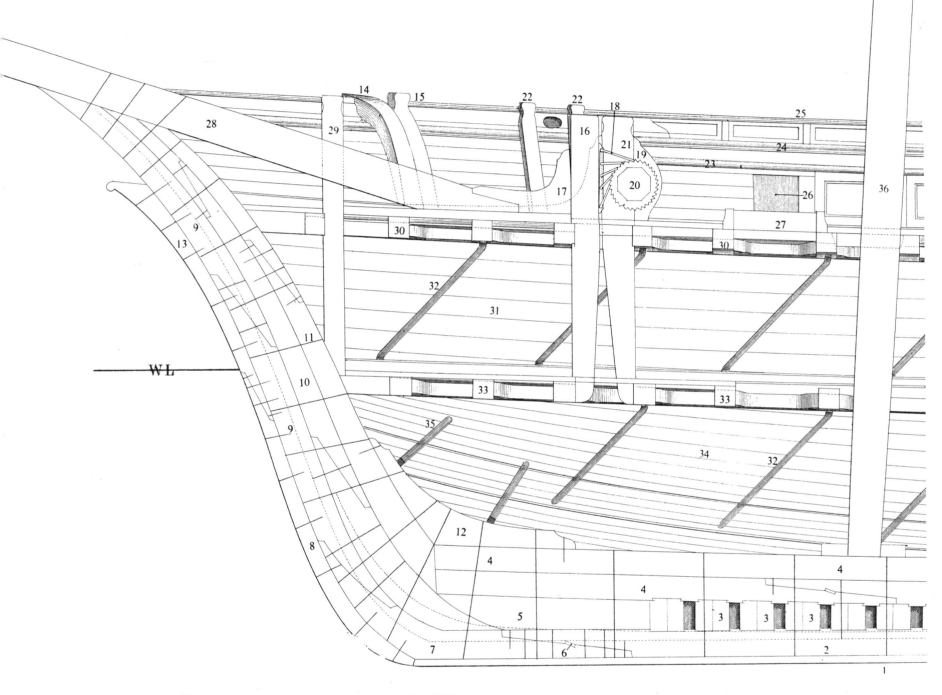

* THREE-MASTED WOODEN SHIP, 500 TONS DWT, LONGITUDINAL SECTION OF THE FOREBODY

1	False keel or shoe	7	Fore foot	14	Cathead	21	Carrick bitt or
2	Keel	8	Cutwater piece, gripe	15	Kevel head		windlass bitt
3	Floors	9	Stem	16	Pawl bitt	22	Mooring bollards
4	Keelson	10	Apron	17	Standard knee	23	Pinrail
5	Fore deadwood	11	Stemson	18	Pawls	24	Main rail
6	Keel scarf	12	Stem knee	19	Pawl rim	25	Topgallant rail
		13	Lace piece	20	Windlass barrel	26	Port

27	Fore hatch coaming	32	Main and 'tween
28	Bowsprit		deck diagonal
29	Foreward bitt		hanging knees
30	Main deck beams	33	Tween deck beams
31	Tween deck ceiling	34	Lower hold ceiling
		35	Breast hooks
		36	Foremast

CARPENTER'S TOOLS

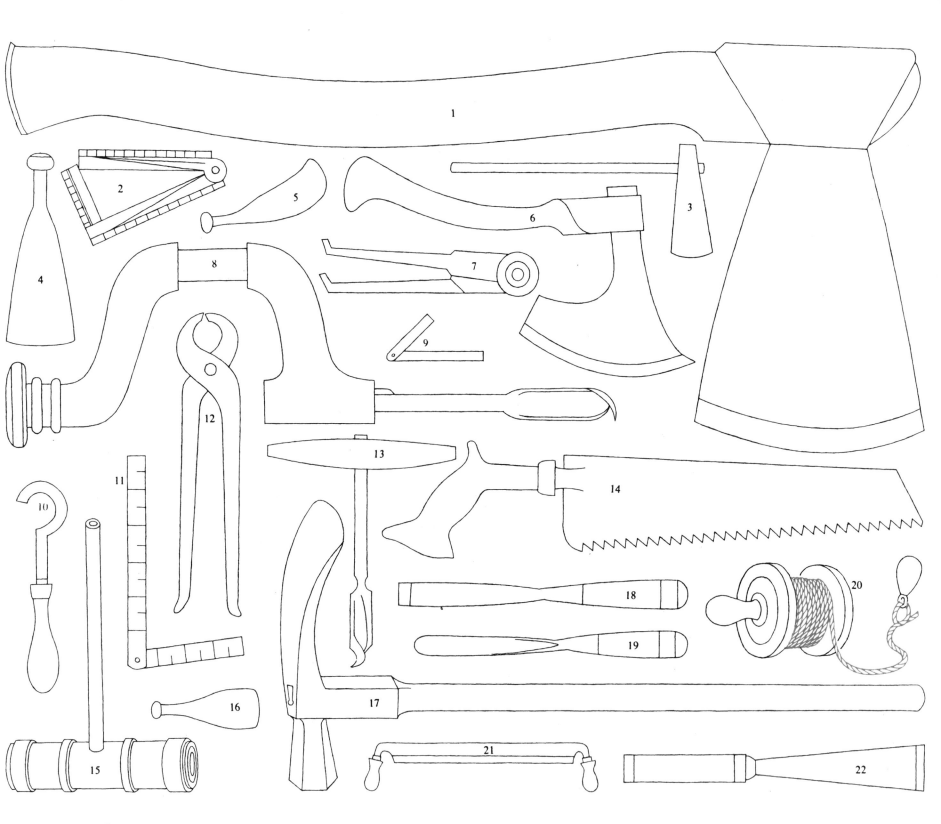

OLD CARPENTER'S TOOLS

From a book on shipbuilding, 1691

1 English broad axe
2 Folding rule, a foot and a half long
3 Horse iron with an iron handle
4 Reeming iron
5 Curved caulking iron
6 Carpenter's hatchet
7 Inside calipers
8 Dutch brace and bit
9 Small bevel
10 Crab iron
11 Dutch rule
12 Pair of pincers
13 English auger with a screw
14 Dutch handsaw
15 Big mallet with iron hoops
16 Caulking iron
17 English adze
18 English chisel
19 Gouge
20 Chalk line and reel
21 Draw knife
22 Chisel with a handle

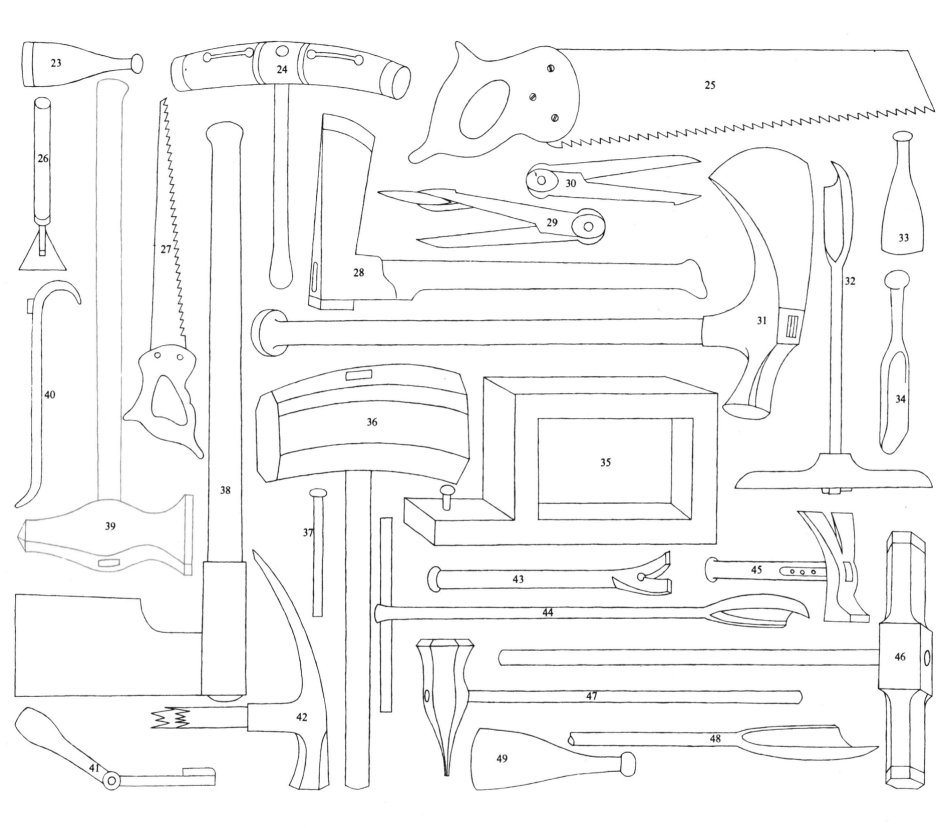

23 Making iron	28 Swedish chopping axe	34 Small gouge to start auger holes	38 Dutch axe	42 Adze, as seen from the side	46 English caulking mallet
24 Swedish caulking mallet	29 Compasses with crayon	35 Grease well to use when caulking	39 Sledge hammer	43 Crowbar	47 Common hammer
25 English handsaw	30 Dividers	36 English maul	40 Rave hook or ripping iron for cleaning caulking from seams	44 English auger with a wooden handle	48 Swedish gouge for pinewood
26 Deck scraper	31 Swedish adze	37 Spike iron	41 Crab iron, made like a clasp knife	45 English claw hammer	49 Reeming iron
27 Compass saw	32 Swedish auger				
	33 Caulking iron				

THREE-DECKED STEAMER

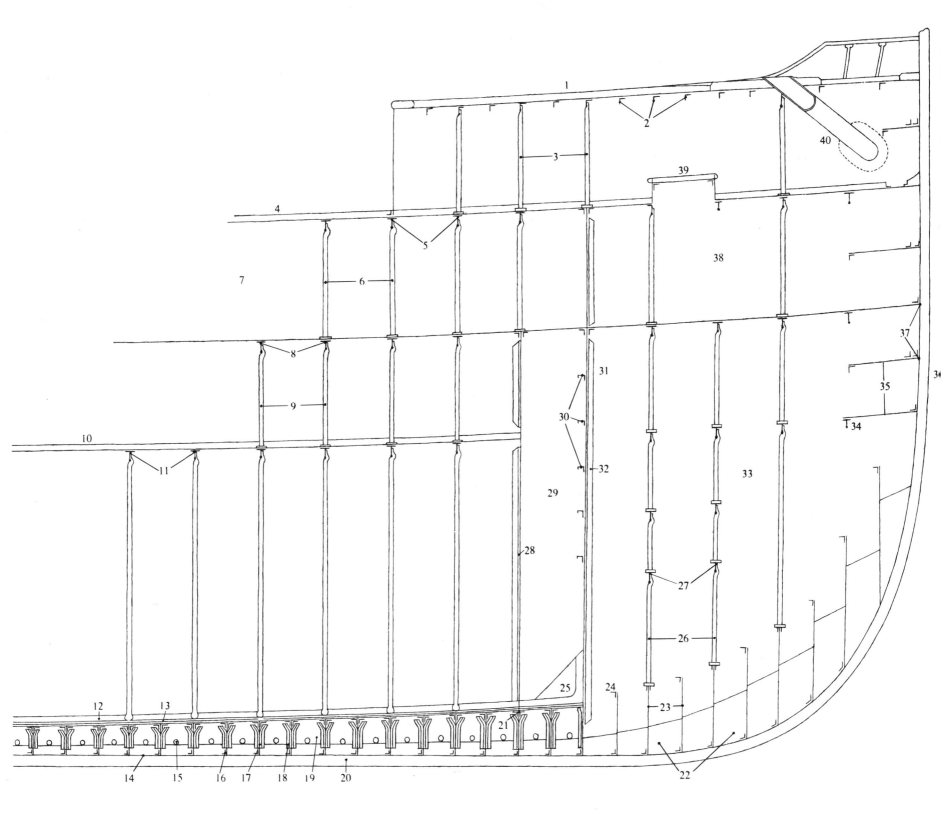

FORWARD ELEVATION OF A THREE-DECKED STEAMER, 1900

1 Fo'c'sle deck	8 Deck beams	15 Limber hole	22 Cement filling	29 Chain locker	36 Stem
2 Deck beams	9 Deck pillars	16 Bottom frame	23 Deep floors	30 Horizontal bulkhead	37 Angle clips
3 Deck pillars	10 Lower deck	17 Floor	24 Reverse frame	stiffeners	38 Storeroom above
4 Main deck	11 Deck beams	18 Angle clips	25 Bracket	31 Forepeak bulkhead,	forepeak tank
5 Deck beams	12 Center keelson	19 Center girder	26 Pillars	collision bulkhead	39 Hatch to storeroom
6 Deck pillars	13 Tank top plating	20 Bar keel	27 Beams	32 Vertical bulkhead	above forepeak tank
7 Tween deck	14 Bottom plating	21 Reverse frame	28 Chain locker bulkhead	stiffeners	40 Hawse pipe
				33 Forepeak tank	
				34 Beam	
				35 Breast hooks	

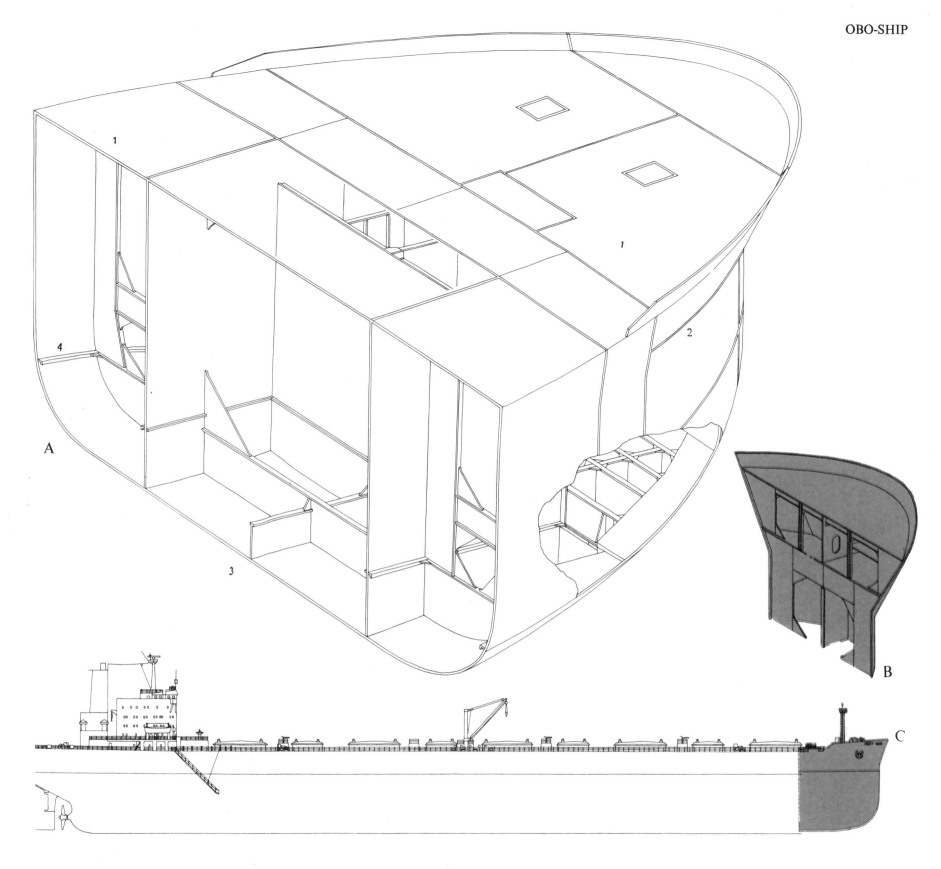

FOREBODY OF A STANDARDIZED OBO-SHIP, BUILT OF PRE-FABRICATED SECTIONS

Construction of forebody of a standardized OBO-ship of 124,000 dwt, 256.5 m (841.5 foot) long and 39 m (128 foot) in beam, built from pre-fabricated sections. The ship *has a cylinder bow, which gives a slightly inferior hydrodynamic performance compared to the bulb bow, but which is easier and cheaper to build.* *The forebody consists of 11 ready-made sections that are lifted into place and welded together in the construction dock. The sections range in weight from 74 to 453 tons.*

A *Assembled forebody with main-sections marked*
1 Upper deck
2 Fore-peak roof
3 Centre line
4 Side stringer

B *Foremost section with cylinder bow. Weight 96 tons*

C *Forebody seen from the side*

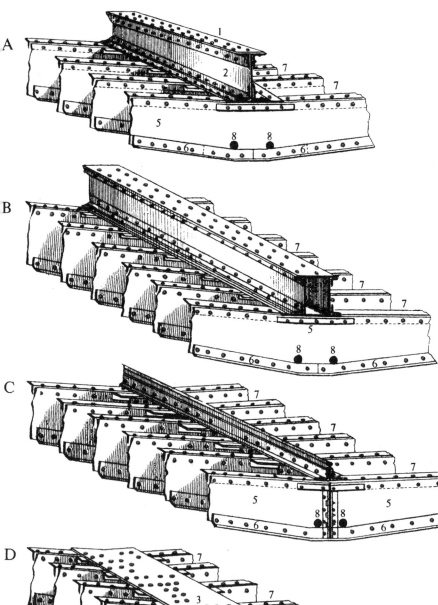

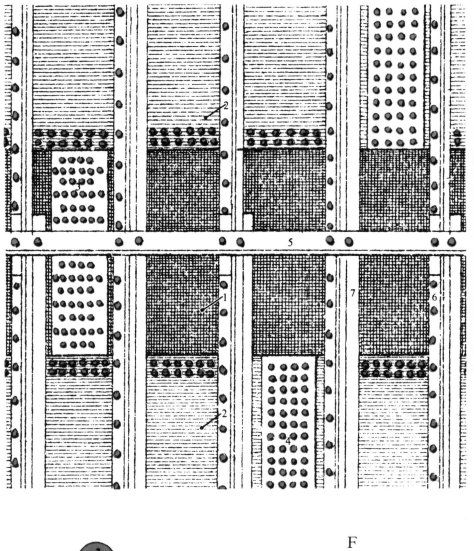

E

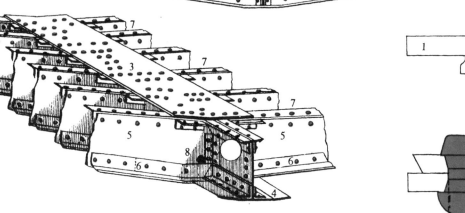

F

G

DETAILS FROM IRON AND STEEL SHIPS

A Single plate keelson

B Box keelson

C Intercostal vertical keel

D Continuous vertical keel

A—D

1 Rider plate
2 Vertical plate
3 Inner bottom center line strake
4 Flat plate keel
5 Floors
6 Frames
7 Reverse frames
8 Limber holes

E Inside view of plating, frames, etc., of an older riveted steel ship

1 Outside strakes
2 Inside strakes
3 Treble-riveted butt strap

4 Double-riveted butt strap
5 Angle bar stringer on top of reverse frames
6 Frames
7 Reverse frames

F Single-riveted end lap

1 Plate
2 Rivet
3 Snap head or button head
4 Rivet shank
5 Driven button head
6 Caulking seam

G Various kinds of riveting

1 Pan head, tapered rivet, button point
2 Pan head rivet, countersunk point
3 Button-headed rivet, countersunk point
4 Countersunk head and point

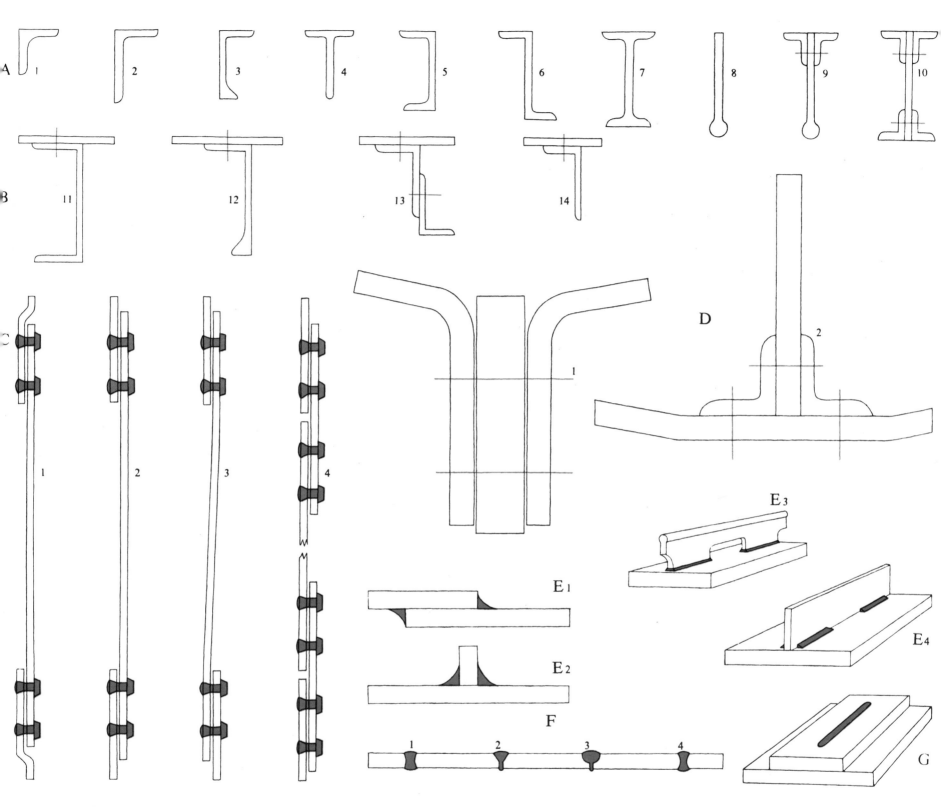

DETAILS FROM IRON AND STEEL SHIPS

A *Various kinds of steel sections*
1 Equal angle bar
2 Unequal angle bar
3 Bulb angle bar
4 Tee bar
5 Channel bar
6 Z-bar
7 I-beam
8 Bulb plate
9 Riveted section formed by two angles and a bulb plate
10 Riveted section formed by four angles and a flat plate

B *Various kinds of riveted frames*
11 Channel
12 Bulb angle
13 Two angles
14 Angle

C *Various kinds of riveting in plating*
1 Joggled outside strakes and flat inside strakes
2 Inside and outside strakes without joggling
3 Clinker built
4 Carvel built

D *Various kinds of keels*
1 Bar keel
2 Flat plate keel

E *Fillet welds*
1 Lap joint
2 T-connection
3 Double continuous weld with scalloped frame
4 Intermittent fillet weld

F *Butt welds*
1 Square weld with gap
2 V-weld without gap
3 U-weld
4 X-weld

G *Slot weld*

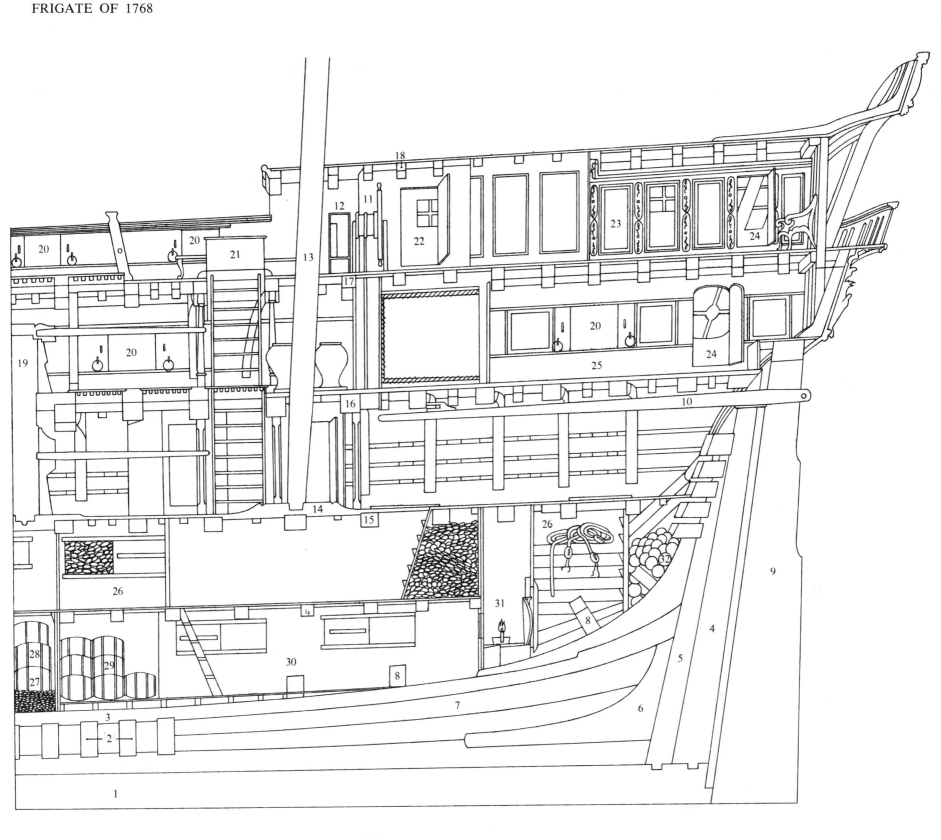

LONGITUDINAL SECTION OF THE AFTERBODY OF A 40-GUN FRIGATE, 1768

1 Keel	7 Deadwood	12 Binnacle	18 Poop deck beams	24 Doorway to quarter	29 Salt meat
2 Floors	8 Crutches	13 Mizzenmast	19 Main capstan	gallery	30 Powder room
3 Keelson	9 Rudder	14 Mast step	20 Gunports	25 Wardroom	31 Lantern for powder
4 Sternpost	10 Tiller	15 Orlop deck beams	21 Companion hood	26 Storerooms	room
5 Inner post	11 Wheel	16 Gun deck beams	22 Officer's room	27 Ballast	32 Shot locker
6 Stern knee		17 Upper deck beams	23 Great cabin	28 Water, beer casks	

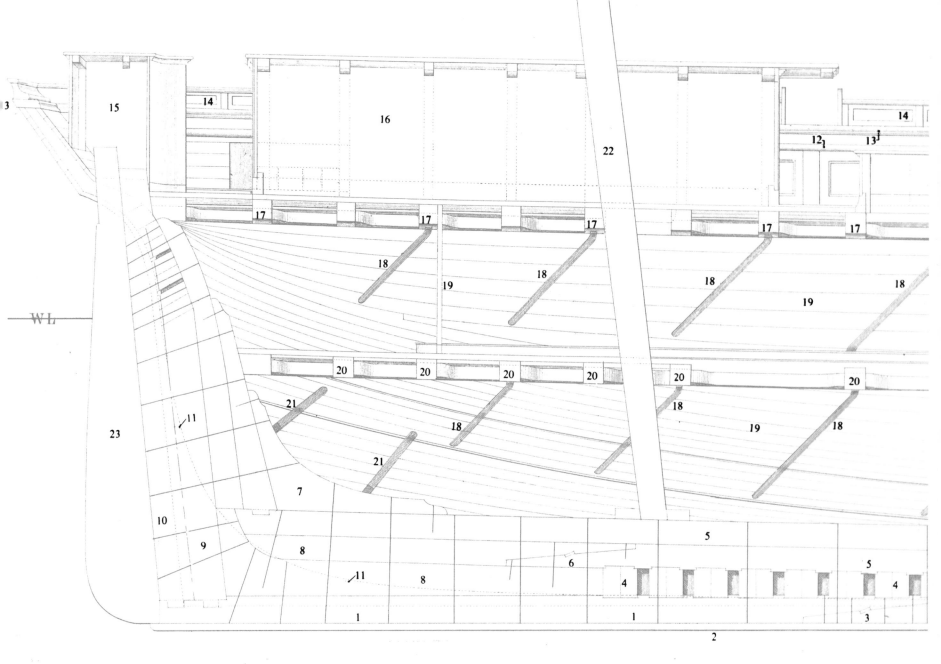

THREE-MASTED BARK, LONGITUDINAL SECTION OF THE AFTERBODY

1 Keel	6 Keelson scarf	11 Bearding line	16 Cabin house	19 Ceiling
2 False keel or shoe	7 Stern knee	12 Pinrail	17 Main deck beams	20 Tween deck beams
3 Keel scarf	8 After deadwood	13 Main rail	18 Diagonal deck beam	21 Crutches
4 Floor	9 Inner post	14 Topgallant bulwark	hanging knees	22 Mizzenmast
5 Keelson	10 Sternpost	15 Lamp locker, round-		23 Rudder
		house		

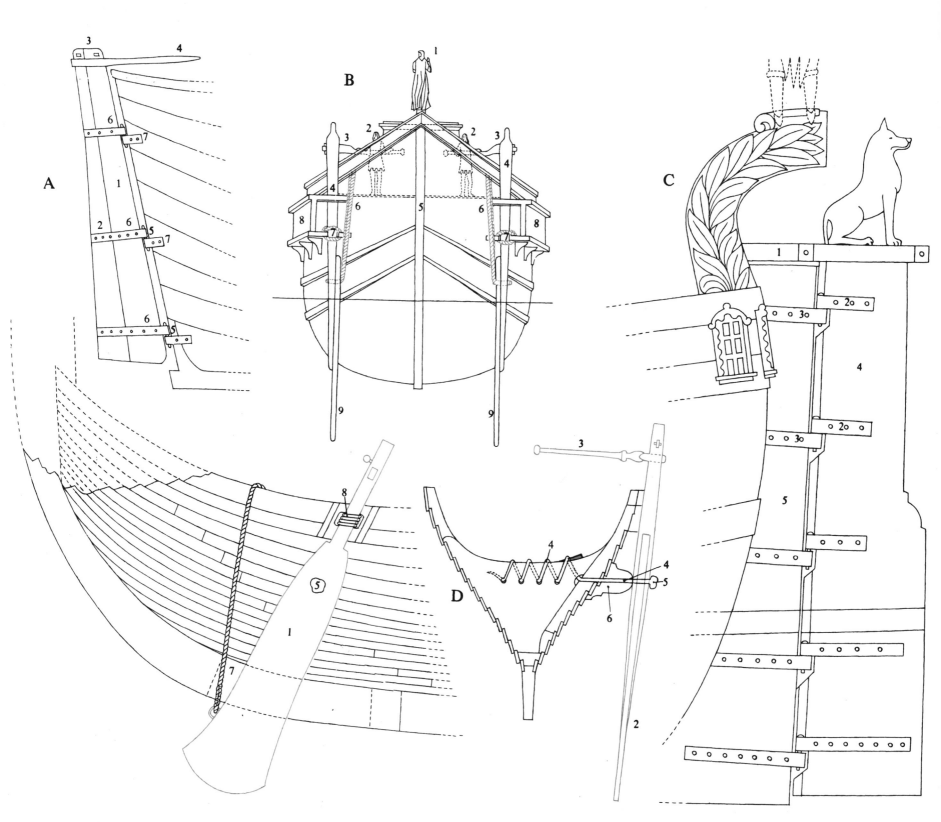

ANCIENT RUDDERS

A *Rudder of small medie-*
val ship
1 Main piece of rudder
2 Back piece
3 Head
4 Tiller
5 Pintles
6 Pintle straps
7 Gudgeon straps

B *Rudder arrangement in*
a Roman merchant ship
about A. D. 200
1 Stern ornament
2 Helmsmen
3 Tillers

4 Rudder stock
5 Sternpost
6 Carrying ropes
7 Lashing
8 Balcony
9 Rudder blade

C *Rudder of a Dutch*
fleut, middle of 17th
century
1 Tiller
2 Pintle straps
3 Rudder braces or
  gudgeon straps
4 Rudder blade
5 Sternpost

D *Rudder arrangement in*
the Viking era
about A.D. 850
(Gokstad ship)
1 Broadside view of
  steering oar
2 Stern view of steering
  oar

3 Tiller
4 Rudder rope
5 Knot
6 "Wart"
7 Tilting rope
8 Collar

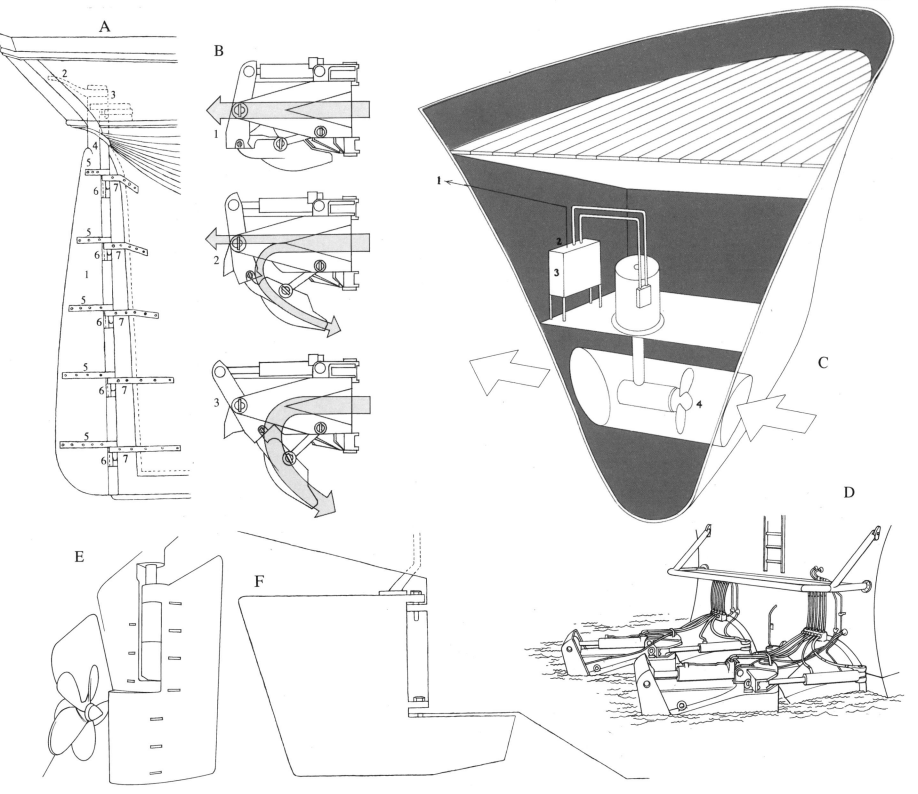

A   *Rudder in a wooden sailing ship*
1 Rudder blade
2 Tiller
3 Rudder head
4 Rudder stock
5 Pintle straps
6 Pintles
7 Gudgeon straps

B   *Water-jet nozzle*
1 Forward power: water is ejected backward
2 Neutral position: the jet splits into two streams that cancel each other
3 Backward power: the water jet reverses

C   *Principle of steering screw in a bow tunnel. The ship is moved sideways by means of water stream through tunnel in hull.*
1 Bridge control
2 Current supply
3 Coupling box
4 Propeller in tunnel

D   *Water-jet nozzle in the stern of a catamaran hull*

E   *Half-spade rudder on a large ship with one propeller*

F   *Balance rudder in a twin-screw ship*

OLD IRON STEAMER

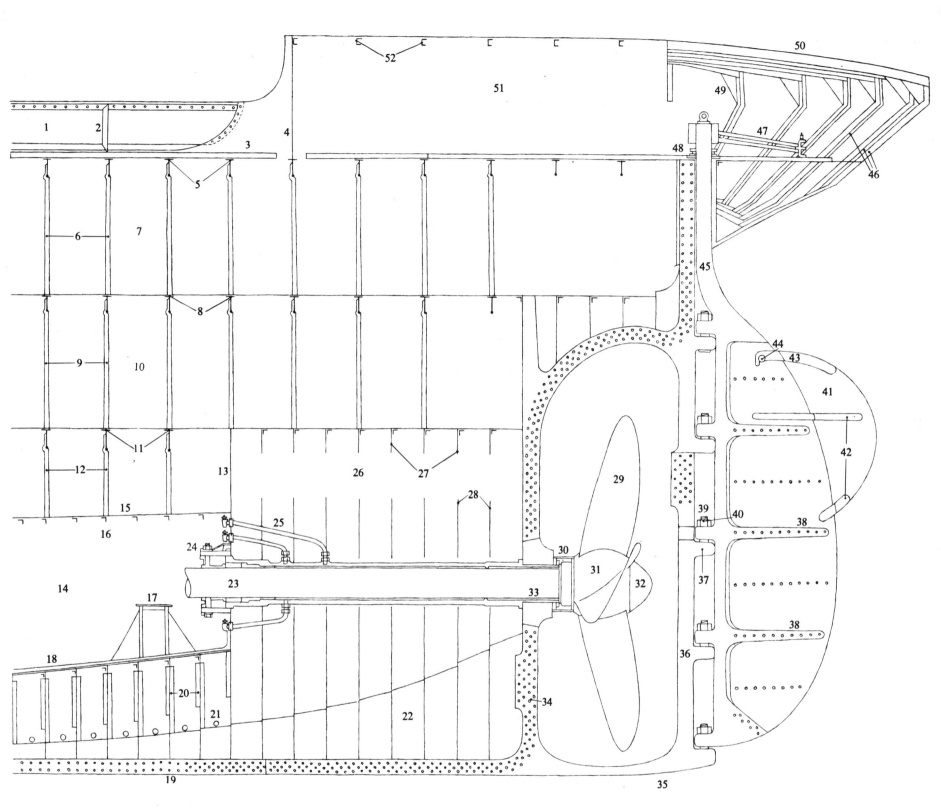

LONGITUDINAL SECTION OF STERN OF AN OLD IRON STEAMER

1 Bulwark	10 Lower deck	18 Tank top	27 Beams
2 Bulwark stanchion	11 Deck beams	19 Bar keel	28 Deep floors
3 Main deck	12 Deck pillars	20 Floors	29 Propeller blade
4 Poop bulkhead	13 Afterpeak bulkhead	21 Limber hole	30 Rope guard
5 Deck beams	14 Shaft tunnel or shaft	22 Cement filling	31 Propeller boss
6 Deck pillars	alley	23 Propeller shaft	32 Propeller nut cap
7 Tween deck	15 Top of shaft tunnel	24 Stuffing box	33 Stern bearing
8 Deck beams	16 Stiffeners on shaft	25 Water outlet pipe	34 Sternpost
9 Deck pillars	alley top	26 Afterpeak tank	35 Sole piece
	17 Pedestal of shaft		
	bearing		

36 Rudder post	45 Rudder stock
37 Gudgeon	46 Cant frames at stern
38 Rudder arms	47 Rudder quadrant
39 Pintle	48 Rudder stock stuffing
40 Nut	box
41 Portable section for	49 Brackets
better steering in	50 Deck beams of whale-
restricted waters	back
42 Stiffeners	51 Poop
43 Connecting strap	52 Deck beams
44 Bolt	

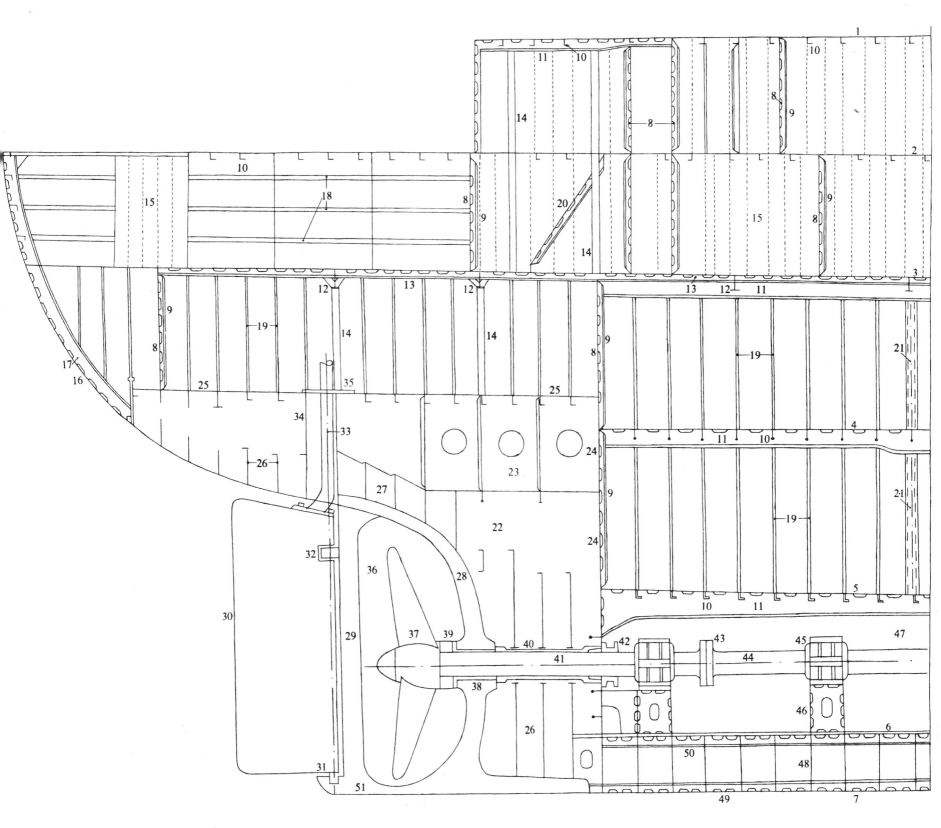

AFTER END OF AN ALL-WELDED CARGO SHIP

1 Boat deck	10 Transverse deck beams	19 Main framing
2 Poop deck	11 Longitudinal deck	20 Stairway
3 Shelter deck	girder	21 Hatch end pillar
4 Main deck	12 Transverse deck web	22 After peak tank
5 Top of shaft alley	13 Deck longitudinal	23 Swash plate
6 Tank top	14 Pillars or stanchions	24 Watertight bulkhead
7 Bottom plating	15 Longitudinal bulkhead	25 Top of after peak tank
8 Bulkhead	16 Cruiser stern	26 Deep floor
9 Bulkhead stiffener	17 Vertical frame	27 Cement filling
	18 Shell longitudinals	

28 Stern post	36 Propeller aperture	44 Line shaft section
29 Rudder post	37 Propeller	45 Line shaft bearing
30 Rudder	38 Stern bearing	(plummer block)
31 Pintle	39 Stern tube nut	46 Bearing foundation
32 Gudgeon	40 Stern tube	47 Shaft alley
33 Rudder stock	41 Tail shaft	48 Bottom floor
34 Rudder stock trunk	42 Shaft stuffing box	49 Bottom longitudinal
35 Stuffing box	43 Coupling flanges	50 Tank top
		longitudinal
		51 Heel of rudder post

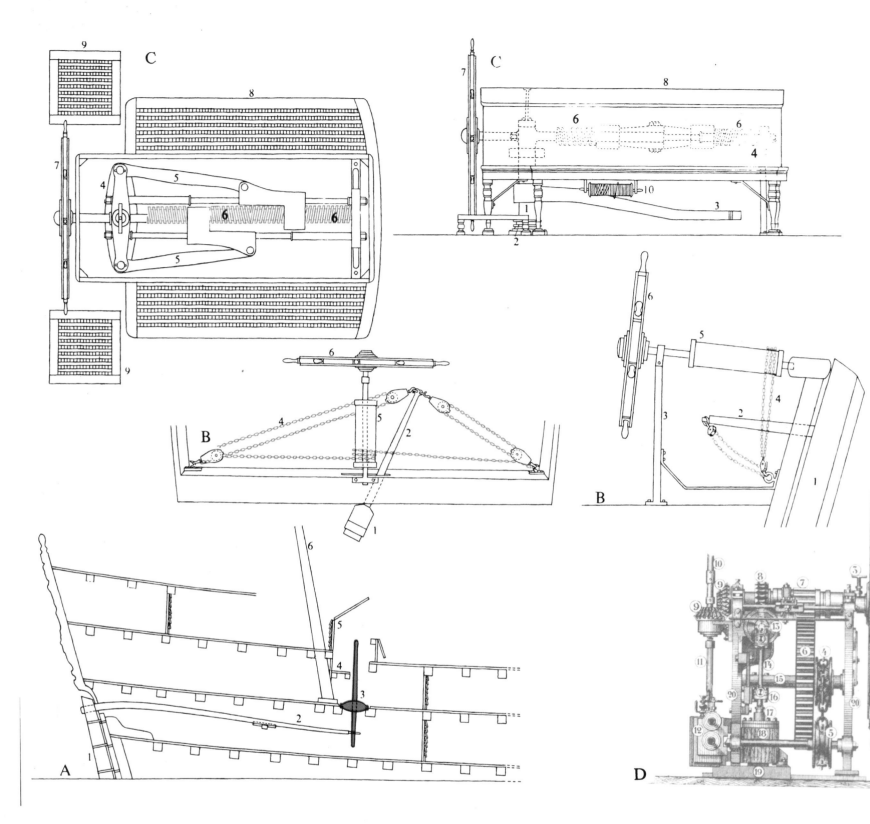

SOME STEERING GEARS

A *Steering arrangement in a big ship of the 17th century, when the rudder was controlled by a vertical lever called the whipstaff*
1 Rudder
2 Tiller
3 Whipstaff
4 Platform for the quartermaster
5 Hood for the quartermaster
6 Mizzenmast

B *Common steering gear in elevation and plan of small wooden sailing ship, 19th century*
1 Rudder
2 Tiller
3 Wheel stand
4 Tiller chain
5 Barrel or drum
6 Wheel

C *Mechanical screw steering gear in plan and elevation of big steel sailing ship, latter part of 19th century*
1 Rudder stock
2 Stuffing box on deck
3 Emergency tiller
4 Cross head
5 Coupling rods
6 Screw spindle-threaded right and left

7 Wheel
8 Wheel box with side seats
9 Wheel gratings
10 Log reel slung underneath wheel box

D *Vertical steering engine, end of last century*
1 Hand-steering wheel
2 Steam-steering wheel
3 Set-screw
4 Messenger wheel and steering chain
5 Guide pulleys
6 Spur wheel
7 Pinion
8 Scroll wheel
9 Miter wheels
10 Valve rod (to pilot bridge)

11 Valve rod
12 Valve casing
13 Crank disc
14 Connecting rod
15 Main shaft
16 Piston rod crosshead
17 Stuffing box
18 Cylinder
19 Bedplate
20 Standards

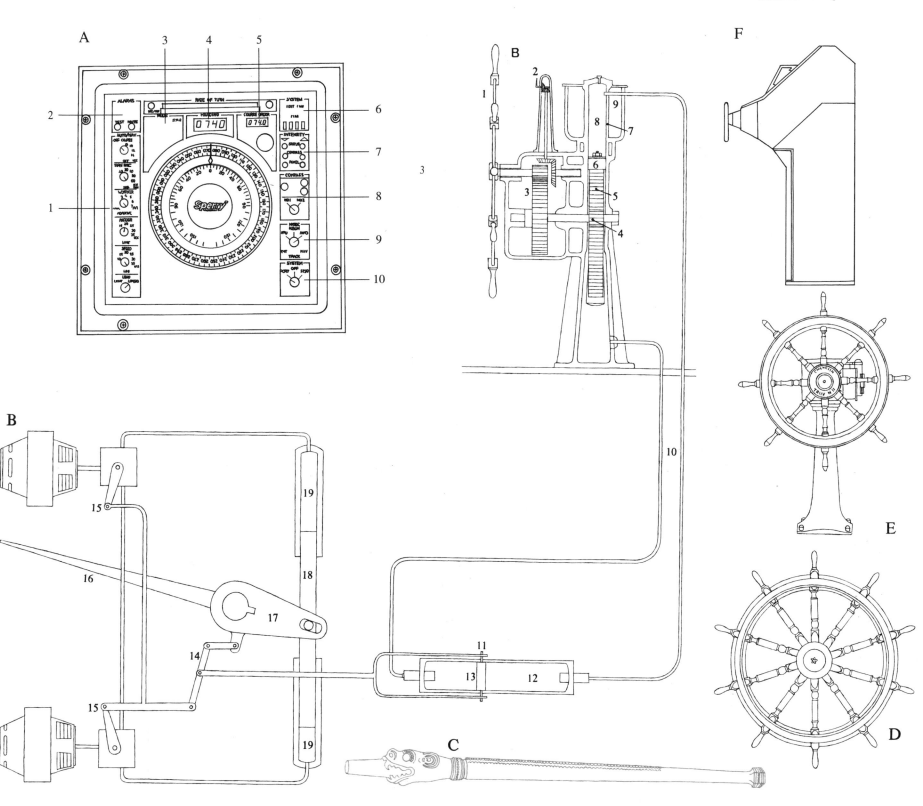

STEERING EQUIPMENT

A *Control and operating panel*
1 Controls and settings
2 Alarm
3 Indicator for steering method
4 Yaw speed
5 Course setting
6 System indicator
7 Instrument lighting
8 Compass selector
9 Selector for steering method
10 System selector

B *Telemotor system*
1 Steering wheel
2 Rudder position indicator
3 Gear pinion
4 Gear
5 Rack
6 Piston
7 Cylinder
8 Fluid
9 Refilling tank
10 Pipes to receiver

11 Receiver
12 Cylinder
13 Piston
14 Floating link, which automatically stops the pumps when the rudder is in position
15 Pumps
16 Rudder
17 Tiller
18 Piston
19 Cylinder

C *Tiller of the Viking ship from Gokstad, ca. A.D. 900*

D *Steering wheel from sailing ship, middle of the 19th century*

E *Steering gear of a steamer, beginning of the 20th century*

F *Steering console*

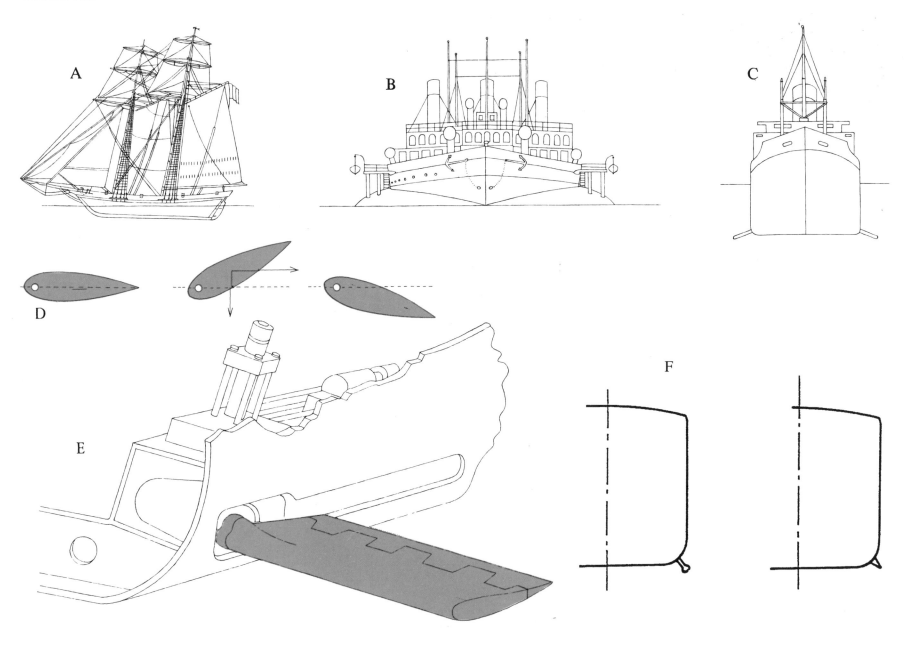

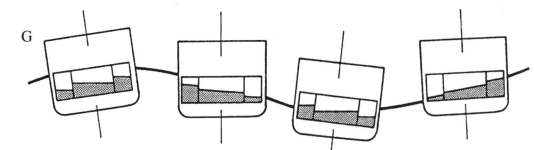

STABILIZERS

A *Sailing ships were stabilized by wind pressure on the sails, decreasing their roll*

B *Among later efforts to reduce rolling was the construction of some very broad ships*

C *Today, ever more ships are equipped with stabilizers*

D *The stabilizers act as horizontal rudders or hydroplanes, and can turn 50 degrees*

E *The stabilizers are guided hydraulically by a gyroscope. When not in use, they can be retracted into slots in the hull*

F *Bilge keels are sheet-metal structures lying longitudinally, at a right angle to the side, in the bilges between the ship's side and bottom. They can reduce its roll by 30%*

G *Stabilizing tanks (so-called flume tanks) are common on ships. Two or three tanks, linked by channels or pipes, lie adjacently athwart a ship. When it begins to roll, water flows back and forth between the tanks. With proper linkage dimensions and quantity of water, the tanks will counteract the ship's rolling.*

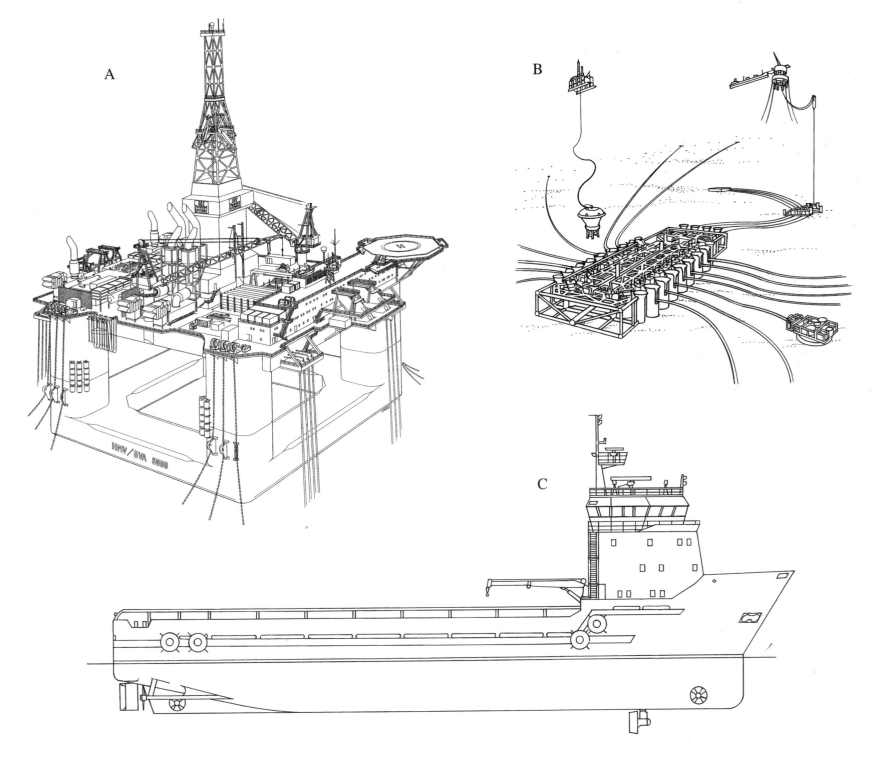

OFFSHORE

A *Production platform in the North Sea, semi-submersible*

B *Offshore underwater-based production plant*

C *Supply ship*

DECORATION

With most people illiterate, the name of a ship was often depicted by painted carvings on the stern, (for example A and B)

A The flower of the English hawthorn on the *Mayflower*, 1620 (from replica built in 1957)

B Stern of the Dutch pinnace *Dromedarus*, middle of the 17th century (from a model)

C Stern of the French ship *Le Soleil Royal*, built at Brest in 1669

D Head ornament of the three-masted fore-and aft schooner *Ellen* of Skärhamn, built at Thurö in 1908

E Name board of the Finnish barkentine *Ida*, wrecked on the west coast of Sweden in 1875

F Stern ornament of the three-masted fore-and aft schooner *Meta-Jan* of Skive, Denmark

DECORATION

A Sculptured lion's head on gun-port lid, perhaps intended to put heart in the crew and to frighten the enemy, the Swedish ship *Wasa*, 1628

B Figurehead of unknown vessel, from the middle of the 19th century

C Figurehead, from the 18th century

D Chinese junk with a painted eye on her bow, known as oculus decoration. "Suppose no eye no can see," the Chinese seamen says in his pidgin English. Such painted eyes may also be seen on fishing craft in the Mediterranean.

E Brigantine from the middle of the 19th century, with painted ports on her sides. This painting was originally intended to make the ship look like a man-of-war, but later it remained as decoration only.

F Dutch pinnace from the middle of the 17th century, with a painted waveline for a water line, to give an impression of speed. (Sketch from a model.)

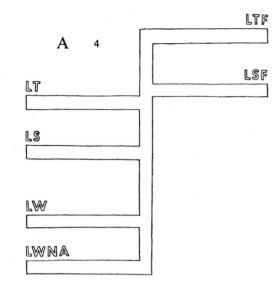

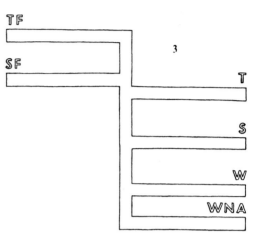

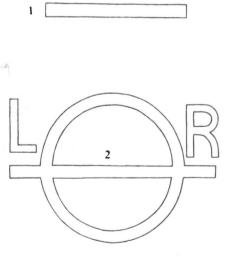

LOAD LINES AND DRAFT MARKS

A *Ordinary and timber loadlines for steamships, starboard side shown*
1 Deck line
2 Loadline disc or Plimsoll mark. (The letters LR denote the classifying society, here Lloyd's Register. American ships have AB, the American Bureau of Shipping)

3 Ordinary loadlines
The letters indicate:
TF=fresh water tropical loadline
SF=fresh water summer loadline
T=salt water tropical loadline
S=salt water summer loadline
W=salt water winter loadline

WNA=winter North Atlantic loadline
4 When loaded with timber (lumber) and with a deck cargo, the ship may be loaded somewhat deeper, and the timber loadlines are shown abaft the disc
The letters indicate:
LTF=fresh water tropical timber loadline

LSF=fresh water summer timber loadline
LT=salt water tropical timber loadline
LS=salt water summer timber loadline
LW=salt water winter timber loadline
LWNA=winter North Atlantic timber loadline

B *Loadlines of a sailing vessel are not so complicated*
1 Deck line
2 Loadline disc or Plimsoll mark (The horizontal bar across the disc gives summer loadline in salt water)
The letters indicate:
F=fresh water loadline

WNA=winter North Atlantic loadline
C *Draft marks*
The draft of ships is measured in feet and marked in six-inch-high Roman figures in such a way that 1 in the diagram indicates 20 feet, 2 indicates 20 feet 6 inches, and so on

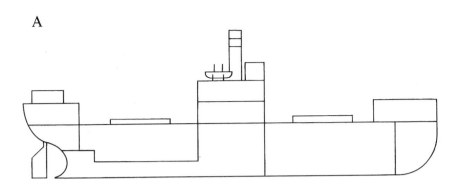

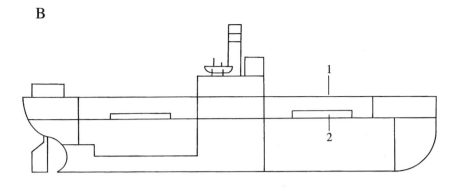

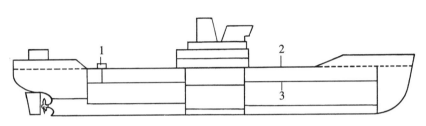

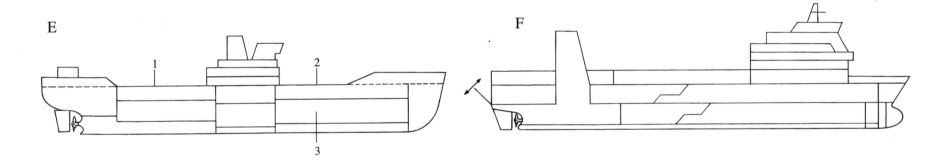

DRY-CARGO SHIP DEVELOPMENT DURING THE 20TH CENTURY

A *Three-Island Vessel. Most dry-cargo ships around 1900 were of this type (named after its looks). They had relatively small holds but were very suitable for cargo of that time (coal, grain, raw wood products etc.).*

B *Awning-decked vessel. With industrialization, bulky piece goods began to be shipped. Such cargo was protected by building a light deck from the bridge to the forecastle and poop (1)*
  2 Awning deck

C *Partially shelter-decked vessel. Openings were left in the ship's sides (1) because the capacity, which is the basis for harbor fees, was calculated from the closed volume. Gross and net capacities were measured in units of a register ton, which was equivalent to 100 ft³ (2.83 m³).*
  2 Shelter deck
  3 Main/freeboard deck

D *An open shelter-decked ship has openings in the shelter deck and transverse bulkhead, which cannot be closed permanently. Thus the space above the main deck is not included in the ship's capacity. Freeboard is measured from the main deck*
  1 Tonnage hatch
  2 Shelter deck
  3 Main/freeboard deck

E *A closed shelter-decked ship has the openings in the shelter deck permanently closed, so this deck becomes the freeboard deck and the ship can take heavier loads. But on harbor visits the ship must pay extra for the space between the shelter and main decks. The shelter deck could be closed as watertight* as the hold hatches etc., *so it was decided in the 1950s that the freeboard deck level should determine which load spaces were counted in the ship's capacity. Spaces above that level were "free"*
  1 Former tonnage hatch
  2 Shelter/freeboard deck
  3 Main deck

F *Ro/ro vessel (roll on, roll off). Since the ramp can never be fully watertight, the main deck is counted as the freeboard deck, so the ship once paid no fees for all loading space above that deck. But new measurement rules, from 1994 onward, base the calculations on all spaces in the ship regardless of location. Thus the gross and net capacities serve only for comparison between different vessels*

ANCHORS

A *Common anchor*
1 Anchor ring
2 Stock
3 Hoops of the anchor
   stock
4 Shank
5 Crown
6 Arm
7 Fluke
8 Pea or bill

B *Part of tree trunk with branches, used as an anchor*

C *Anchor, made from tree branches and stone*

D *Roman anchor of Caligula from Lake Nemi*

E *Viking anchor from the Oseberg ship*

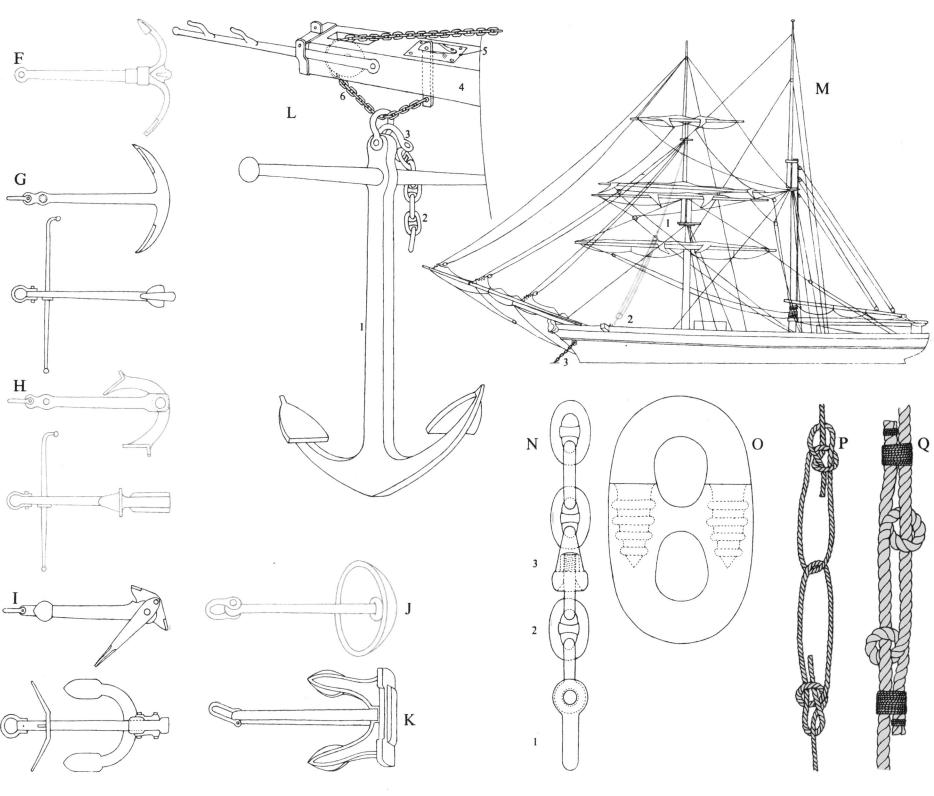

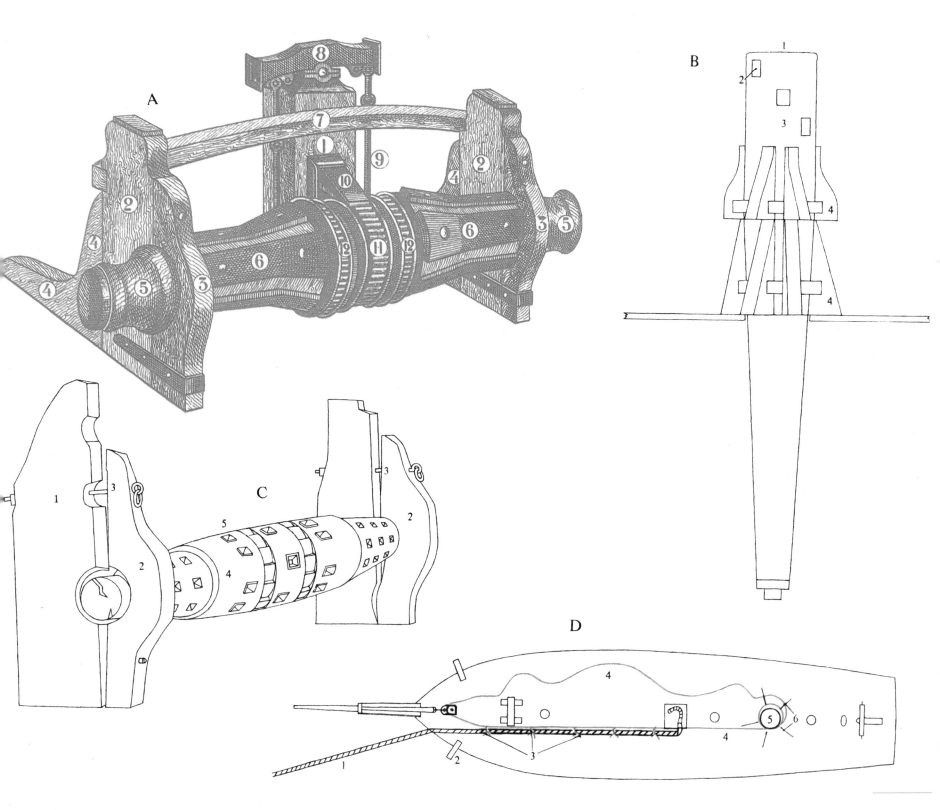

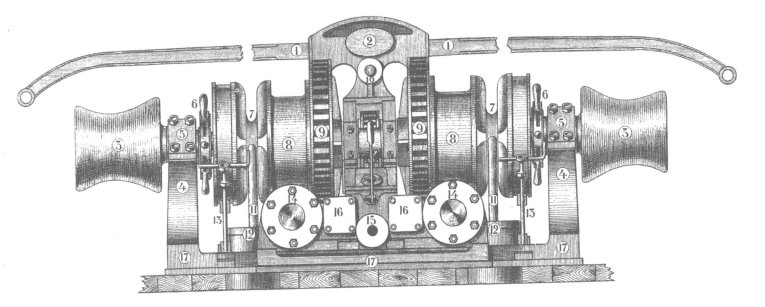

A

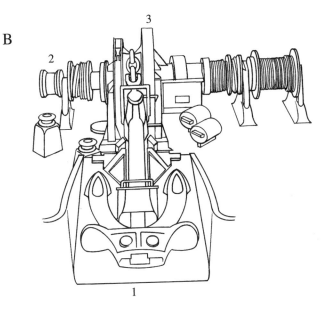

B

C

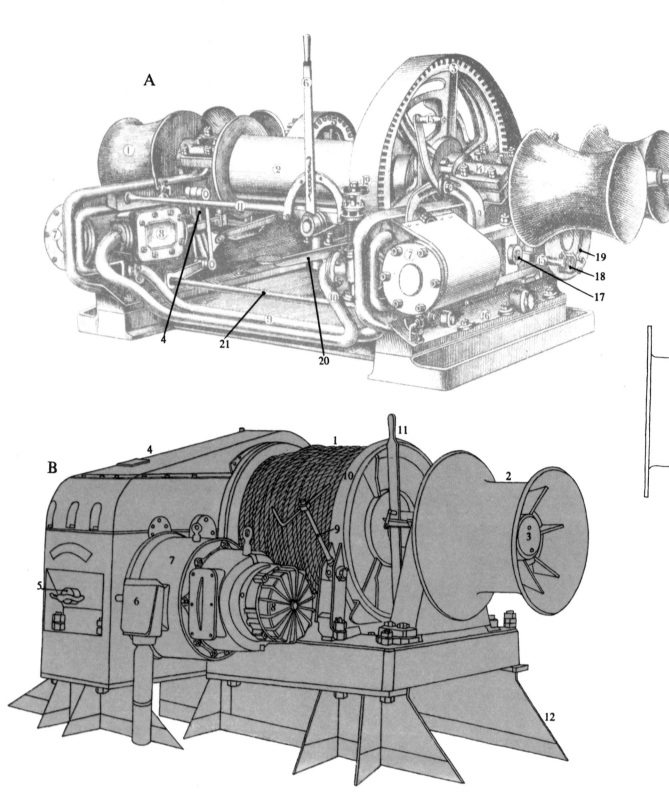

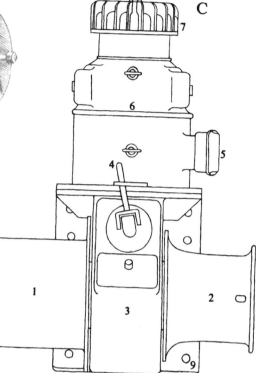

WINCHES

A *Steam winch*
1 Warping heads or gypsy heads
2 Winch drum
3 Main cogwheel
4 Reversing link
5 Pinion shaft cogwheel
6 Clutch lever
7 Cylinders
8 Slide-valve box
9 Steam exhaust pipe
10 Inlet steampipe
11 Tie rod, stay
12 Throttle valve
13 Reversing lever
14 Drum shaft bearing
15 Connecting rod
16 Bedplate
17 Piston rod and cross-head
18 Crank pin
19 Combined gear- and flywheel
20 Strap-brake pedal
21 Weigh shaft

B *15/5 ton automatic or constant-tension mooring winch*
1 Winch drum
2 Warping head
3 Drum shaft
4 Gear casing
5 Gear lever, 5 or 15 tons
6 Electric coupling box
7 Electric driving motor
8 Lamina brake
9 Strap-brake tightening screw
10 Strap-brake
11 Warping head coupling handle
12 Foundation

C *Worm-geared vertical cargo winch*
1 Winch drum
2 Warping head
3 Worm-gear house
4 Gear lever, 2 or 5 tons
5 Electric coupling box
6 Electric motor (vertical shaft)
7 Lamina brake
8 Bedplate
9 Foundation

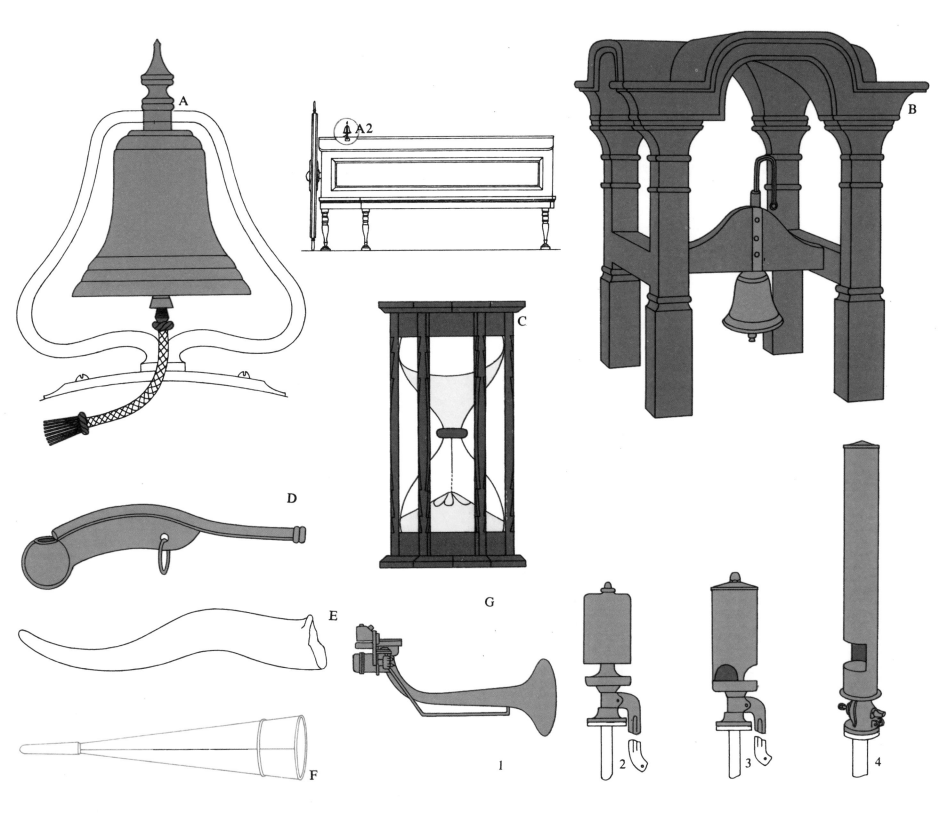

BELLS, HOURGLASS, AND WHISTLES

A A little bell placed aft, on which the helmsman struck the time, and which was repeated by the lookout at the main bell

B A bell hanging in a belfry, Nelson's *Victory*

C Hourglass, measuring half an hour. Each glass on board accounts for half an hour, and is sounded by one stroke of the bell; each watch of four hours is divided into eight glasses, corresponding to eight bells. The six watches are: the 1st watch 20—24, the 2nd watch (middle watch) 00—04, the day watch (morning watch) 04—08, the forenoon watch 08—12, the noon watch 12—16, and the afternoon watch 16—20. Three bells thus mean that the time is 01.30, 05.30, 09.30, 13.30, 17.30, or 21.30.
Eight bells mean that a watch is over. The number of glasses is struck on the bell as a series of double strokes. For instance, 15.30 (seven glasses):

+ + + + + + +

D Boatswain's call

E Fog horn made from a bullock's horn

F Fog horn of copper

G Sirens and whistles

1 Siren

2 Bell whistle

3 Chime whistle

4 Organ pipe whistle

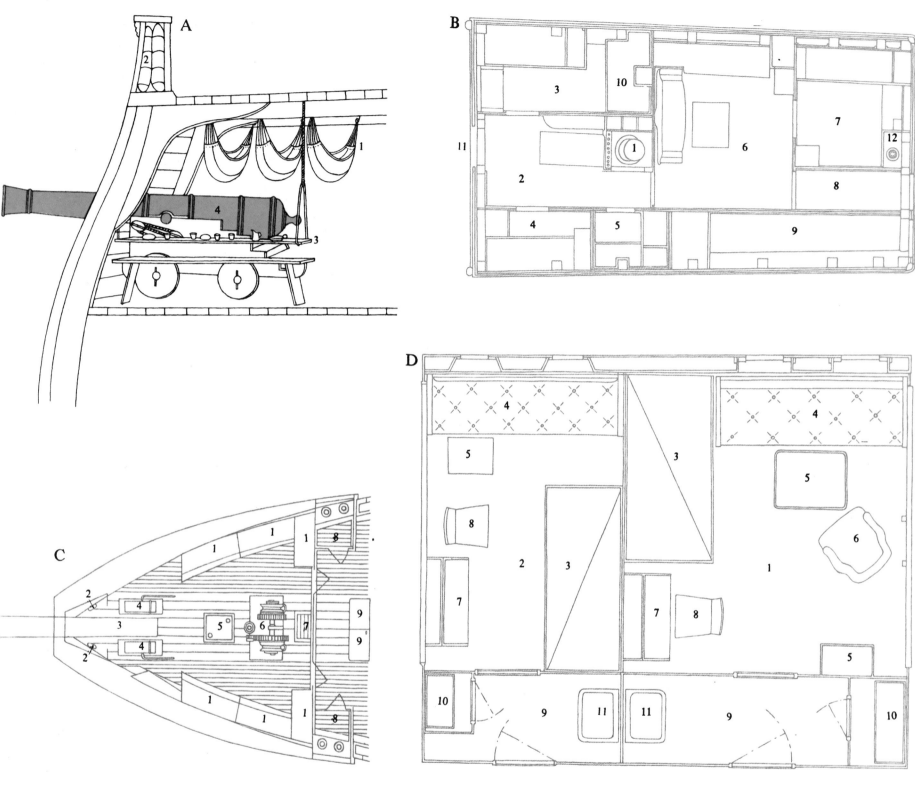

Up to the middle of the 17th century the crew had no special accommodations but had to sleep on the bare deck or find a place for themselves. Meals were eaten on deck without tables or chairs.

A *Early 19th century When hammocks were used in the navy they were slung from the*

deck-head beams; they were stowed in the top-gallant bulwark for protection against musket fire when not in use

1 Hammocks slung under deck beams
2 Hammocks stowed in bulwark
3 Mess table slung from overhead beam
4 Muzzle-loading gun with wooden carriage

B *Cabin accommodations on board a Swedish barkentine, built in Gävle, 1878*

1 Mizzenmast
2 Mess room
3 Mate's room
4 Second mate's and steward's room
5 Pantry
6 Cabin
7 Captain's bedroom
8 Alleyway

9 Sail locker and deck stores
10 Provisions
11 Entrance from deck
12 Steering compass

C *Accommodation for 12 seamen in fo'c'sle on board a British three-masted iron bark of 900 tons, built in Glasgow, 1879*

1 Upper and lower bunks
2 Hawse pipes

3 Bowsprit
4 Cable compressors
5 Fore peak hatch
6 Windlass
7 Hatch to chain locker
8 Crew's lavatory with light house above
9 Fore hatch

D *Modern staterooms*

1 Officer's room
2 Seaman's room
3 Berth
4 Sofa
5 Table
6 Armchair
7 Desk
8 Chair
9 Washroom
10 Wardrobe
11 Washstand

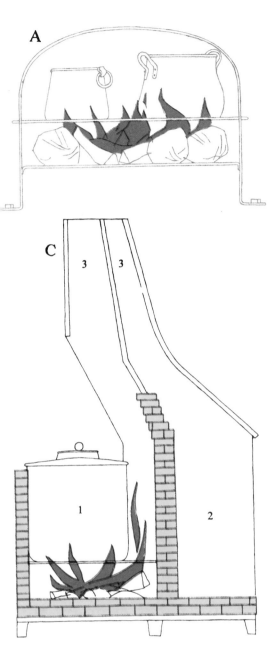
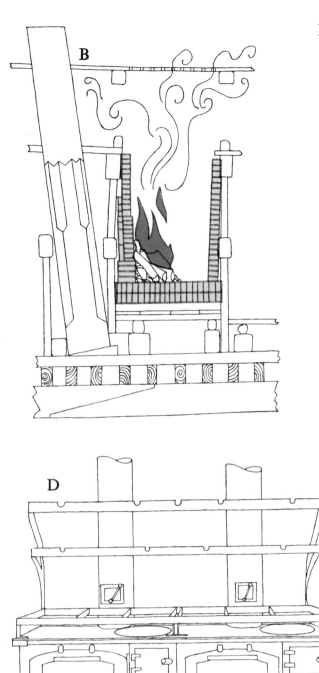
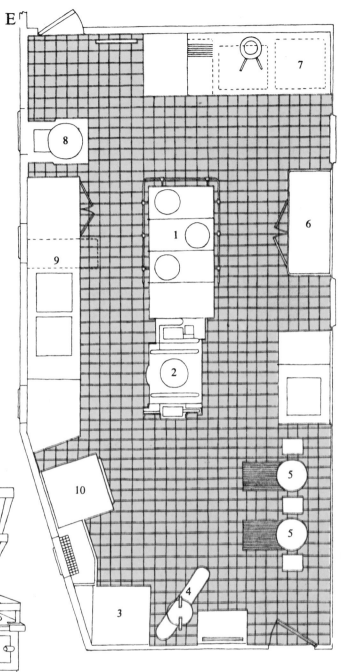

GALLEY

A *Open sheet-iron fire-place, on the deck of a coaster in the Indian Ocean*

B *Brick fireplace on board the Swedish ship Wasa, 1628. There was no chimney and the smoke had to find its way out wherever it could.*

C *Ship's galley, according to Chapman, 1768*
1 Pea-soup kettle
2 Brick fireplace
3 Galley stacks

D *Big galley stove, from the beginning of the 20th century*

E *Modern ship's galley*
1 Electric stove
2 Roaster
3 Dumbwaiter
4 Garbage chute
5 Steamer, steam kettles
6 Electric control panel
7 Refrigerator
8 Mixer
9 Sink
10 Oven

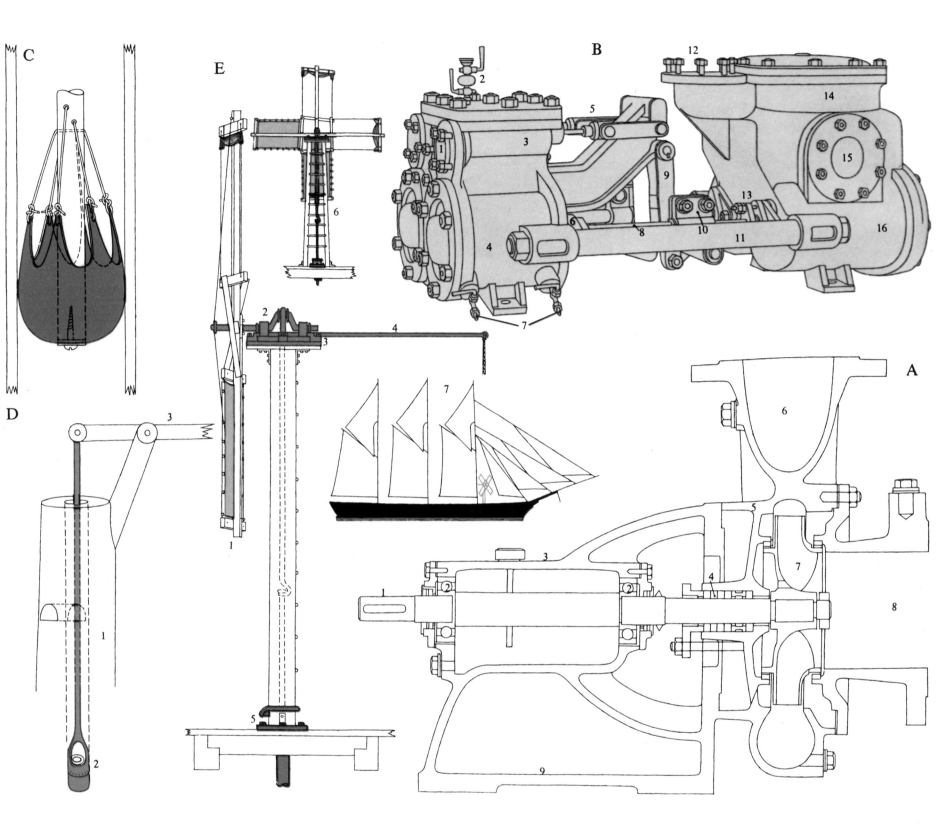

A *Single-stage centrifugal pump*
1 Pump shaft drive
2 Ball bearing
3 Oil-filled bearing box
4 Gland sealing
5 Pump casing
6 Discharge flange
7 Impeller
8 Suction flange
9 Mounting flange

B *Duplex-type, direct-acting pump*
1 Steam inlet
2 Cylinder lubricator
3 Slide-valve box
4 Steam cylinder
5 Slide-valve rod
6 Gland sealing
7 Drain and air cocks
8 Piston rod
9 Rocker arm
10 Crosshead connection
11 Column

12 Discharge flange
13 Gland sealing
14 Suction and discharge valve box
15 Suction flange
16 Pump cylinder

C *Old-type bilge pump, once common in small craft in the Baltic area. It was constructed from a piece of leather, which formed a bag, and gave good service.*

D *The standard bilge pump in small wooden sailing vessels. It was made from a straight tree trunk, bored through the heart.*
1 Trunk of pump
2 Pump bucket
3 Pump brake, handle

E *Windmill pump with four sails, mounted on a turntable on top of a bipod erection. The windmill pump always had rigging. The three-masted fore-and-aft schooner, Eufrosine of Reval, had a windmill pump forward of the foremast.*

1 Sails as seen from the side
2 Crankshaft
3 Turntable
4 Arm with braces, for setting the mill to the wind
5 The pump deck seating
6 Front view of windmill, showing two sails furled and two set
7 Three-masted fore-and-aft schooner with a windmill pump

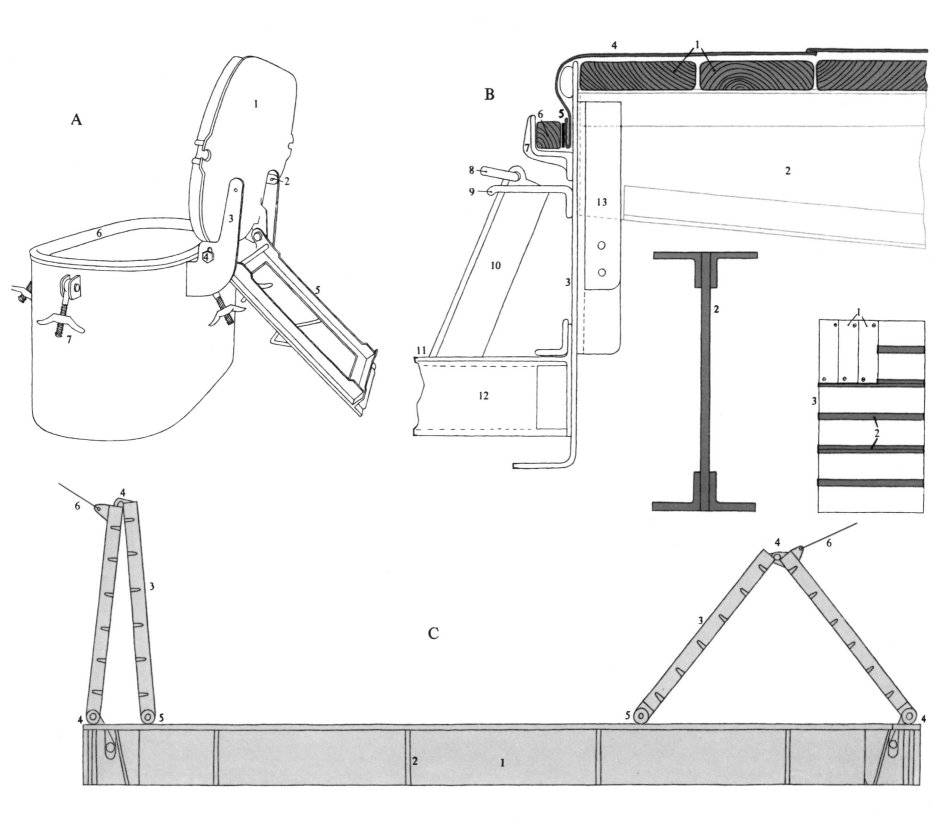

HATCHES

A *Oil tanker hatch cover*
1 Cover
2 Locking lug
3 Stop
4 Hinge pin

5 Strongback (opening lever)
6 Coaming
7 Locking screw with butterfly nut

B *Hatchway*
1 Wooden hatch covers
2 Hatch beams
3 Hatch coaming
4 Tarpaulin
5 Flat bar batten
6 Batten wedge
7 Batten cleat

8 Frapping ring
9 Bulb angle for stiffening
10 Coaming stanchion
11 Deck plating
12 Deck beam
13 Hatch beam support

C *Steel hatch cover*
1 Hatch coaming
2 Coaming stanchion
3 Folding steel hatch cover
4 Hinge
5 Rollers
6 Operating wire rope

LANTERNS

LANTERNS

A *Swedish poop lantern from the 18th century*

B *Lantern with horn windows from the 18th century*

C *Riding light with a round wick lamp and Fresnel lens (A.J. Fresnel, French physicist, 1788-1827)*

D *Development of the poop lantern*
1 1514, *Great Harry*
2 Middle of the 16th century, Sir Francis Drake's *Golden Hind*

3 The 17th century, Dutch poop lantern
4 The 17th century, English poop lantern, *Prince Royal*

5 The 18th century, poop lantern of a big French ship, built at Brest in 1756
6 The 18th century, Swedish poop lantern (same as A)

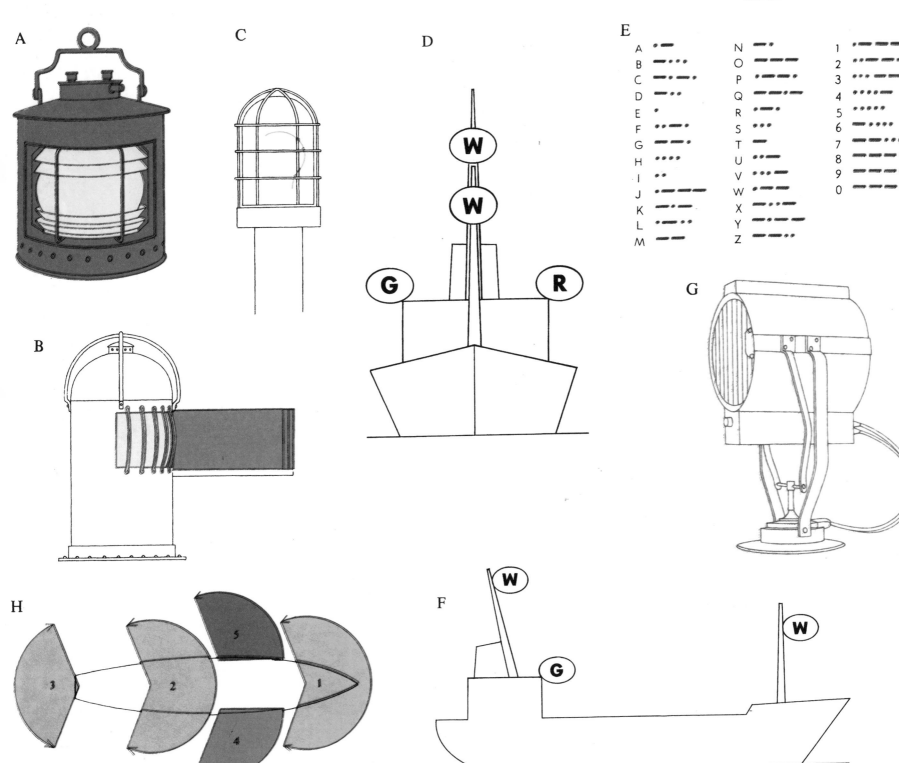

LANTERNS AND SIDELIGHTS

A *Sidelights from the early 20th century*

B *Sidelights in tower on forecastle, 19th and 20th centuries*

C *Morse lamp for a merchant ship, all-around illumination*

D *Lighting on engine-powered ship, seen from front. W=white, G=gold/yellow, R=red.*

E *Morse code, invented by S.F.B. Morse (1791-1872)*

F *Lighting on engine-powered ship, seen from side. W=white, G=gold/yellow, R=red.*

G *Searchlight*

H *Arcs of ship lights:*
1 Masthead light (fore steaming light), from right ahead over 112.5° to each side (total arc 225°)
2 Range light (after steaming light), from right ahead over 112.5° to each side
3 Stern light (overtaking light), from right astern over 67.5° to each side (total arc 135°)
4 Starboard side light, from right ahead over 112.5° to starboard
5 Port side light, from right ahead over 112.5° to port

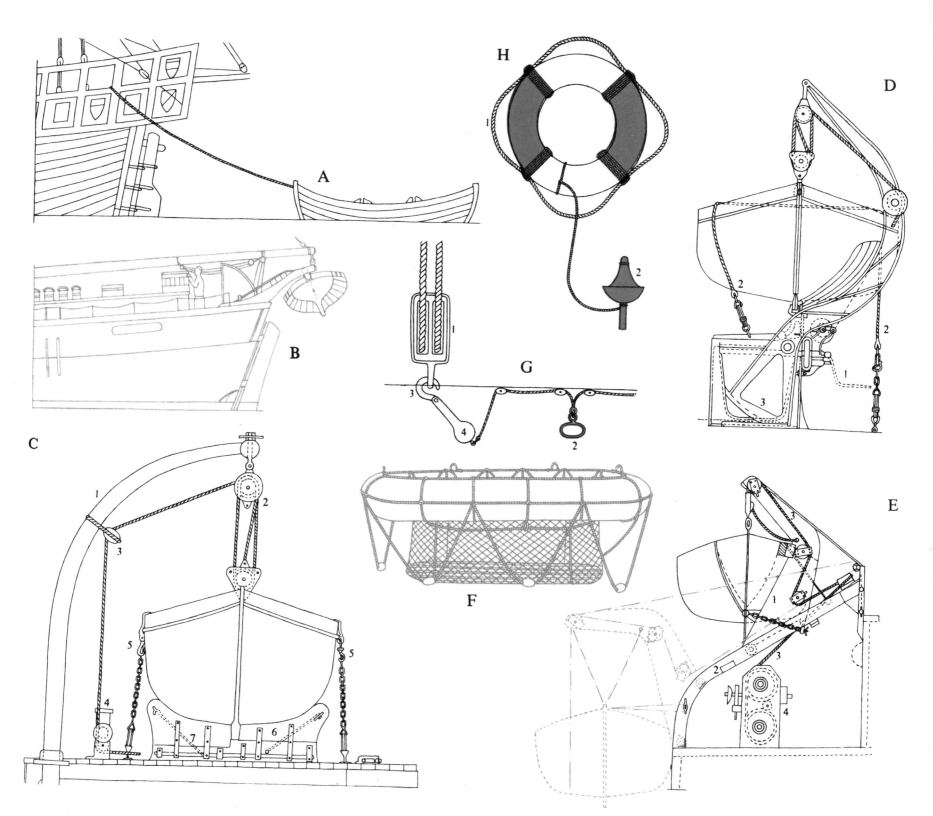

SOME TYPES OF LIFEBOAT DAVITS

A *Medieval ship towing her barge*

B *Auxiliary coaster with her boat slung from short davits across her transom stern*

C *Radical davit*
1 Davit
2 Boat fall
3 Leading block
4 Staghorn bollard
5 Gripes
6 Boat chocks
7 Hinged chocks on the outboard side

D *Quadrant davit*
1 Crank for turning out davit
2 Gripes holding boat steady
3 Toothed quadrant

E *Gravity Davit*
Davits with details shall, according to the 1960 Convention for Safety of Life at Sea, be constructed for quintuple safety, but wires must have sextuple safety. Further, gravity davits must fall into position even if the ship lists 25° to either side, and the track-way must have an angle of at least 30° to the horizontal plane.
1 Cradle mounted on rollers
2 Trackway
3 Boat fall
4 Winch

F *Carley life float*

G *Mills release apparatus*
1 Block
2 Releasing handle
3 Hook holding the block until the handle is pulled
4 Weight keeping the hook in place

H *Life buoy*
1 Life line
2 Battery operated self-igniting buoyant light

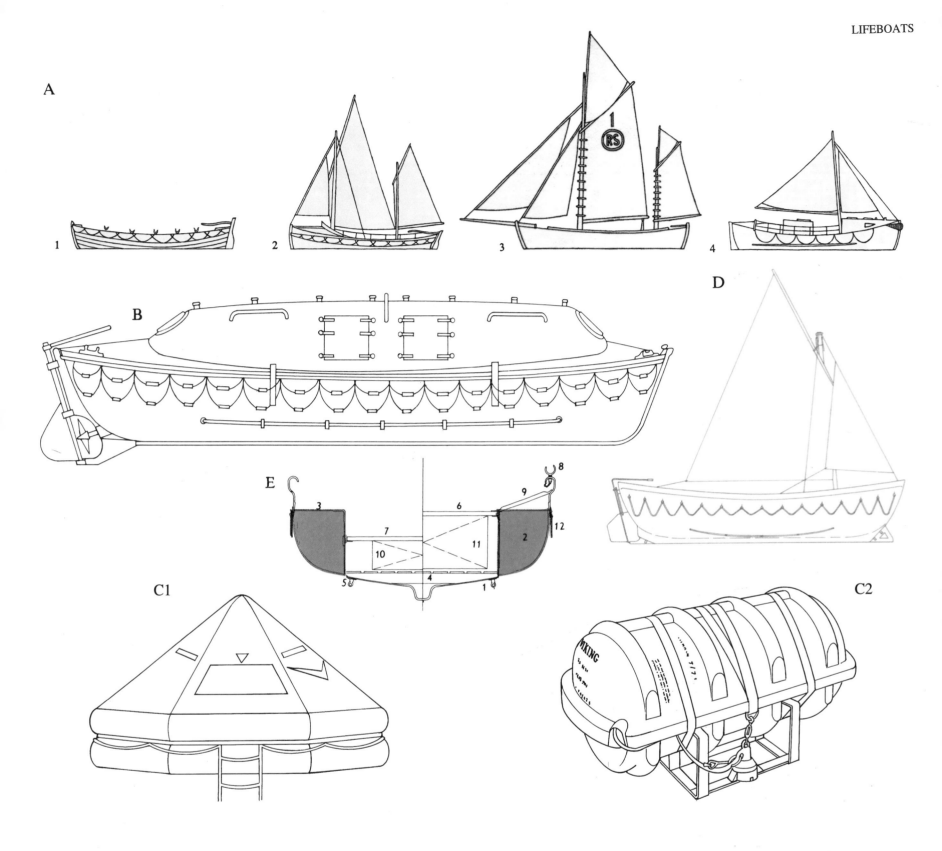

A

1

2

3

4

D

B

E

9 8

3 6

7 11 2 12

10

5 4 1

C1

C2

LIFEBOATS

A *Historical examples*
1 Old lifeboat equipped only with oars
2 English sailing lifeboat, ca. 1900
3 Norwegian "rescue boat" *Colin Archer*, built 1893
4 British self-erecting sail/motor lifeboat

B *Fireproof tanker lifeboat*

C *Raft for large ships*
1 Inflatable life raft
2 Fibreglass-reinforced plastic container for storage of life raft

D *Typical fibreglass lifeboat with sail*

E *A standard-approved fibreglass lifeboat (cross-section)*
1 Fibreglass hull
2 Polyurethane foam-filled float-tank
3 Fibreglass side bench

4 Wooden rails and floor
5 Grab-rail
6 Thwart
7 Lower sitting bench
8 Movable oar-lock with safety chain
9 Rail stanchion
10 Water tank
11 Food storage tank
12 Grab-rope

The SANTA MARIA is shown once again to introduce the chapter on spars and rigging. There is not much rigging left on modern ships, therefore most of this chapter will deal with times gone by.

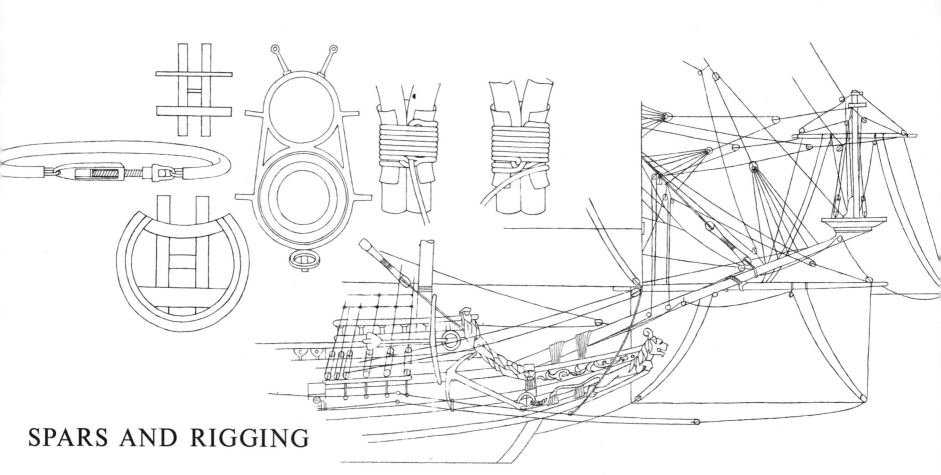

SPARS AND RIGGING

BY SAM SVENSSON

Exactly when and where primitive man first rigged a mast and sail to his simple boat remains a mystery. But quite early, he must have noticed that if he stood up in his craft, he would drift in the direction in which the wind was blowing. If he wanted to go in this direction, he might very well have speeded up his journey by holding up a cloak or animal hide to catch the wind. The time that elapsed between this first step and the introduction of the first real mast was certainly extremely long. And for many thousands of years a single mast and a simple square sail were the limit of the ancient sailor's ability to rig a boat.

Far along through the ages, from the Old Empire in Egypt and well into the European Middle Ages, the single mast remained the only rig. One break in the monotony comes in the Roman era, when the Roman sailing ship had a bowsprit, sometimes seen as a greatly inclined foremast.

In Mediterranean lands, where the rowing galley played an important role, the mast and sail evolved somewhat differently than in Western Europe, where the single mast and square sail were prevalent up to the beginning of the 15th century. The standing rigging was very simple. Smaller ships at times had none, as in the rudimentary sailing boats of the early Scandinavian fishermen.

The running gear also was very simple. The halliard hoisting the sail was led aft and acted as a backstay, thus also serving to strengthen the mast when sailing. In the early Middle Ages bowlines were added to the sail and led forward to a spar, called the bowsprit, which was rigged out over the stem.

The shrouds were set up with deadeyes and lanyards, and the rigging was rattled down, forming rope ladders to facilitate going aloft. The Northern ship was also given a fighting top at the masthead. This top is actually very old. In fact, our oldest reproduction of the fighting top is to be found on an Egyptian relief from about 1200 B.C. The oldest top mentioned in Scandinavia is in the saga of Haakon Hardabred, 1159, contained in *Snorres Konungasagor.*

Sometime during the first half of the 15th century larger ships were built with two or three masts. In northwest Europe evolution quickly culminated in three masts. The mainmast kept its location in the middle of the ship, and from the beginning the new masts were stepped in the fore- and aftercastles. As improvements were made, it was most likely that flags or banners were first flown there, a common practice during the Crusades, and that it was just as easy to hoist a small sail on this same flag-pole. One could even go so far as to say that every square sail, except the first, of course, was preceded by a flag on a pole. Thus, big ships unfurled a banner aloft on a staff in the fighting top, and toward the end of the 15th century they appeared with a small sail on the same staff. From the beginning this small sail was handled by the men in the top, and it was from this that the name topsail was derived. The Dutch, Germans, and Scandinavians used a similar term; to them the sail was known as the "märssegel." The main topsail was soon followed by a second sail on the foremast. Both were small at first, but they continually increased in size as they came to be used more and more. The clews were sheeted to the yardarms below, and, with braces and clewlines leading down to the deck, the sail became more functional. As it could be set flatter, it could be used when sailing on the wind.

The triangular lateen sail, in general use in galleys and fishing boats of the Mediterranean, was eventually used as the mizzen in big ships all along the European coast. Its use had spread all the way to the Baltic Sea by the end of the Middle Ages. There, it gradually supplanted the older square sail as the mizzen. In the 250 years that followed, the lateen mizzen continued to be used in all larger ships.

The bowsprit had originally served only to lead the bowlines. By the end of the Middle Ages, however, a square sail had been rigged under the bowsprit. This sail was called a blind in Medieval English, as it wholly blocked the view ahead. It was, perhaps, the blind that prompted the need for a lookout aloft. Later, it became known as the spritsail.

By the last quarter of the 15th century larger ships began to have as many as four masts. The two aftermost masts generally had lateen sails only, but the main mizzenmast could carry a triangular topsail on a topmast as well. The smaller mizzen, known as the bonaventure mizzen, usually reached abaft the ship where it was sheeted to a spar rigged out over the stern.

The topsail continued to grow in size, and around the middle of the 16th century larger ships began to carry a third square sail, the topgallant sail, on the fore- and mainmasts. Until this time, however, the topmasts had been fixed extensions of the masts themselves and could not be rigged down. But around the 1570's, topmasts began to be stepped, to be fidded as the term was, so they could be rigged up or taken down depending on circumstances. This innovation, credited to the Dutch, was found to be very practical and was soon adopted for general use. Consequently, the fidded topmasts grew larger in relation to the lower masts; the topsail grew deeper, and the lower sail shallower.

Around 1620 it was common to equip the third mast with a square topsail. At the same time, the bonaventure mizzenmast was discarded. This marked the creation of the three-masted ship, with square sails on each mast. These early ships always had one yard less on the mizzenmast than on the fore- and mainmasts.

It was not until the latter half of the 18th century that rigging had evolved to the point where each mast had the same number of yards. This was the time when the term full-rigged ship became universal. The full-rigged ship usually referred to a merchant vessel, while sailing warships with such a rig were referred to by their rating: ship of the line, frigate, or sloop. The ships of the early 17th century were built with low heads and high sterns.

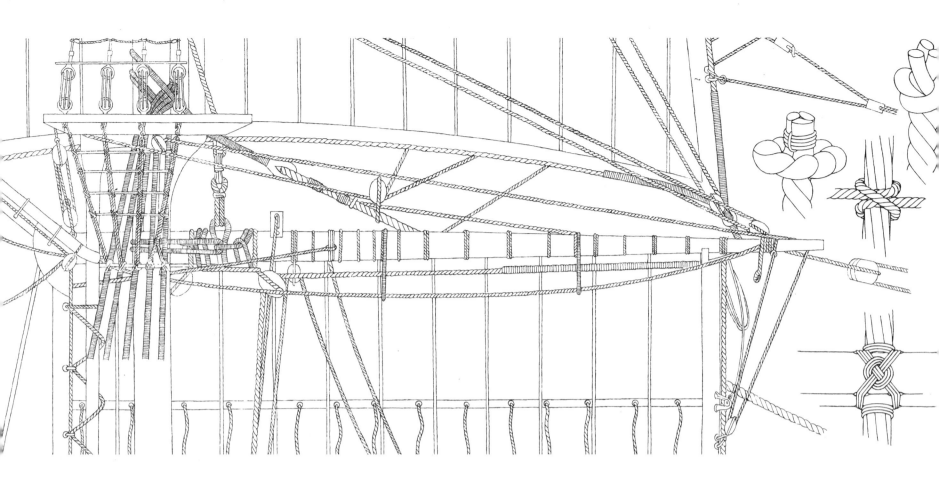

This design made them very hard to steer when the wind was abaft the beam, and the need for more headsail was keenly felt. To remedy the problem all larger ships of the 19th century were rigged with a spritsail topsail on a small mast at the end of the bowsprit. This sail was very impractical, though it was found to be very necessary, and it remained in use for over a hundred years before it was replaced with more practical and effective staysails.

Staysails had been used quite early in small craft, but not in the big ships. By the 1670's, however, the larger ships began carrying staysails, first between the masts and later over the bowsprit. This fore topmast staysail over the bowsprit was difficult to set because of the complicated rigging of the spritsail and sprit topsail. This was also the case with the staysails between the masts, because of the braces and bowlines leading to the stays. The staysails won out over the others, though, and in the beginning of the 18th century the spritsail topmast was discarded and the running gear was gradually changed to make more room for the staysails of the mainmast. This development continued through the entire 18th century, and by the end of the century larger ships carried a staysail on every possible stay.

When the spritsail topmast was discarded in the first decade of the 18th century, a new spar, the jib boom, was rigged out on the bowsprit. A new staysail, called the jib, was placed over it ahead of the fore topmast staysail. After the middle of the same century the lateen mizzen's long yard was exchanged for a gaff. This change occurred earlier in the smaller vessels than in the big ones.

During the Napoleonic wars, at the end of the century, other changes began to take place in the rigging. The mizzen was enlarged and sheeted to a boom extending over the stern. Under the bowsprit a new spar, called the martingale or dolphin striker, was inserted to improve the staying of the jib boom. This all developed into a new spar and staysail, the flying jib boom and flying jib, which were rigged outside the jib. A fourth yard above the topgallant yard, called the royal yard, now became

more and more common on larger ships. Men-of-war always set it flying, while merchant ships set it as a standing sail carried on the upper part of the long topgallant mast. Only on hard winter trips was it rigged down. But this, of course, was true of all unnecessary rigging in prolonged bad weather.

The 19th century's mechanical revolution gradually began to influence the rigging of sailing ships. At first, it was merely a replacement on masts and yards of rope fittings, strops, and so on, with forged iron bands. Then the rope trusses of the lower yards were replaced with iron trusses, called patent trusses. Wherever possible, the heavier running rigging was replaced with chain, first the topsail ties and sheets and then the topgallant ties and sheets, and then just about anywhere chain could be used to advantage. By the middle of the 19th century British ships began to have the standing rigging replaced with wire. The rigging had previously been made of tarred hemp rope, but wire was cheaper and stronger and more durable. It had less surface exposed to the wind, and as the early attempts to build iron vessels were crowned with success, wire rigging was used more and more on larger ships, especially on steamships, which always had rigging and sails by the 19th century.

The huge topsails on larger sailing ships were extremely hard to handle during storms, when they had to be reefed. The American captain, Robert Forbes, devised a rig with double topsails in 1841. In 1854, another American sea captain, named Howes, improved this rig, and it became common in big ships. Twenty years later, in 1874, the largest ships were also rigged with double topgallant yards, as well as double topsail yards.

By this time the use of wire for standing rigging and of chain for sheets and halliards was entirely accepted. Standing rigging now featured turnbuckles instead of deadeyes and lanyards, the system used ever since the early Middle Ages. Strong but stiff tarred hemp was replaced with Manila rope for running gear. Manila rope was softer and easier to work and just as strong, though

not as durable as the hemp used formerly. Block sheaves were furnished with roller bearings, which also served to lighten the work on board ship. In fact, so much was done to ease the work on deck and aloft that the vessels could now be sailed with fewer hands, and larger ships could be sailed with the same crew as had been required for a smaller ship twenty years earlier. Sail handling became more mechanized in the large ships. In the 1890's, the Scottish sea captain, J.C.B. Jarvis, devised a geared mechanical winch that allowed a couple of men to brace the yards in the largest ships in rough weather. This was, of course, a big help. In the last of the big ships the topsail and topgallant halliards of chain were replaced with wire regulated by a hand-operated drum winch. Equipped with a conical drum, the winch considerably eased the effort of raising the yard.

All these innovations were part of that universal sequence of events that provided labor-saving devices in many areas of trade. For the sailing ship, these innovations had to be adapted to the special needs of the sea. They were needed to enable the sailing ship, with only the wind for power, to face up to the competition now provided by the coal- and oil-burning ships of the new age. It was obviously not a successful struggle, and the new means of propulsion became a prime factor in the disappearance of the sailing ship from all the seas of the world.

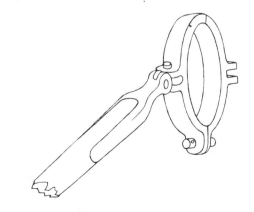

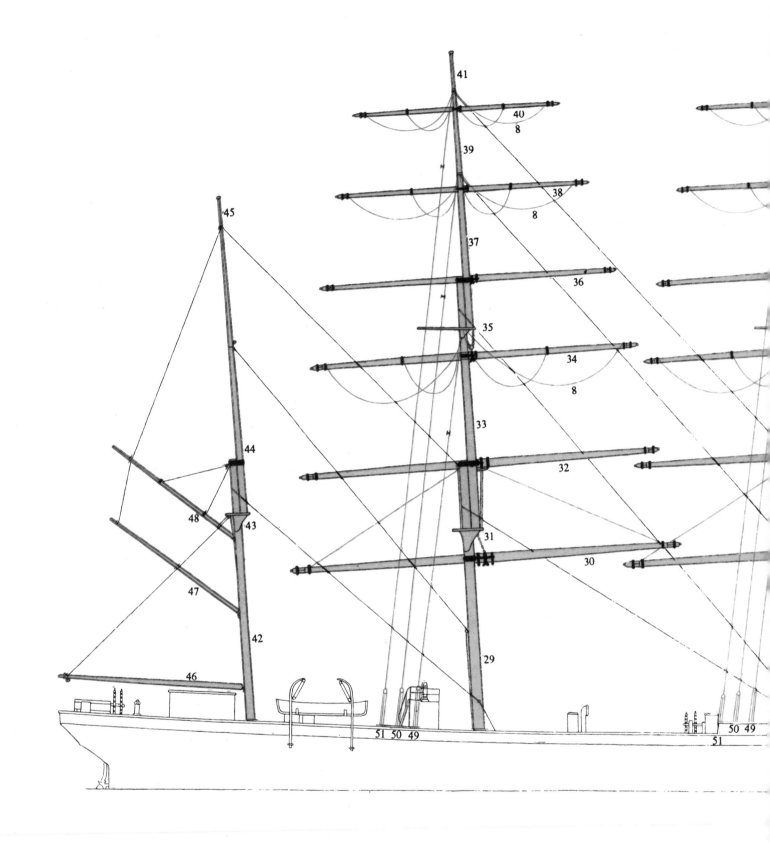

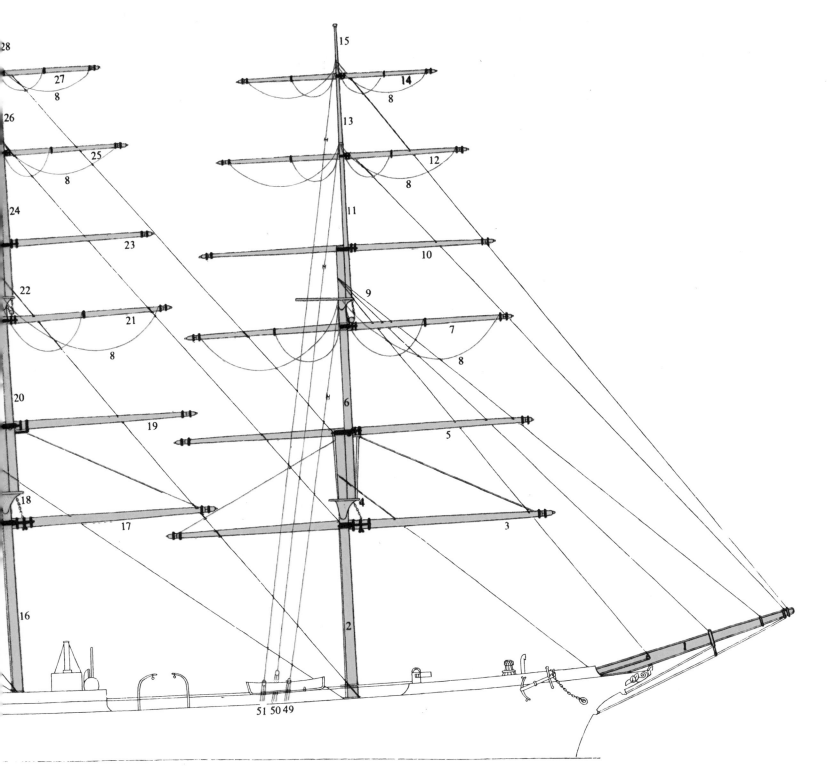

SPARS OF A FOUR-MASTED BARK

1 Spike bowsprit
2 Fore lower mast
3 Fore yard
4 Fore top
5 Fore lower topsail yard
6 Fore topmast
7 Fore upper topsail yard, hoisted
8 Lifts
9 Fore topmast crosstree

10 Fore lower topgallant yard
11 Fore topgallant mast
12 Fore upper topgallant yard, hoisted
13 Fore royal mast in one with topgallant mast
14 Fore royal yard, hoisted
15 Fore royal pole
16 Main lower mast
17 Mainyard

18 Main top
19 Main lower topsail yard
20 Main topmast
21 Main upper topsail yard, hoisted
22 Main topmast crosstree
23 Main lower topgallant yard
24 Main topgallant mast
25 Main upper topgallant yard, hoisted

26 Main royal mast
27 Main royal yard, hoisted
28 Main royal pole
29 Mizzen lower mast
30 Crossjack yard
31 Mizzen top
32 Mizzen lower topsail yard
33 Mizzen topmast

34 Mizzen upper topsail yard, hoisted
35 Mizzen topmast crosstree
36 Mizzen lower topgallant yard
37 Mizzen topgallant mast
38 Mizzen upper topgallant yard, hoisted
39 Mizzen royal mast
40 Mizzen royal yard, hoisted

41 Mizzen pole
42 Jigger lower mast
43 Jigger top
44 Jigger topmast
45 Jigger pole
46 Spanker boom
47 Lower spanker gaff
48 Upper spanker gaff
49 Upper topsail halliard
50 Upper topgallant halliard
51 Royal halliard

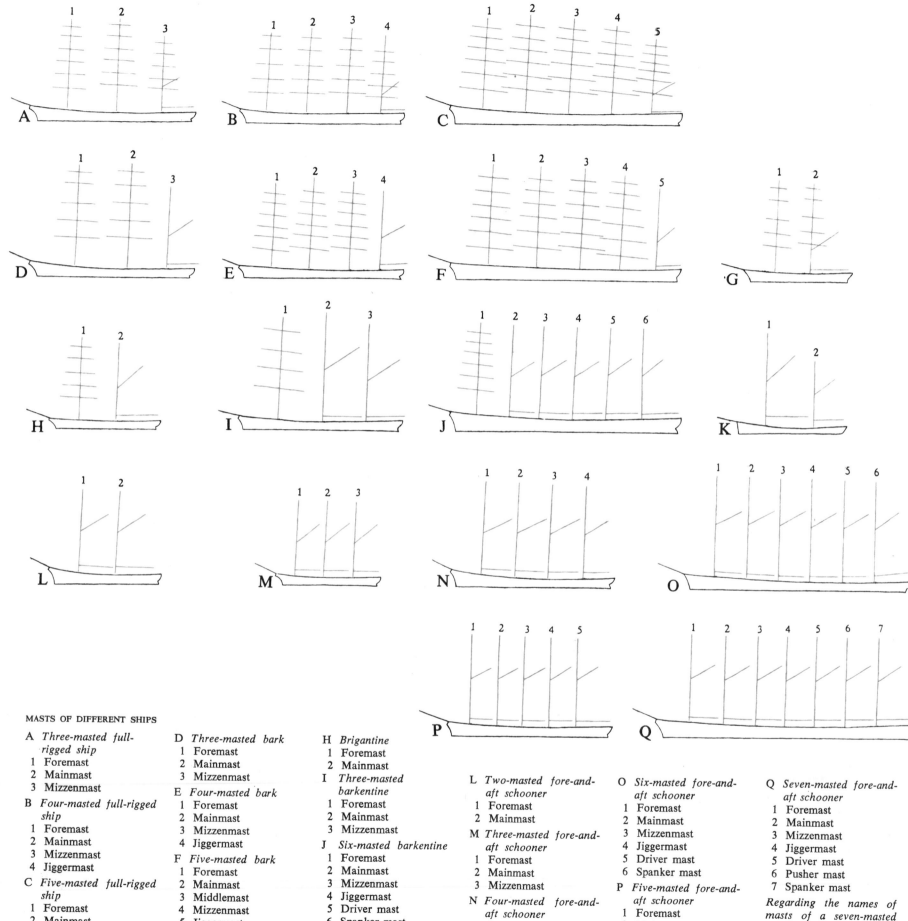

MASTS OF DIFFERENT SHIPS

A *Three-masted full-rigged ship*
 1 Foremast
 2 Mainmast
 3 Mizzenmast

B *Four-masted full-rigged ship*
 1 Foremast
 2 Mainmast
 3 Mizzenmast
 4 Jiggermast

C *Five-masted full-rigged ship*
 1 Foremast
 2 Mainmast
 3 Middlemast
 4 Mizzenmast
 5 Jiggermast

D *Three-masted bark*
 1 Foremast
 2 Mainmast
 3 Mizzenmast

E *Four-masted bark*
 1 Foremast
 2 Mainmast
 3 Mizzenmast
 4 Jiggermast

F *Five-masted bark*
 1 Foremast
 2 Mainmast
 3 Middlemast
 4 Mizzenmast
 5 Jiggermast

G *Brig*
 1 Foremast
 2 Mainmast

H *Brigantine*
 1 Foremast
 2 Mainmast

I *Three-masted barkentine*
 1 Foremast
 2 Mainmast
 3 Mizzenmast

J *Six-masted barkentine*
 1 Foremast
 2 Mainmast
 3 Mizzenmast
 4 Jiggermast
 5 Driver mast
 6 Spanker mast

K *Ketch*
 1 Mainmast
 2 Mizzenmast

L *Two-masted fore-and-aft schooner*
 1 Foremast
 2 Mainmast

M *Three-masted fore-and-aft schooner*
 1 Foremast
 2 Mainmast
 3 Mizzenmast

N *Four-masted fore-and-aft schooner*
 1 Foremast
 2 Mainmast
 3 Mizzenmast
 4 Spanker mast

O *Six-masted fore-and-aft schooner*
 1 Foremast
 2 Mainmast
 3 Mizzenmast
 4 Jiggermast
 5 Driver mast
 6 Spanker mast

P *Five-masted fore-and-aft schooner*
 1 Foremast
 2 Mainmast
 3 Mizzenmast
 4 Jiggermast
 5 Spanker mast

Q *Seven-masted fore-and-aft schooner*
 1 Foremast
 2 Mainmast
 3 Mizzenmast
 4 Jiggermast
 5 Driver mast
 6 Pusher mast
 7 Spanker mast

Regarding the names of masts of a seven-masted schooner, see also page 132

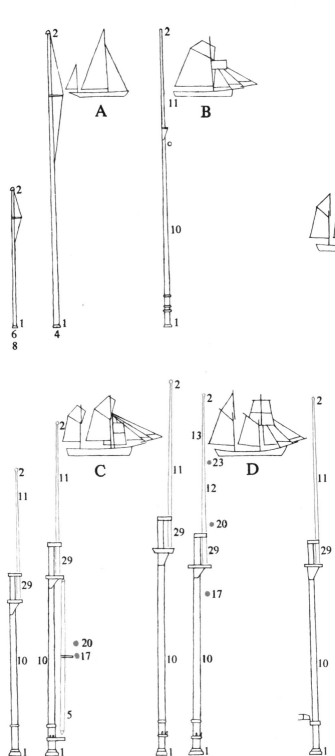

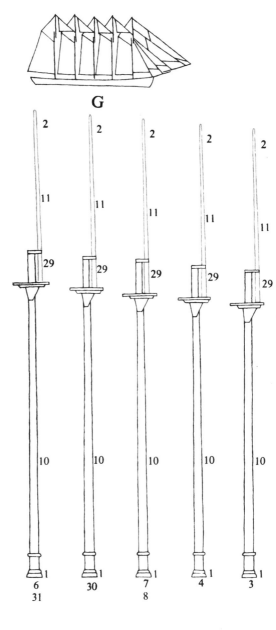

MASTS AND SPARS IN DIFFERENT SHIPS

A *Yawl*
B *Sloop, about 1900*
C *Ketch, end of the 19th century*
D *Topsail schooner*
E *Barkentine*
F *Three-masted fore-and-aft schooner*
G *American five-masted fore-and-aft schooner*

1 Mast coat
2 Truck
3 Foremast
4 Mainmast
5 Snow mast
8 Mizzenmast
9 Laeisz mast
10 Lower mast
11 Fore-and-aft-rigged topmast
12 Square-rigged topmast

13 Topgallant mast
14 Royal mast
15 Skysail mast
16 Moonsail mast
17 Fore yard
18 Main yard
19 Crossjack yard
20 Topsail yard for single topsail
21 Lower topsail yard
22 Upper topsail yard
23 Topgallant yard for single topgallant sail

24 Lower topgallant yard
25 Upper topgallant yard
26 Royal yard
27 Skysail yard
28 Moonsail yard
29 Masthead and housing of topmast
30 Jiggermast
31 Spankermast
32 Flagpole
33 Laeisz yard
34 Jigger yard

The terminology for masts varies in different languages. Numbers 6 and 7, missing in list above, refer to Teutonic languages only.

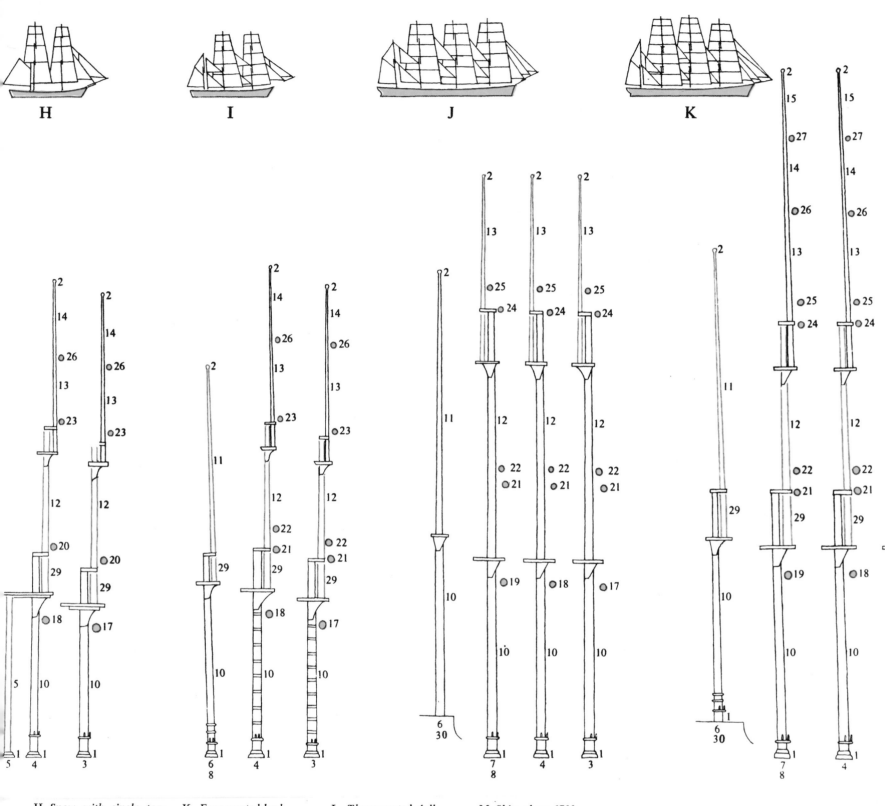

H Snow with single top-
   sails
I Three-masted bark with
   double topsails
J Four-masted bark
   with short topgallant
   masts abaft the top-
   masts

K Four-masted bark
   with royals and double
   topgallant sails, skysails
   on the main and the
   mizzen

L Three-masted, full-
   rigged ship, American
   clipper, about 1850,
   with skysails and a main
   moonsail

M Ship, about 1700
N Five-masted full-rigged
   ship (Preussen, the
   only ship of this
   rig ever built)

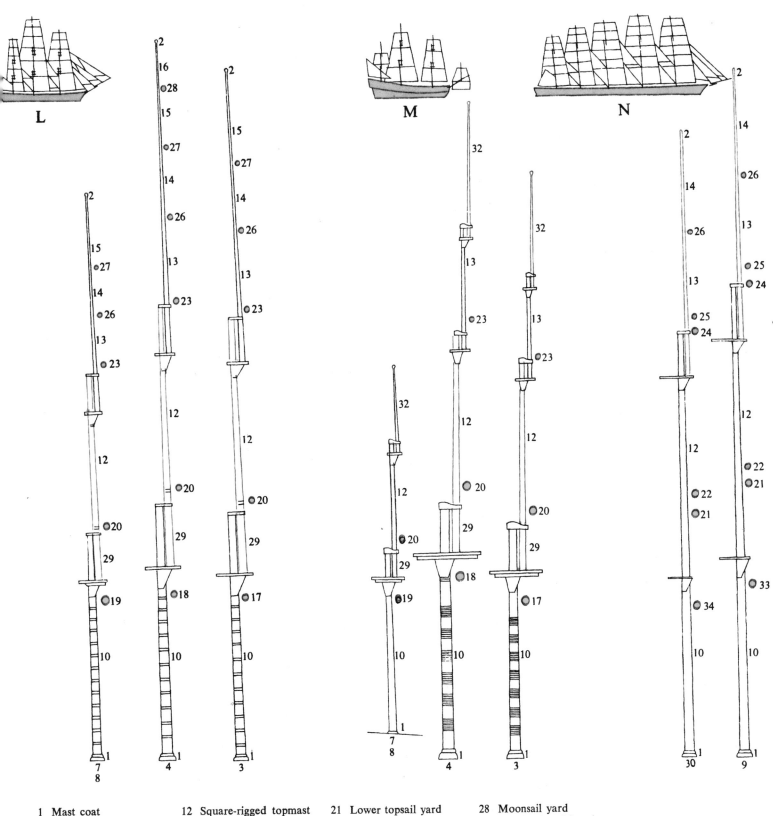

1	Mast coat	12	Square-rigged topmast	21	Lower topsail yard	28	Moonsail yard
2	Truck	13	Topgallant mast	22	Upper topsail yard	29	Masthead and housing
3	Foremast	14	Royal mast	23	Topgallant yard for		of topmast
4	Mainmast	15	Skysail mast		single topgallant sail	30	Jiggermast
5	Snow mast	16	Moonsail mast	24	Lower topgallant yard	31	Spankermast
8	Mizzenmast	17	Fore yard	25	Upper topgallant yard	32	Flagpole
9	Laeisz mast	18	Main yard	26	Royal yard	33	Laeisz yard
10	Lower mast	19	Crossjack yard	27	Skysail yard	34	Jigger yard
11	Fore-and-aft-rigged	20	Topsail yard for single				
	topmast		topsail				

The terminology for masts varies in different languages. Numbers 6 and 7, missing in list above, refer to Teutonic languages only.

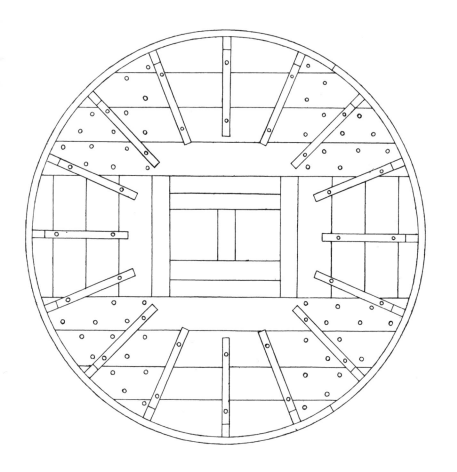

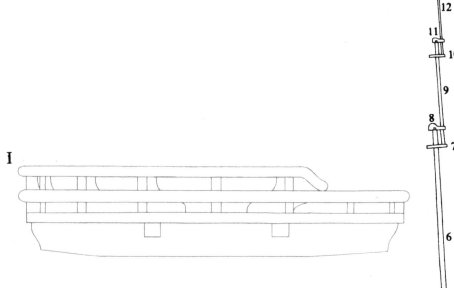

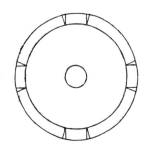

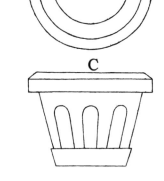

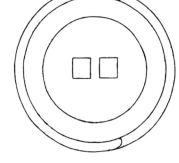

A   **B**   **C**   **D**

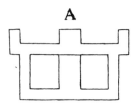

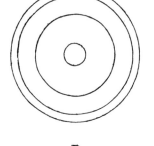

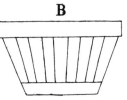

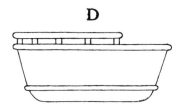

MASTS AND TOPS

A *Early medieval top*
B *Medieval top*
C *Medieval top*

D *Top, about 1550*
I *Top from the end of the 17th century*
J *Mast from the end of the 17th century (from an old book on ship building)*

1 Mast step in keelson
2 Lower mast
3 Cheeks
4 Trestletrees supporting rigging and topmast

5 Lower cap
6 Topmast
7 Topmast crosstree
8 Topmast cap
9 Topgallant mast

10 Topgallant crosstree
11 Topgallant cap
12 Flagpole
13 Truck

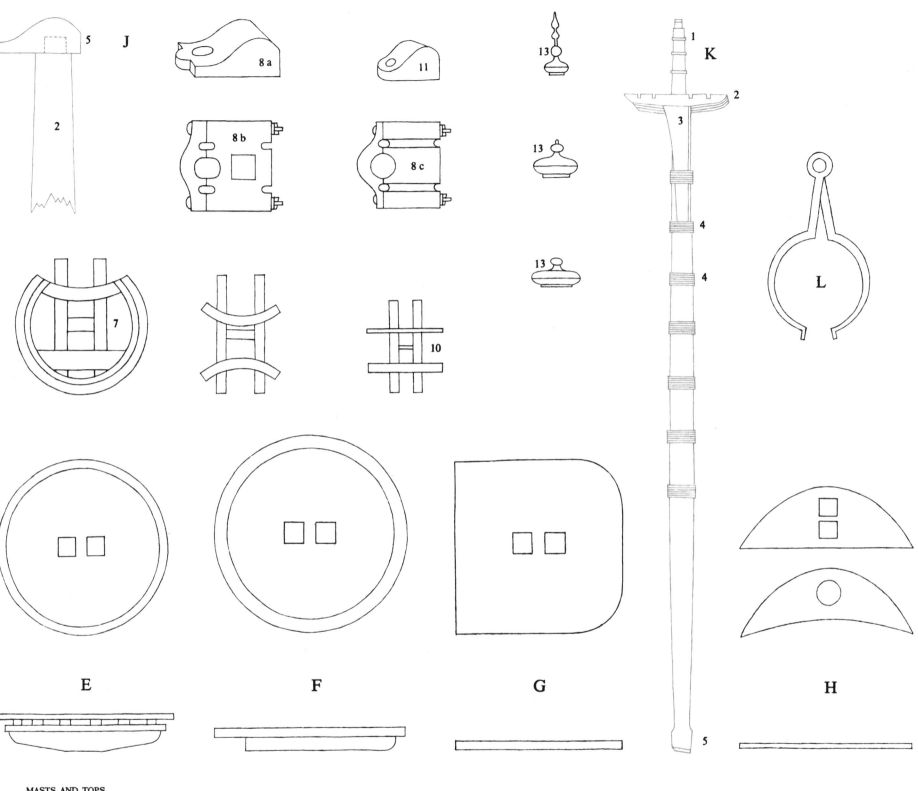

MASTS AND TOPS

E *Top in the 17th century*
F *Top in the 18th century*
G *Top in the 19th century*
H *Tops, about 1900*

J *Mast from the end of
   the 17th century (contin-
   ues from J on page 78)*
2 Lower masthead
5 Lower cap

7 Topmast crosstree
8 Dutch cap made in one
   piece, a: as seen from
   the side, b: another
   Cap made in two pieces
   as seen from below, c:
   the same as seen from
   above

10 Topgallant crosstree
11 Small Dutch cap
13 Trucks from the 17th
    century

K *Lower mast seen from
   port side*
1 Lower masthead
2 Trestletrees
3 Cheeks
4 Rope wooldings
   around the mast
5 Heel of mast

L *Mast calipers*

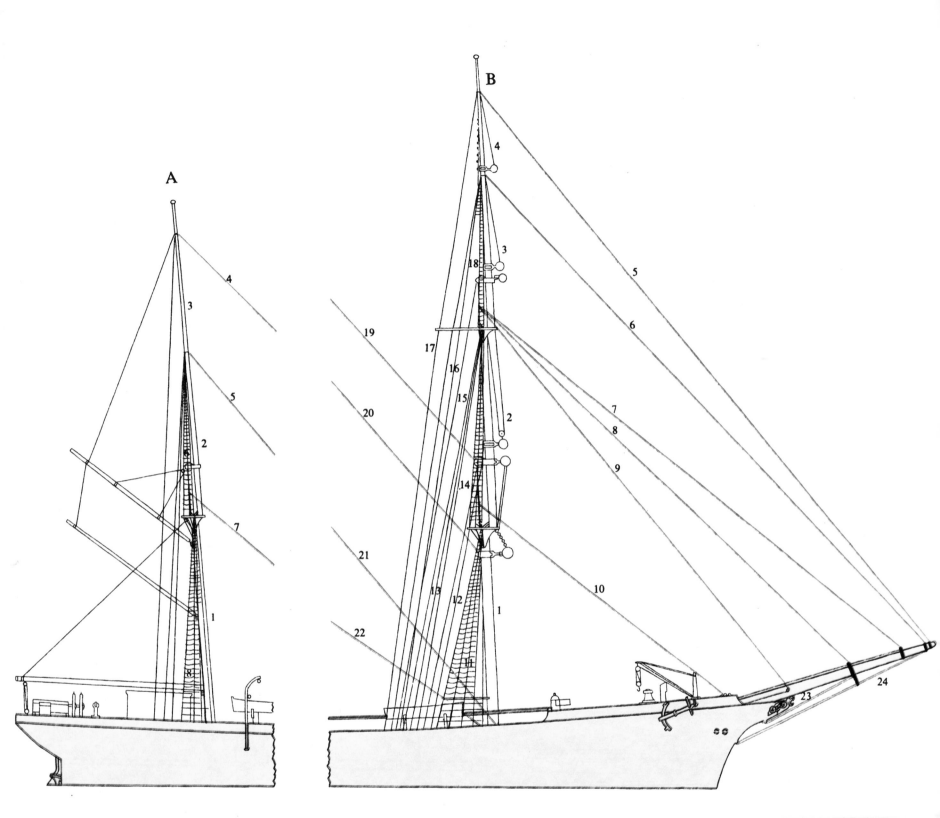

STANDING RIGGING OF A FOUR-MASTED BARK

A *Jigger mast* (identical with mizzenmast of a three-masted bark)
1 Jigger lower mast
2 Jigger topmast
3 Jigger topgallant mast
4 Jigger topgallant stay
5 Jigger topmast stay
6 Jigger topmast rigging or shrouds
7 Jigger stay
8 Jigger rigging or jigger shrouds

B *Foremast* (identical with mainmast and mizzenmast except in the lead of the stays)
1 Fore lower mast
2 Fore topmast
3 Fore topgallant mast
4 Fore royal mast
5 Fore royal stay
6 Fore topgallant stay
7 Outer jib stay
8 Inner jib stay
9 Fore topmast stay
10 Fore stay
11 Fore rigging or shrouds
12 Fore cap backstays
13 Fore topmast backstays
14 Fore topmast rigging or shrouds
15 Fore topmast cap backstay
16 Fore topgallant backstays
17 Fore royal backstay
18 Fore topgallant rigging or shrouds
19 Main royal stay
20 Main topgallant stay
21 Main topmast stay
22 Main stay
23 Bob stay
24 Outer bob stay

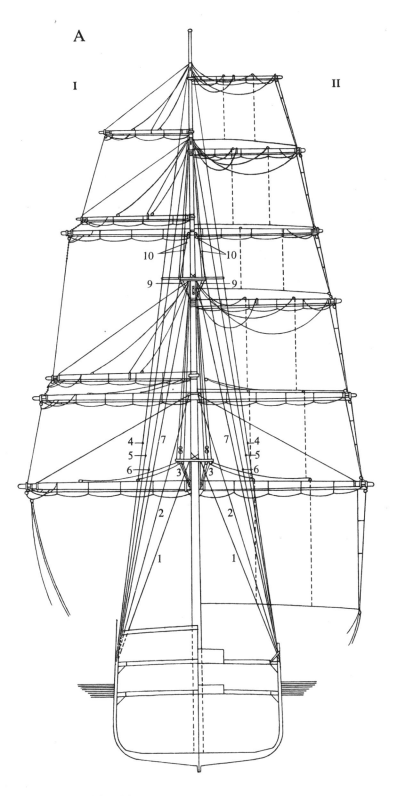

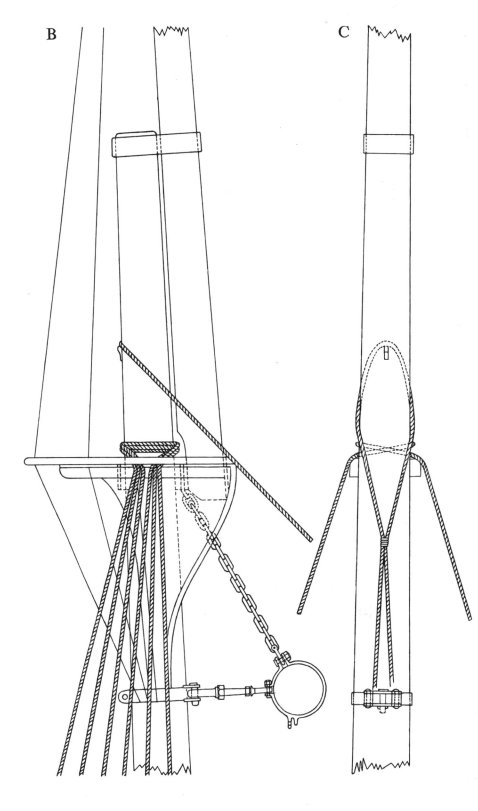

STAYS AND SHROUDS

A *Square-rigged foremast of a big modern sailing ship as seen from aft, with the sails furled on the port side (I) and set on the starboard side (II)*

1 Lower rigging or shrouds
2 Cap backstay
3 Futtock rigging, futtock shrouds
4 Royal back stay
5 Topgallant backstay(s)
6 Topmast cap backstay

7 Topmast backstay(s)
8 Topmast rigging, topmast shrouds
9 Topmast futtock rigging
10 Topgallant rigging, topgallant shrouds

B *This picture of a top, seen from the side, shows how shrouds and stays are fastened to the mast*

C *The same top as B, here seen from ahead*

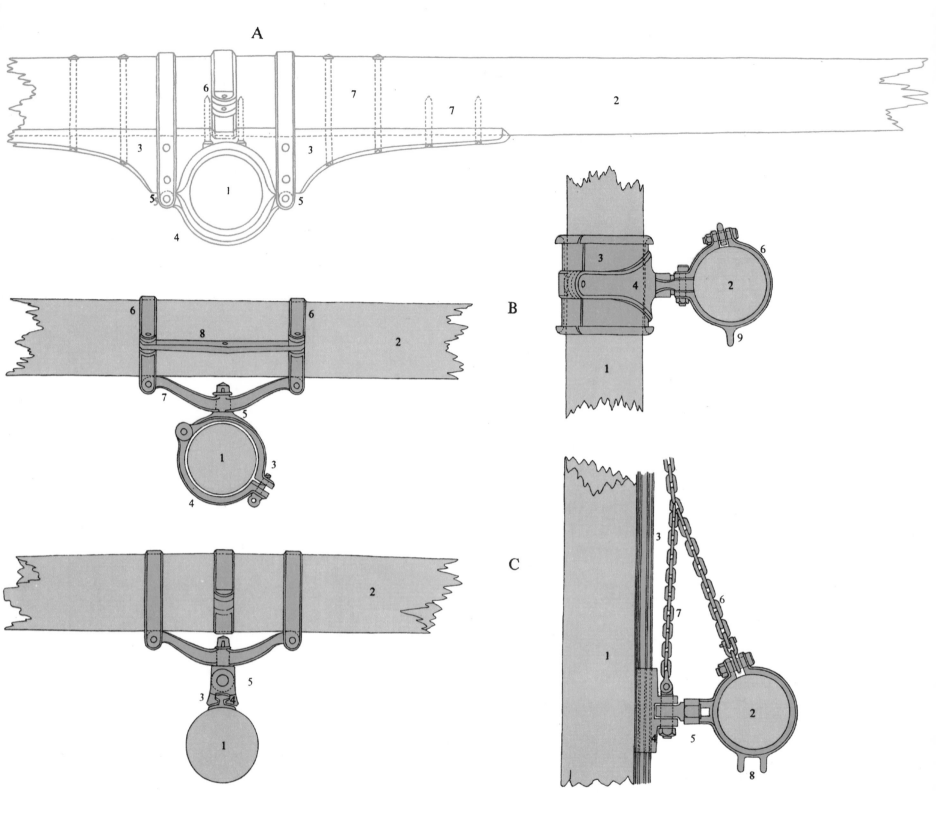

A

B

C

DIFFERENT PARRELS

A *Parrel with cleats on a wooden yard*
1 Topmast
2 Yard
3 Wooden cleats
4 Half-iron hoop served with leather

5 Pins forming hinges to open the parrel
6 Iron band to take the tie
7 Iron straps and bolts securing parrel to yard

B *Tub parrel for iron yard*
1 Topmast
2 Yard
3 Tub divided in halves
4 Iron binding for same
5 Gooseneck bolt

6 Iron bands to take parrel and tie
7 Yoke for the parrel
8 Yoke for the tie
9 Eye bolt for quarter-block

C *Parrel, sliding on T-bar in a big ship*
1 Topmast
2 Topsail yard
3 T-bar
4 Slide

5 Two-way coupling
6 Tie
7 Connecting chain keeping slide in place
8 Eye bolts for quarter-blocks

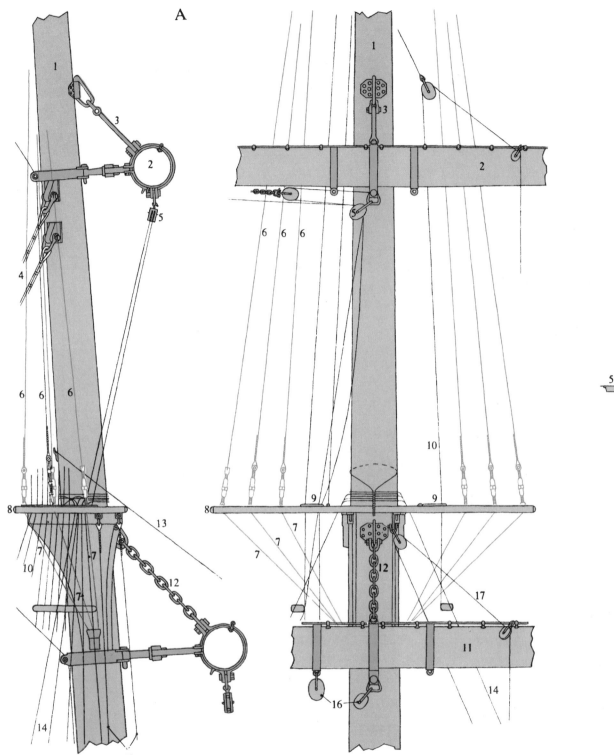

A

B

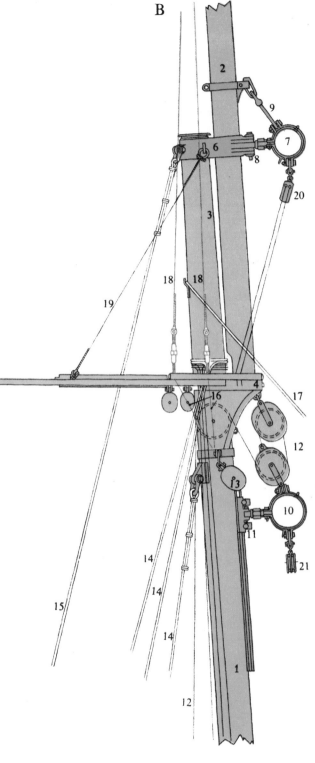

TOP AND CROSSTREES IN A BIG MODERN SAILING SHIP

A *Details around the top*
1 Topmast, built in one with lower mast
2 Lower topsail yard with its truss
3 Lower topsail yard tie
4 Lower cap backstays
5 Quarter block for upper topsail sheet and topsail clewline
6 Topmast rigging, ratlines not shown
7 Futtock shrouds
8 Top
9 Fairleader
10 Running gear rove through fairleader
11 Lower yard with its truss
12 Lower yard tie
13 Lower stay, doubled
14 Lower rigging, ratlines not shown
15 Pendants for braces from mast ahead, leading to brace winch
16 Quarterblock for topsail sheet and the course clewgarnet
17 Buntline with its leading blocks

B *Details around the topgallant crosstrees*
1 Topmast
2 Topgallant mast
3 Topmast head
4 Topgallant crosstrees
5 Spreader of topgallant backstays
6 Topmast cap
7 Lower topgallant yard
8 Lower topgallant truss
9 Lower topgallant tie
10 Upper topsail yard
11 Upper topsail parrel, slide running on a T-bar
12 Topsail halliard, wire tackle leading to winch on deck
13 Leading block for topsail brace from mast ahead
14 Topmast backstays
15 Topmast cap backstay
16 Topgallant futtock shrouds
17 Topmast stay
18 Topgallant rigging
19 Spreader lift
20 Quarterblock for lower topgallant clewline and upper topgallant sheet
21 Quarterblock for topsail downhaul and lower topgallant sheet

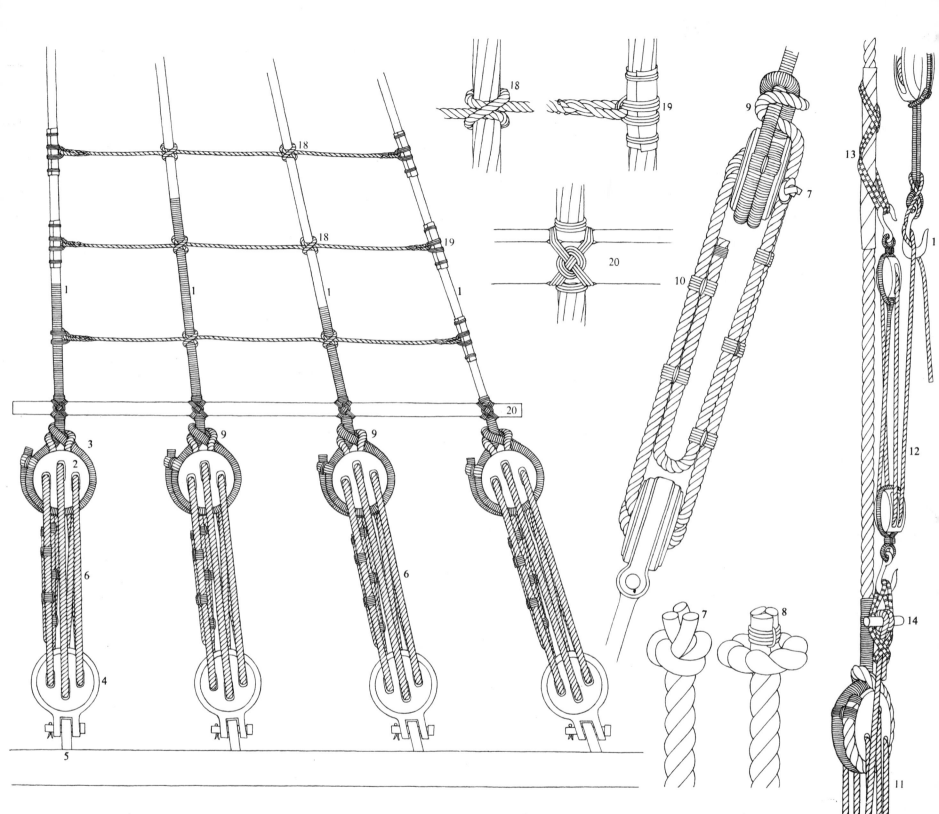

LOWER PART OF RIGGING, PORT SIDE

1 Shrouds, lower ends of which are served with spun yarn
2 Upper deadeye
3 Deadeye turned in cutter-stay fashion
4 Lower deadeye in iron strap

5 Chain plate
6 Lanyard, standing part with wall knot
7 Wall knot
8 Double wall knot
9 Hauling end of lanyard hitched

10 Surplus end of lanyard made up
11 Setting up a shroud by luff upon luff
12 Luff clapped on lanyard up and down
13 Selvagee on shroud parceled for protection

14 Selvagee strapped on lanyard with a toggle
15 Double Blackwall hitch
16 Lower block of burton from masthead
17 Standing end of lanyard passed around neck of deadeye

18 Ratlines in rigging
19 Seizing of ratline to shroud
20 Wooden batten secured to shroud with seizing wire

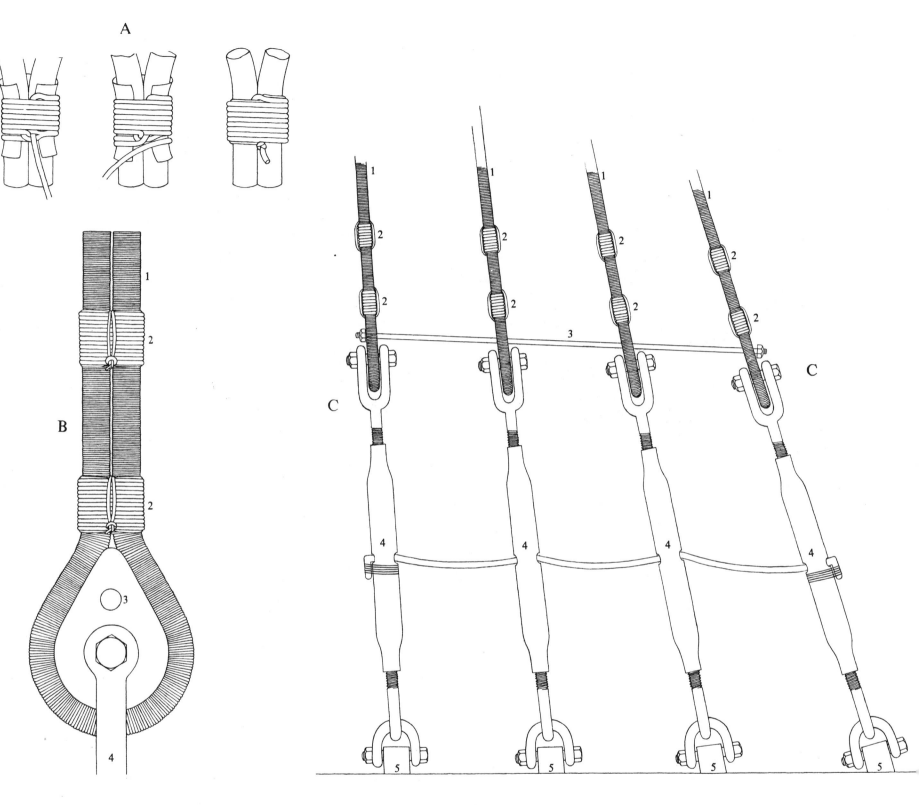

SEIZINGS AND RIGGING SCREWS

A Three stages of making an old-fashioned round seizing; formerly used on hemp shrouds

B 1 Shroud or backstay of wire served over with spun yarn
   2 Rigging seizings of galvanized wire

   3 Solid heart thimble with a hole for the sheer pole
   4 Upper end of rigging screw

C 1 Lower ends of four port side shrouds
   2 Rigging seizings
   3 Sheer pole

   4 Rigging screws or turnbuckles
   5 Upper ends of chain plates

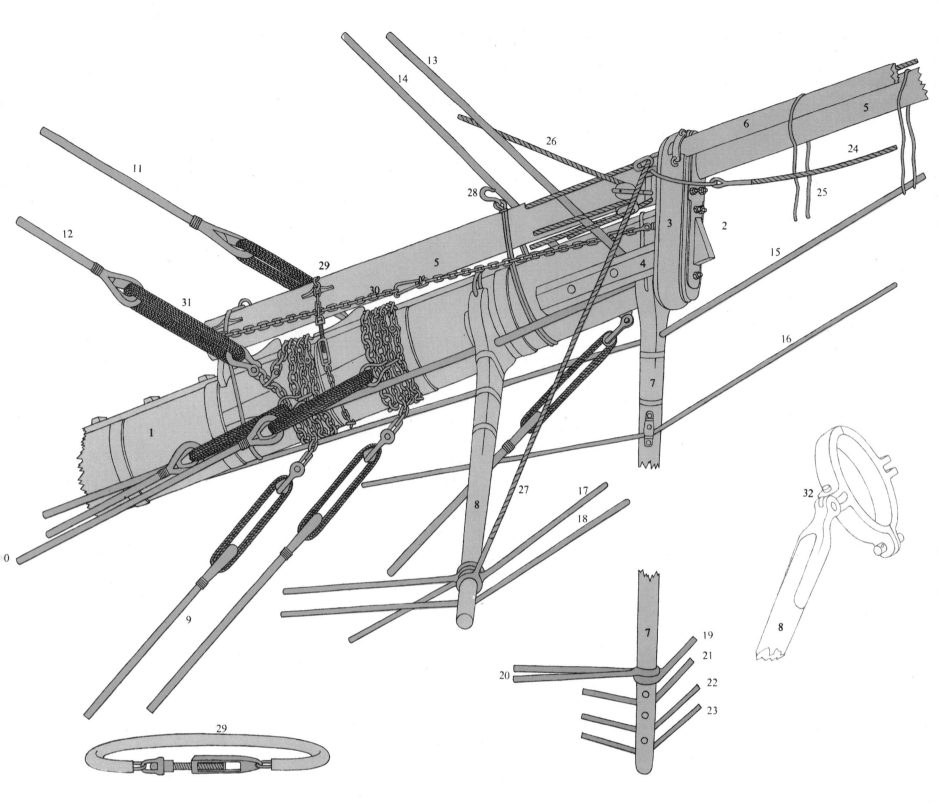

BOWSPRIT OF A FRIGATE, 1890

1 Bowsprit	7 Martingale boom or dolphin striker	12 Preventer forestay	17 Jib boom guy	23 Fore royal stay	28 Fore topmast staysail tack
2 Tenon for bowsprit cap	8 Whisker	13 Fore topmast stay	18 Flying jib boom guy	24 Jib boom horse, footrope	29 Jib boom gammoning
3 Bowsprit cap	9 Inner and outer bobstays	14 Fore topmast preventer stay	19 Martingale stay	25 Gaskets	30 Jib boom heel stay
4 Bowsprit bees		15 Jib stay	20 Backropes or martingale guys	26 Fore topsail bowline	31 Lanyards for stays
5 Jib boom	10 Bowsprit shrouds	16 Jib outhaul	21 Flying jib stay	27 Whisker lift	32 Iron fitting for whiskers
6 Heel of flying jib boom	11 Forestay		22 Fore topgallant stay		

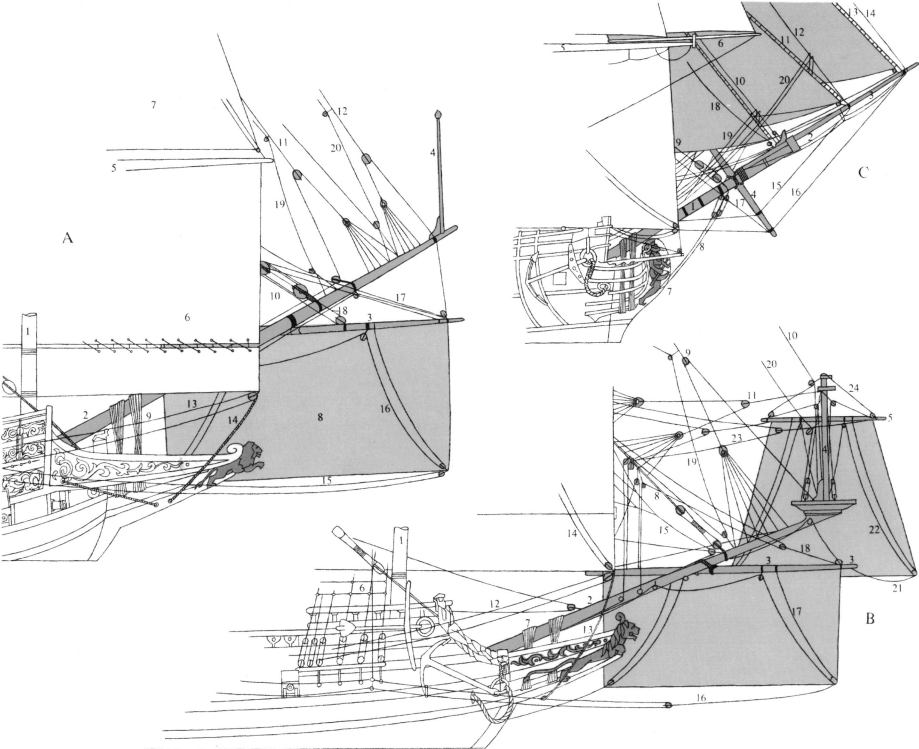

THE BOWSPRIT DURING THREE CENTURIES

A *The bowsprit and its rigging at the end of the 16th century*
1 Foremast
2 Bowsprit
3 Spritsail yard
4 Jackstaff
5 Foreyard
6 Foresail with bonnet
7 Fore topsail
8 Spritsail
9 Gammoning
10 Forestay lanyard
11 Fore topmast stay
12 Fore topgallant stay
13 Fore sheet
14 Fore tack
15 Spritsail sheet
16 Spritsail clewline
17 Spritsail braces
18 Spritsail lifts
19 Fore topsail bowline
20 Fore topgallant bowline

B *Bowsprit with spritsail topmast and rigging, from the 17th century*
1 Foremast
2 Bowsprit
3 Spritsail yard
4 Spritsail topmast
5 Spritsail topsail yard
6 Fore rigging
7 Gammoning
8 Forestay
9 Fore topmast stay
10 Fore topgallant stay
11 Spritsail topmast backstay
12 Fore sheet
13 Fore tack
14 Fore clewgarnet
15 Fore bowline
16 Spritsail sheet
17 Spritsail clewline
18 Spritsail braces
19 Fore topsail bowline
20 Fore topgallant bowline
21 Spritsail topsail sheet
22 Spritsail topsail clewline
23 Spritsail topsail braces
24 Spritsail topsail lift

C *Bowsprit with jib boom and rigging, end of the 18th century*
1 Bowsprit
2 Jib boom
3 Flying jib boom
4 Spritsail yard
5 Foreyard
6 Studdingsail boom
7 Fore tack bumpkin
8 Bobstay
9 Forestay
10 Fore topmast stay
11 Jibstay
12 Fore topgallant stay
13 Flying jibstay
14 Royal stay
15 Jib boom guy
16 Flying jib boom guy
17 Spritsail braces
18 Fore topmast staysail downhaul
19 Weather side jib sheet
20 Weather side flying jib sheet

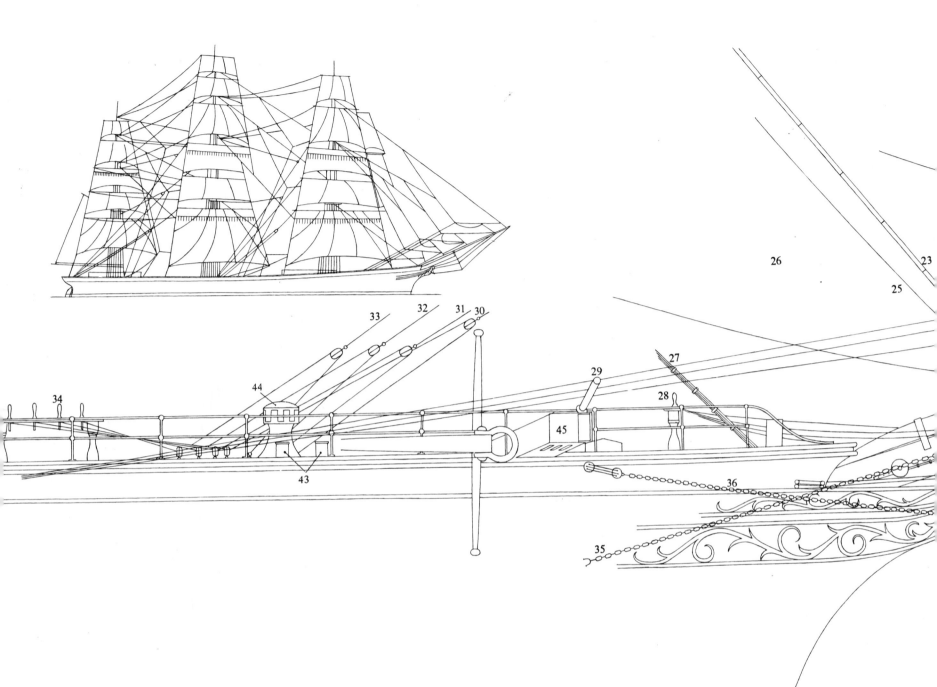

BOWSPRIT OF THE SHIP, PRINCE OSCAR, BUILT IN 1864

1 Shark's tail	10 Outer jib downhaul	19 Bowsprit cap
2 Fore royal stay	11 Outer jib	20 Swinging boom fore
3 Fore topgallant stay	12 Inner jib stay	guy lead block
4 Flying jib tack	13 Inner jib tack	21 Jib boom
5 Flying jib downhaul	14 Inner jib downhaul	22 Bowsprit
6 Flying jib	15 Inner jib	23 Fore topmast stay
7 Flying jib boom	16 Flying jib boom guy	24 Fore topmast staysail
8 Outer jib stay	17 Outer jib boom guy	tack
9 Outer jib tack	18 Inner jib boom guy	

25 Fore topmast staysail	32 Inner jib sheet	39 Inner martingale
downhaul	33 Fore topmast staysail	(stay)
26 Fore topmast staysail	sheet	40 Middle martingale
27 Fore stay	34 Pinrail	(stay)
28 Pinrail for staysails'	35 Bowsprit shroud	41 Outer martingale
downhauls	36 Martingale backrope	(stay)
29 Whisker boom	(Martingale guy)	42 Foot rope
30 Flying jib sheet	37 Bobstay	43 Bitts
31 Outer jib sheet	38 Martingale or Dolphin	44 Capstan working the
	striker	windlass
		45 Cathead

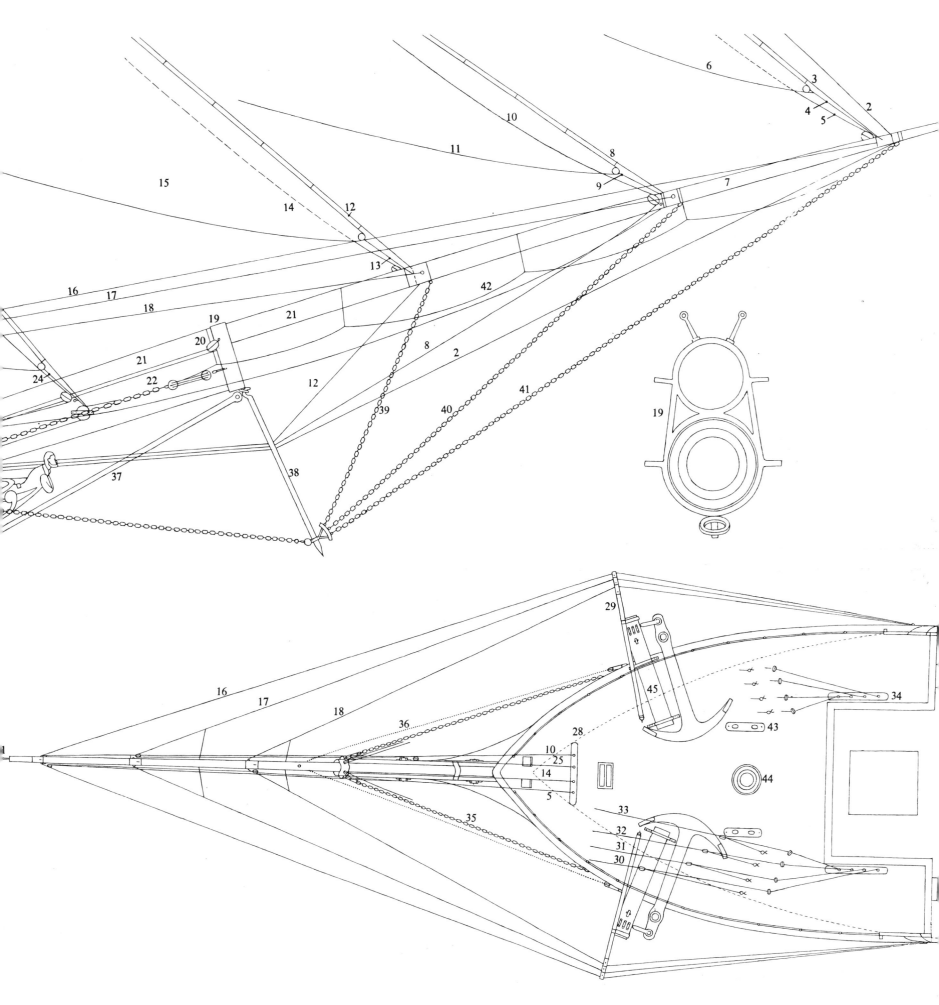

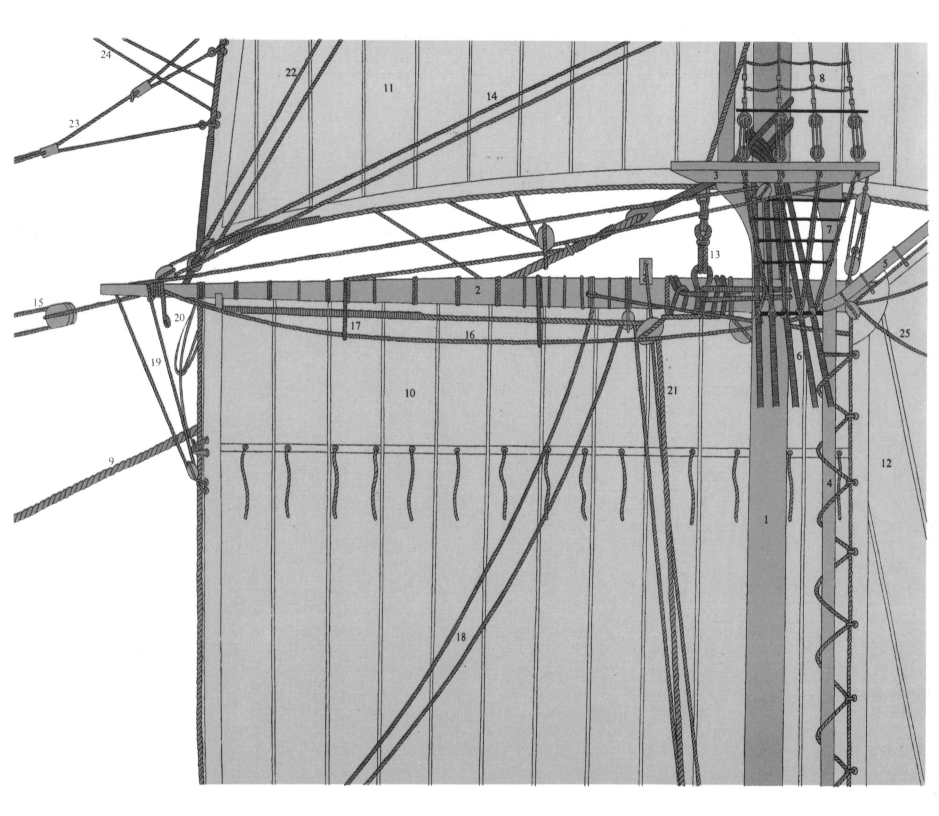

DETAILS OF MAINMAST AND MAINYARD OF A SNOW, ABOUT 1800

1 Mainmast	6 Main rigging	11 Main topsail	16 Mainyard footrope	21 Topsail sheet
2 Mainyard	or shrouds	12 Trysail	17 Mainyard stirrups	22 Topsail clewline
3 Main top	7 Futtock shrouds	13 Mainyard sling	18 Main clewgarnet	23 Topsail bowline bridle
4 Trysail mast	8 Topmast shrouds	14 Main lift	19 Reef tackle	24 Fore topsail brace
5 Trysail gaff	9 Mainstay	15 Main brace	20 Reef earing	25 Trysail brails
	10 Mainsail			

DETAILS OF MAINMAST HEAD, SHIP OF THE LINE, 1750

1 Mainmast	5 Heel of topmast	9 Parrel tackle
2 Trestle trees	6 Main cap	10 Main rigging or
3 Maintop	7 Mainyard	shrouds
4 Lower masthead	8 Main parrel	11 Mainstay
		12 Spring stay

13 Futtock shrouds	17 Main footrope
14 Topmast shrouds	18 Main clewgarnet
15 Mizzen topmast stay	19 Main topsail sheet
16 Main lift	20 Main jeers

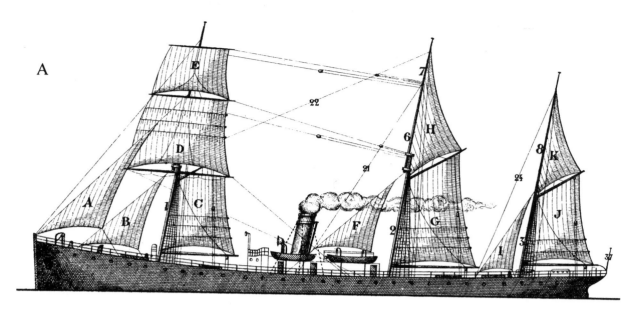

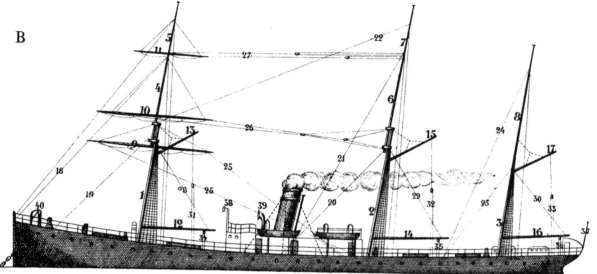

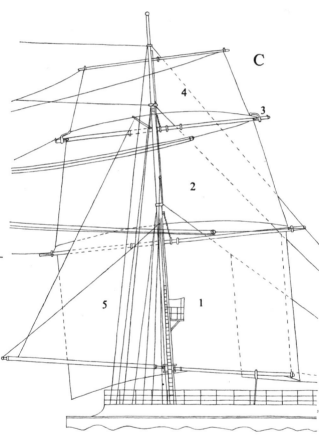

RIGGING OF OLDER STEAMERS

A, B

Steamer from about 1890, rigged as a three-masted topsail schooner

A Fore topmast staysail
B Fore staysail
C Foresail; Boom foresail
D Topsail
E Topgallant sail
F Main staysail
G Mainsail
H Main gaff topsail
I Mizzen staysail
J Mizzen
K Mizzen gaff topsail

1 Foremast
2 Mainmast
3 Mizzenmast
4 Fore topmast
5 Fore topgallant mast
6 Main topmast
7 Main topgallant mast
8 Mizzen topmast
9 Fore yard
10 Topsail yard

11 Topgallant yard
12 Fore boom
13 Fore gaff
14 Main boom
15 Main gaff
16 Mizzen boom
17 Mizzen gaff
18 Fore topmast stay
19 Fore stay
20 Main stay

21 Main topmast stay
22 Main topgallant stay
23 Mizzen stay
24 Mizzen topmast stay
25 Fore braces
26 Topsail braces
27 Topgallant braces
28 Fore boom topping lift
29 Main boom topping lift

30 Mizzen boom topping lift
31 Fore vang
32 Main vang
33 Mizzen vang
34 Boom foresail sheet
35 Main sheet
36 Mizzen sheet
37 Flagstaff
38 Pole compass
39 Ventilator
40 Anchor davit

C *Patent reefing topsails were not unusual in the old steamers carrying sails, because of the possibility of reefing without a man leaving the deck*

1 Foresail
2 Topsail with Collin's and Pinkney's Patent (3)
4 Topgallant sail
5 Bermuda-type trysail traveling on a bar abaft the mast

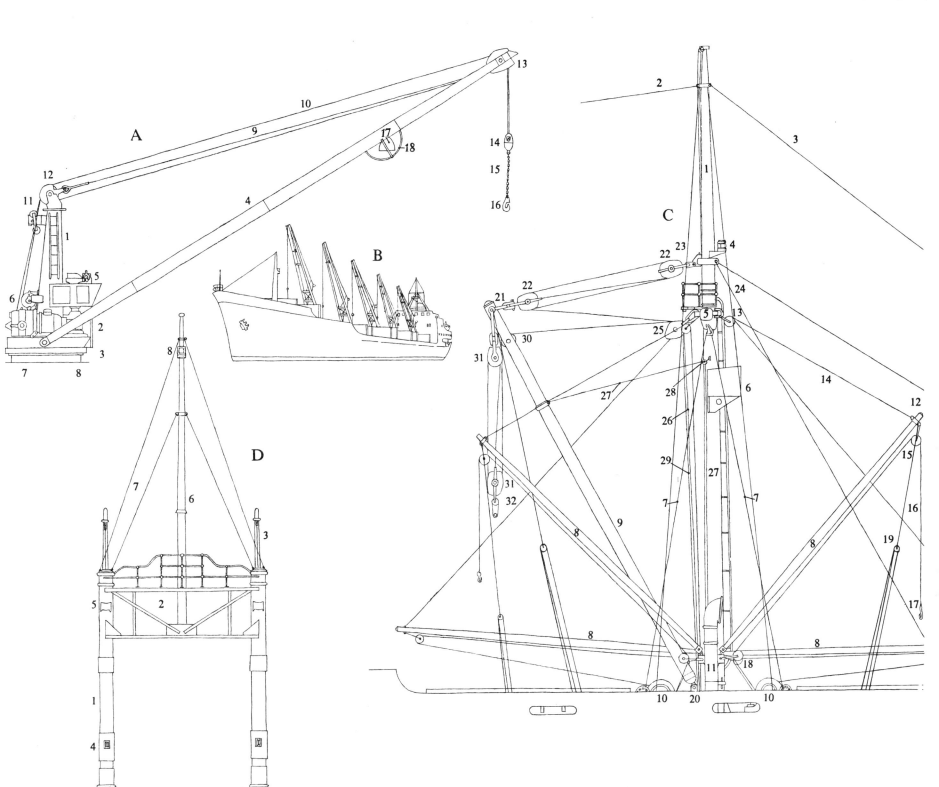

A *Electric deck crane*	12 Triple sheave block	C *Rigging and derrick arrangement*	11 5-ton boom, gooseneck	22 Four-fold topping lift tackle
1 Crane post	13 Triple sheave block	1 Foremast	12 Boom band	23 Mast band
2 Electric equipment platform	14 Weight and swivel	2 Signal stay	13 Topping lift block	24 Preventer stays
3 Turning rim	15 Chain	3 Topmast stay	14 Topping lift	25 Topping lift and cargo fall block
4 Crane jib	16 Cargo hook	4 Masthead light	15 Cargo hoist block	26 Topping lift hauling part (wire)
5 Maneuvering stand	17 Electric light	5 Outrigger	16 Cargo fall	27 Topper
6 Topping motor	18 Cage guard	6 Crow's nest	17 Cargo hook	28 Topper block
7 Hoisting motor		7 Shrouds	18 Topping lift and cargo fall heel blocks	29 Cargo fall hauling part
8 Slewing motor	B *Cargo vessel with deck cranes*	8 5-ton booms	19 5-ton boom guy	30 Cargo fall sheave
9 Topping rope		9 20-ton heavy boom	20 Heavy boom heel fitting	31 Four-fold cargo tackle
10 Hoisting rope		10 Topping and cargo winches	21 Boom head eye plate	32 20-ton cargo hook
11 Slack rope switch				

D *Goal-post mast, pair mast*	
1 King post	
2 Transverse girder	
3 Boom (behind post)	
4 Gooseneck fitting	
5 Band for lashing boom	
6 Topmast	
7 Topmast shrouds	
8 Masthead light	

*Opposite is a 1492 nao;
it is Columbus'
SANTA MARIA and it
introduces the section
about sails. The color
in the picture illustrates
the fact that the chapter
deals with flags as well.*

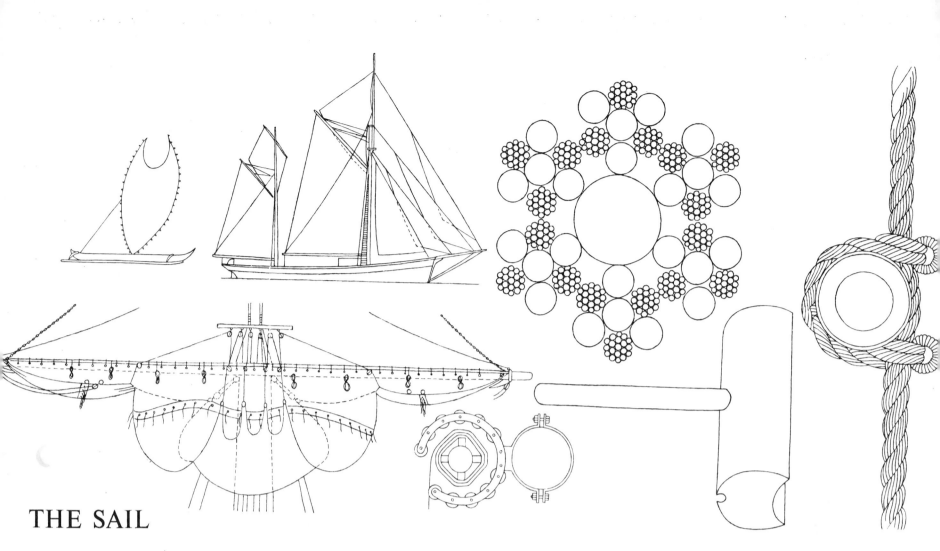

THE SAIL

BY SAM SVENSSON

The oldest sail we know is the square sail. For many thousands of years no other types were used. The distinguishing feature of the square sail is that the same side is always turned to the wind. This is a simple, fundamental principle, and none of the aerodynamic inventions of recent years have changed the square sail or influenced its value for sailing on the high seas.

The fore-and-aft sail, which can face into the wind with either side, is a more recent development. What aerodynamics could not do for the square sail it has succeeded in doing for the fore-and-aft sail. The latter is very effective in close-hauled sailing and is superior for use while cruising. Today it is the sail most used for sport sailing among off-shore islands where winds are variable and the water is smooth. Because the fore-and-aft sail always has its forward bolt rope as the windward edge and the leech as the leeward edge, it can be cut with a favorable curvature. The square sail, on the other hand, has the starboard or port leech alternately as the windward edge, resulting in a different curvature. The value of the modern fore-and-aft sail on the wind is, however, outweighed by the advantages of the more secure square sail in running before the wind in stormy and high seas. Almost all sailing on the high seas has been done with the square sail. The oldest known reproduction of a boat equipped with a sail is painted on an Egyptian clay urn from the predynastic period. Estimated to be from about 4000 B.C., it could actually be even older. Furthermore, the evidence is not conclusive that this painting shows the world's first sail. Past cultures of which we have no knowledge may very well have had sailing vessels thousands of years before.

Contemporary writings and pictures prove that the sailors of ancient lands in the eastern Mediterranean used sails.

In the twenty-seventh chapter of Ezekiel, the ships of Tyrus are described as having cedar masts from Lebanon, gay, embroidered sails of fine Egyptian linen, and awnings of blue and purple cloth from the Isles of Elisha. The decoration of the sails indicates that they were used both for propulsion and as a means of identification.

We have no record of when the art of sailing was brought to Scandinavia, but by the Viking Age it was certainly hundreds, perhaps even thousands, of years old. Early Nordic sails were made of homespun wool, and lacked the durability of linen sail. The cloth would stretch under the force of the wind, and the large sail would sag more and more until it burst. To strengthen the sail and hold it more evenly, a supporting net was fastened to the forward side. The net, often of a different color than the sail, was either of rope, of cloth bands, or of interwoven sennit. The foot of the sail was held down by a number of sheets, forming bridles, all to hold the sail flatter. By the Viking Age, linen sails were in use on larger ships. These sails could be set flatter, making for better sailing on the wind. The long journeys made by the Vikings in European waters and over the Atlantic Ocean would have been impossible, if their ships had not been able to sail with all kinds of wind. At the dawn of Swedish history, the cruising ability of the ships of the time is illustrated in the saga of the King of the Sveas, Erik Väderhatt, who, according to history, could turn the wind so that he never had a headwind.

The majority of ships continued to have only one mast and a single sail for many years. Only after the later Middle Ages did larger ships commonly appear with two or three masts and sails — one sail on each mast. By the end of the 15th century, however, a new sail was set at the head of the mainmast. It was originally

very small, and was handled by the men in the top (an early masthead castle). It derived its name, the topsail, from this position. Another sail was added under the bowsprit; this was called the spritsail or blind, as it blocked the view ahead. Eventually a topsail was also added to the foremast. By the middle of the 16th century, then, a large three-masted ship carried six sails: the spritsail under the bowsprit, two sails on the foremast, two sails on the mainmast, and one sail on the mizzenmast. The sail on the mizzenmast was always a triangular lateen sail at this time.

The origin of the lateen sail is unknown. At the fall of the Roman Empire in 476 A.D., all ships had square sails. After that, sources of information on ships and navigation in the Mediterranean are not available for several hundreds of years. Not until the end of the 9th century do Greek manuscripts show some miniatures of ships with triangular sails under an inclined yard. Even today these sails are called lateen sails. These were probably introduced into the Mediterranean by the Arabs, but no one knows whether their origin is Arabian or Polynesian. Up to the 13th century the lateen sail was in use exclusively along the Mediterranean. But from that time on, the square sail began to make a comeback under western European impetus. The lateen sail was used, at this time, along the whole European coastline, especially as a mizzen on larger ships. It probably reached the Baltic by the latter half of the 15th century, about the same time as the carvel or smooth-sided shipbuilding technique came along. Down to the middle of the 18th century the lateen sail was in general international use as the mizzen. It was then replaced by the gaff mizzen. The coastal galleys of the Swedish navy continued to employ lateen sails as long as these ships were in use, the last one being built in 1749. But the development of sail went

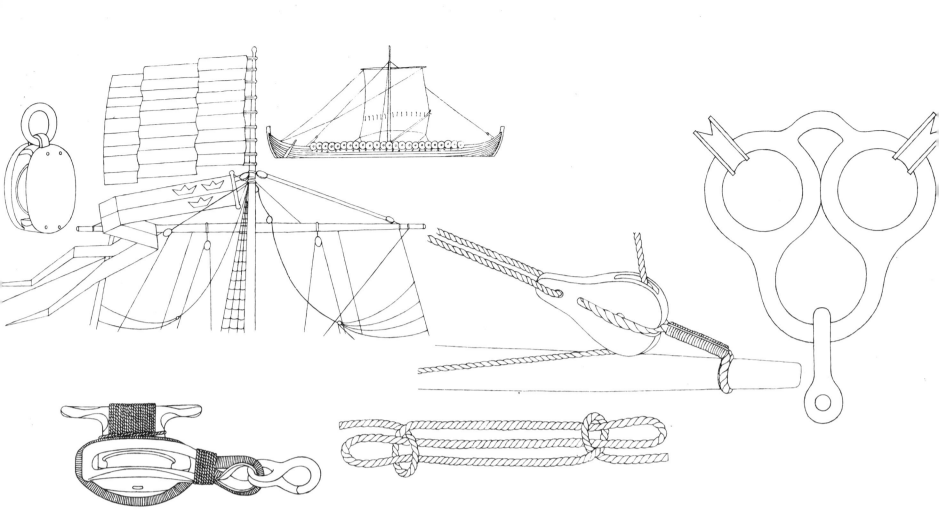

in the opposite direction in small barges and boats, and in the Mediterranean, the Red Sea, and the Persian Gulf. The lateen sail can be seen on these craft even today.

As the lateen sail has to be set on the leeward side of the mast, it is not suitable for tacking with short boards in a narrow channel. The rule is that lateen-rigged craft wear, and the sail is taken around forward of the mast and sheeted on the new lee side when the craft is wearing. Large Arab dhows still sail in this same manner from the Persian Gulf to East African ports, as far down as Zanzibar. They never beat against the wind, but run to Africa in the favorable wind of the northeast monsoon and return with the southwest monsoon to the Persian Gulf. They are, therefore, limited to only one such round trip a year, the same as the Indian grain carriers that make only one voyage a year to Rangoon to pick up rice for Ceylon.

The lateen sail was the world's first fore-and-aft sail. While it enjoyed great popularity in the Near East and Mediterranean for a long time, other types of sail began to appear in Europe. We can follow this development especially well in Holland and Friesland.

During the 16th century, Holland became the world's most powerful maritime nation, replacing the sea power of the Hanseatic League. Using the rich Rhineland inland waterways, the Dutch had developed navigation with small ships in canals and rivers and in the shallow coastal waters between the islands. The inability to beat and especially to tack in a narrow channel, when using a square sail, created the need for new types of sail, and Dutch art records two new fore-and-aft sails, the spritsail and staysail. The former was a simple rectangular sail with one side laced to the mast and extended by a diagon-

ally placed sprit. The sail was found to be very practical, and, as a result, it became the most commonly used sail in small sailing boats of Northern Europe. It was eventually used in larger craft as well, and is now best known on the Thames River barges, which still use it today.

With the spritsail set abaft the mast, there was an empty space under the stay on the forward side of the mast, and it was only natural to set a triangular sail on that stay before the mast. By the middle of the first half of the 16th century, boats with a spritsail and fore staysail were in use in Holland. The development of the fore staysail was followed by a new staysail called the jib, which was set on a jib boom outside the stem. These staysails were soon in general use in small vessels in Western Europe, but it was not until the end of the 17th century that staysails appeared in the larger, square-sailed ships.

Another fore-and-aft sail, the lug sail, came to Europe somewhat later. The lug sail was a rectangular one that was hoisted with an inclined yard, with the halliard nearer the forward yardarm. Again there is evidence that the lug sail was known in the eastern Mediterranean about 100 A.D.

We are not sure whether the lug sail evolved from the lateen sail by cutting away the forward section or whether it came from the square sail by moving the halliard nearer one end of the yard and at the same time shifting the sail's tack amidships. The lug sail was used mostly in Western Europe, in the English and French waters of the English Channel. French fishermen and smugglers, as well as privateers and customs boats with sharp lines and fast hulls, were often rigged with lug sails; the type was sometimes called the *Chasse Marée*. English and Scottish

fishermen in the North Sea also employed the lug sail, until they gave up the use of sails. Sailing ship's boats, both in the merchant marine and the navy, generally had lug sails as well, most often in one-masted, but also in two- or three-masted, rigs.

There were two types of lug sails: the standing and the dipping. The tack of the dipping lug was made fast a little before the mast, near the stem. It was always set to the lee of the mast and had to be shifted to the new leeward side at every tack. A standing lug had the tack at the mast and could take the wind from either side, though it was most effective when the yard was on the lee side of the mast. In ancient times it was very common for the masts of fishing boats to have no shrouds, and one sailed only "on the wood," as it was called. The sail was set on the lee side of the mast, with the halliards leading to the weather quarter and serving as a backstay to sail on. Coming about, the sail was shifted to the new lee and the halliard to the new weather side.

In addition to the fore-and-aft sail on fishing boats and smaller vessels, the lateen sail in the Mediterranean, the lug sail in Western Europe, and the spritsail in Northern Europe, there were many small craft that still used square sails. The "Roslagen" sloops from Stockholm's archipelago used square sails until the end of the 18th century, as did the Norwegian "Nordland" yachts—for as long as they used sails.

The original square sail, which had served maritime navigation for several thousand of years, was entirely different from the various kinds of fore-and-aft sails. When ships became larger and masts taller, the number of sails on each mast also increased. After the middle of the 16th century the larger ships set a third sail, the topgallant

sail, which was rigged above the topsail. In the beginning of the 17th century a square sail, the spritsail topsail, was rigged on a topmast at the end of the bowsprit. An impractical square sail, its mast was very badly stayed and often prone to damage. It remained in use on larger ships, however, for more than a hundred years, before it was replaced by a more practical staysail, the jib.

The first staysails on larger ships were set between the masts as the main staysail, the main topmast staysail, and the mizzen staysail. In addition, there was the fore topmast staysail, which was placed on a special stay from the fore topmast head and parallel with the fore topmast stay. This stay was actually so cluttered with blocks and running gear for the spritsail that the additional rigging for the new staysail caused many difficulties. The fore topmast staysail was, however, a more effective headsail than either of the square sails on the bowsprit, and at the beginning of the 18th century the spritsail topsail disappeared. It was replaced, as was said earlier, by a new staysail called the jib. This was set on a new spar, the jib boom, which was rigged on the extension of the bowsprit.

By the beginning of the 18th century rigging became more functional. The sails could be reefed effectively, and the rigging allowed for better bracing, which meant better sailing to windward. The studding sail, which on occasion was already used in the previous century, became more common. It was used, when running free, to increase the sail area, much as the modern spinnaker functions on sailing yachts.

Toward the end of the 18th century larger ships began to use a fourth square sail above the topgallant sail. It was called the royal. In men-of-war it was always set flying, i.e., it was set from the deck, and when furled, it was taken down on deck. But in merchant ships it became a standing sail with the royal yard left aloft.

An important improvement in types of sail was made at the beginning of the 19th century, as the jackstay on the yards came into use. The head of the sail was bent to the jackstay on the forward upper side of the yard instead of having lashings around the yard. This made the work easier when bending and unbending sail, and especially when furling sail. The sail could then be rolled up on top of the yards, where it could be easily secured under the gaskets. Without the jackstay on the yards, the larger steel ships of a later period could not have sailed with the small crews they had.

After the Napoleonic era larger ships were rigged with a fifth sail, the skysail, which was carried over the royal. It was never widely used, but was seen mostly at the

time of the clipper ships, in the middle of the century. Some clippers carried still another sail, the moonsail, usually set only on the mainmast. Exaggerations could always be found, and one of the most unusual occurs in a story of the English corvette hunting for slavers in the steaming heat and calm waters of the Bay of Benin. Seamen tell of it carrying a royal, skysail, moonsail, heaven poker, angel poker, and cloud disturber—all over the topgallant sail.

Expanding 19th century industry gave rigging a more delicate look. Mechanical improvements in the rigging also influenced the sails. Thimbles and clasp hooks were introduced, and, later, shackles. Both square sail halliards and sheets were made of chain. Previously, the clews of square sails had been part of the bolt rope, which formed an eye in which the sheet and clewline were fastened. It now became common to put a thimble in the clew, and later to lead a cringle from the eye. Still later, a wrought-iron clew was spliced into the bolt ropes. In larger ships, with double topsail sheets, the clew was formed by a stropped block through which the sheet was reeved. The sheet was still made of hemp. In navy ships, where working the sails quickly became more and more important, all running gear was equipped with toggles, so that bowlines, buntlines, clewlines, and sheets could be let go in just a few seconds and a topsail shifted in just a few minutes.

When large ships began to be built of iron and then of steel, during the last half of the century, the standing rigging and then the running gear was made of wire. Even the sails were influenced. The huge square sails were given both leech and foot ropes of wire, and a bolt rope of wire could be used for foot and leech on the staysail but not for the luff, as this had to be folded along the stay when the sail was hauled down.

In addition to the fore-and-aft sails already mentioned—the lateen sail, spritsail, staysail, and lug sail—there is still another, the gaff sail, that gradually came to dominate all the others. It evolved from the spritsail by means of shortening the sprit, raising it, and fastening it to the sail's head. To keep it in place, with the forward end against the mast, the end was shaped as a throat or gaff with a branch fork, which partly covered the mast and gave both the spar and the sail its name, the gaff. To be able to hoist the gaff sail the mast had to be made higher than the sail, so that the gaff's halliards, the inner throat halliard, and the outer peak halliard could be fastened above the gaff.

Pictures of the gaff sail appear later than those of the spritsail, but also go as far back as the middle of the

17th century. Slowly, the gaff sail won out over the other fore-and-aft sails. Mail packets and other semi-official craft, which sailed with mail and passengers between specified ports, revenue cutters, the larger pilot boats, and similar craft were among the first to use the gaff sail. During the 18th century, smaller merchant ships and warships began more often to be rigged with the gaff sail. Various types of early schooners and sloops all had gaff sails.

During the 19th century, larger merchant ships, for example, the three-masted fore-and-aft schooners and barkentines, began to employ the gaff rig. Particularly in North America, by the end of the century, multi-masted fore-and-aft schooners began to show up. Many were four- or five-masted, several six-masted, and one was seven-masted. Some of them were extremely large sailing vessels that required steam winches to hoist their large gaff sails. They were at their best sailing on the wind in calm coastal waters; but they were difficult to run before the wind in hard weather. When they were used on deep-water voyages, their performance was usually much poorer than that of the square-riggers.

The gaff sail, however, soon became the most important sail for pleasure yachts. By the 17th century the Dutch, English, and even the Swedes had gaff-rigged pleasure yachts. With the development of sport sailing and yacht clubs in the maritime nations, the gaff-rigged cutter became more and more popular; though it was sometimes surpassed in size by two- and three-masted, gaff-rigged pleasure schooners. At the beginning of the 20th century the gaff sail was almost universally used in the yachting field.

Here, aerodynamic research performed a great service for sport sailing. As a result of new inventions, the wide gaff sail with a long boom is now almost as rare as the square sail. The only sail that has survived the extensive use of the motor yacht is the tall, narrow, gaffless boom sail, known as the Bermuda sail. Two hundred years ago fishermen in Bermuda were using a triangular mainsail without a gaff, but with a long boom. The modern yacht uses a sail which has only the name in common with that original Bermuda sail.

DIFFERENT SAILS

1 Spritsails
2 Standing lug sail
3 Gaff sail
4 Gunter rig
5 Bermuda sail
6 Staysail rig
7 Lateen sails
8 Square sail

SAILS OF A FOUR-MASTED BARK

(Herzogin Cecilie)
This four-masted bark was built in 1902 by Rickmers ship yard at Bremerhaven for the Norddeutscher Lloyd at Bremen. It was a big sailing vessel of 3,242 gross tons or 4,350 dw.

The Norddeutscher Lloyd, a large shipowner and in Germany second only to the Hamburg—America Line, employed the Herzogin Cecilie to train cadets as officers for their own fleet of ships. In addition to the officers, teachers, and a skeleton crew of tradesmen and seamen, she was fitted out to carry ninety cadets. She had the best possible equipment, but with plenty of man power on board to pull the braces she was rigged without any brace winches, as was customary at that time in big sailing ships of this class. She was a good sailer and made many excellent voyages. During World War 1 she was interned at Coquimbo, Chile. After the war she brought a cargo of nitrate to Ostend, and was there allocated to the French government. In November, 1921, she was purchased by Gustaf Erikson, Marie-hamn, and under his flag was employed chiefly in the Australian grain trade. She foundered on April 25, 1936, off Salcombe, Devonshire, after running aground in heavy fog.

SAILS OF A FOUR-MASTED BARK

1 Flying jib
2 Outer jib
3 Inner jib
4 Fore topmast staysail
5 Fore sail, fore course
6 Fore lower topsail
7 Fore upper topsail
8 Fore lower topgallant sail

9 Fore upper topgallant sail
10 Fore royal
11 Main topmast staysail
12 Main topgallant staysail
13 Main royal staysail

14 Main sail, main course
15 Main lower topsail
16 Main upper topsail
17 Main lower topgallant sail
18 Main upper topgallant sail

19 Main royal
20 Mizzen topmast staysail
21 Mizzen topgallant staysail
22 Mizzen royal staysail
23 Crossjack, mizzen course

24 Mizzen lower topsail
25 Mizzen upper topsail
26 Mizzen lower topgallant sail
27 Mizzen upper topgallant sail
28 Mizzen royal

29 Jigger staysail
30 Jigger topmast staysail
31 Jigger topgallant staysail
32 Lower spanker
33 Upper spanker
34 Gaff topsail

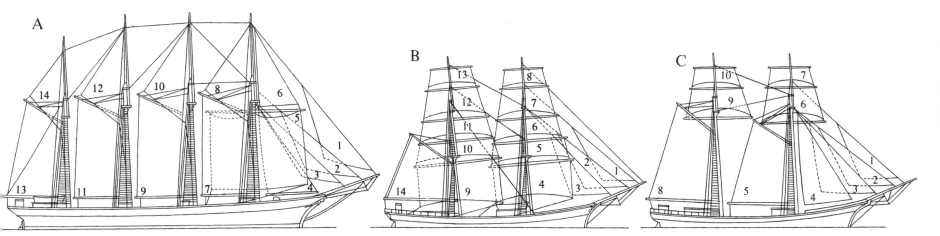

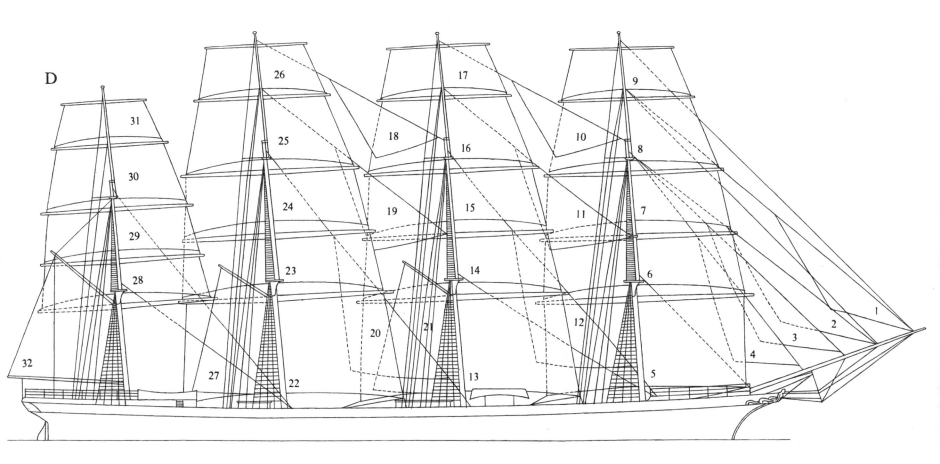

SAILS IN VARIOUS SAILING VESSELS

A *Four-masted fore-and-aft schooner*
1 Flying jib
2 Outer jib
3 Inner jib
4 Fore staysail
5 Square foresail
6 Raffee
7 Foresail
8 Fore gaff topsail
9 Mainsail
10 Main gaff topsail
11 Mizzen

12 Mizzen gaff topsail
13 Jigger or spanker
14 Jigger gaff topsail
B *Brig*
1 Flying jib
2 Jib
3 Fore topmast staysail
4 Foresail
5 Fore lower topsail
6 Fore upper topsail
7 Fore topgallant sail
8 Fore royal
9 Mainsail

10 Main lower topsail
11 Main upper topsail
12 Main topgallant sail
13 Main royal
14 Trysail
C *Two-topsail schooner*
1 Flying jib
2 Outer jib
3 Inner jib
4 Fore staysail
5 Foresail
6 Fore topsail
7 Fore topgallant sail

8 Mainsail
9 Main topsail
10 Main topgallant sail
D *Full-rigged four-masted ship*
1 Flying jib
2 Outer jib
3 Inner jib
4 Fore topmast staysail
5 Foresail
6 Fore lower topsail
7 Fore upper topsail

8 Fore topgallant sail
9 Fore royal
10 Main royal staysail
11 Main topgallant staysail
12 Main topmast staysail
13 Mainsail
14 Main lower topsail
15 Main upper topsail
16 Main topgallant sail
17 Main royal
18 Mizzen royal staysail
19 Mizzen topgallant staysail

20 Mizzen topmast staysail
21 Main spencer
22 Crossjack
23 Mizzen lower topsail
24 Mizzen upper topsail
25 Mizzen topgallant sail
26 Mizzen royal
27 Mizzen spencer
28 Jigger lower topsail
29 Jigger upper topsail
30 Jigger topgallant sail
31 Jigger royal
32 Spanker

SAILS IN VARIOUS SAILING VESSELS

A *Three-masted staysail schooner*
1 Flying jib
2 Jib
3 Fore staysail
4 Fore trysail
5 Main staysail
6 Main trysail
7 Mizzen staysail
8 Jib-headed spanker

B *Ketch*
1 Flying jib
2 Outer jib
3 Inner jib
4 Fore staysail
5 Mainsail
6 Main gaff topsail
7 Mizzen
8 Mizzen gaff topsail

C *Sloop*
1 Jib topsail
2 Jib
3 Fore staysail
4 Square foresail
5 Mainsail
6 Gaff topsail

D *Four-masted barkentine*
1 Flying jib
2 Outer jib
3 Inner jib
4 Fore topmast staysail
5 Foresail
6 Fore lower topsail
7 Fore upper topsail
8 Fore lower topgallant sail
9 Fore upper topgallant sail
10 Main staysail
11 Middle staysail
12 Main topmast staysail
13 Mainsail
14 Main gaff topsail
15 Mizzen topmast staysail
16 Mizzen
17 Mizzen gaff topsail
18 Jigger topmast staysail
19 Jigger or spanker
20 Jigger gaff topsail

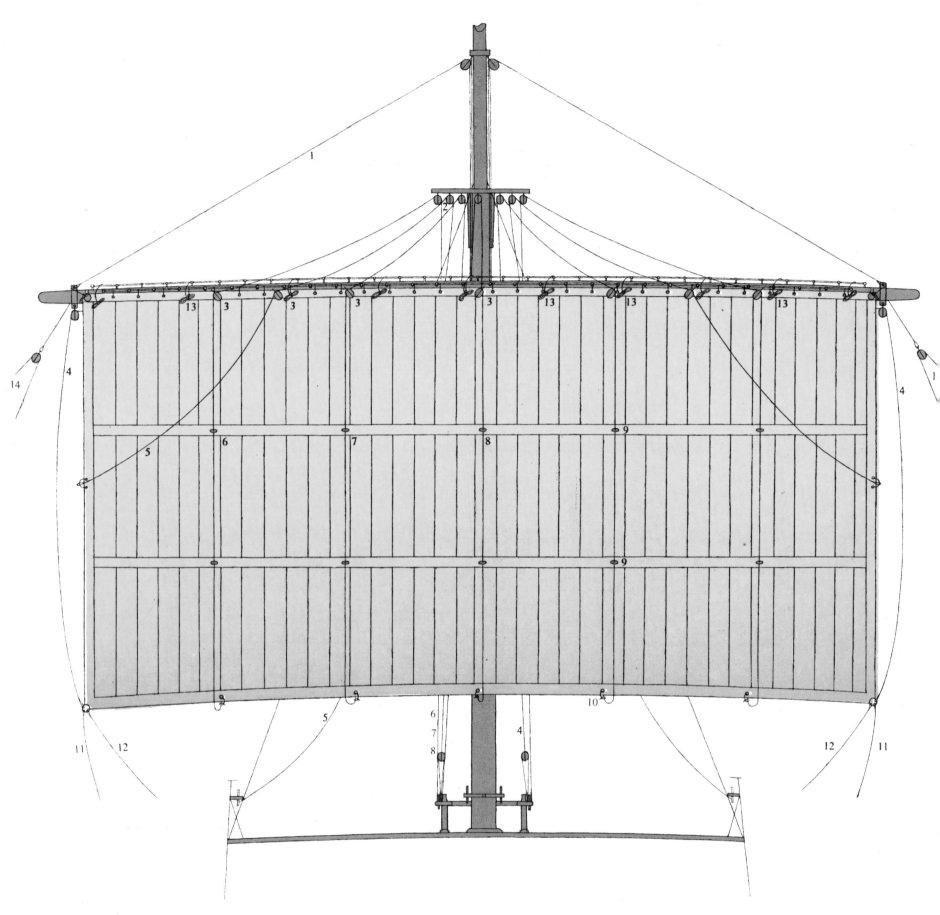

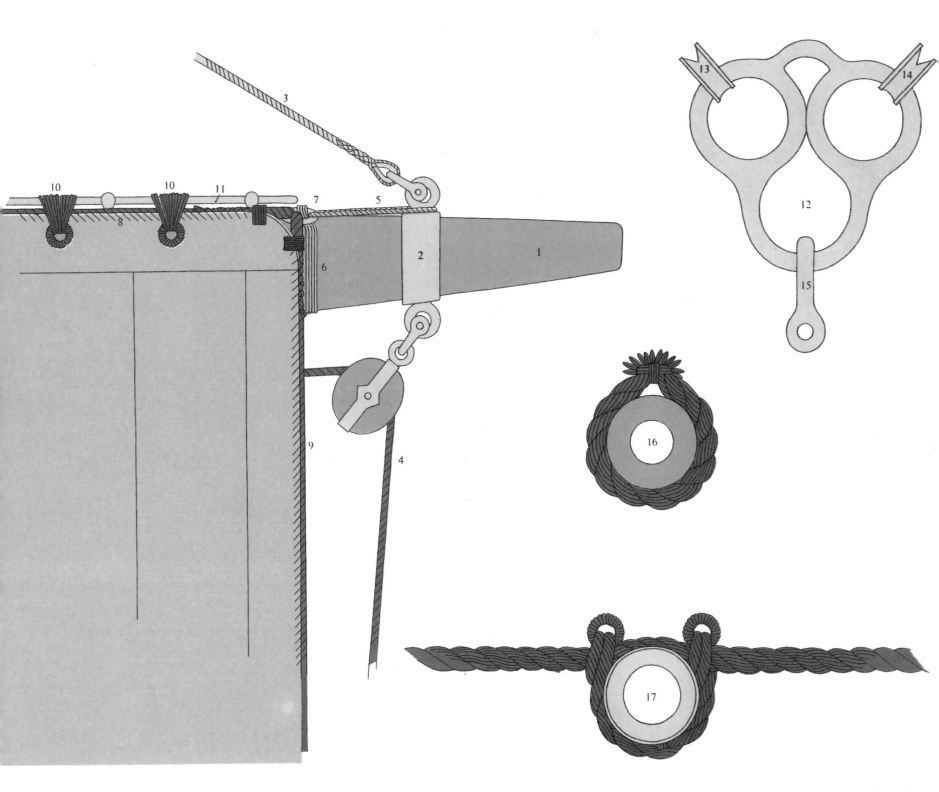

1 Lift by which the yard can be trimmed either way out of the horizontal. In port, this can be done independently of the yards above and to a considerable angle. At sea, when sails are set, the movement is restricted, but affects all the yards on the mast.

2 Buntline blocks under rim of top

3 Buntline blocks on yard seized to jack stay

4 Clewgarnet by which the clews of the sail are hauled up to the yardarms

5 Leech line

6 Outer buntline

7 Inner buntline

8 Middle buntline

9 Bull's eye sewn to the sail to lead the buntlines

10 Buntline hitch

11 Tacks leading forward

12 Sheets leading aft; the clews of the sail are trimmed to the wind by tacks and sheets

When the sail is to be furled, the tacks and sheets are let go and the sail is hauled up to the yard by the clewgarnets and buntlines. Then the men go aloft,

lie out on the yard, and roll up the sail tightly and secure it by tying the gaskets around yard and sail.

13 Gaskets

14 Braces leading aft, by which the yard is braced to different winds

1 Yardarm

2 Yardarm band

3 Lift shackled to yardarm band

4 Clewgarnet

5 Hauling out part of head earing

6 Round turns of head earing

7 Ring for head earing

8 Head of sail

9 Leech of sail

10 Robands, tied with a square knot

11 Jack stay

12 Clew of galvanized iron

13 Thimble for foot of sail

14 Thimble for leech

15 Shackle for sheet

16 Bull's-eye sewed into sail

17 Cringle on bolt rope with round thimble

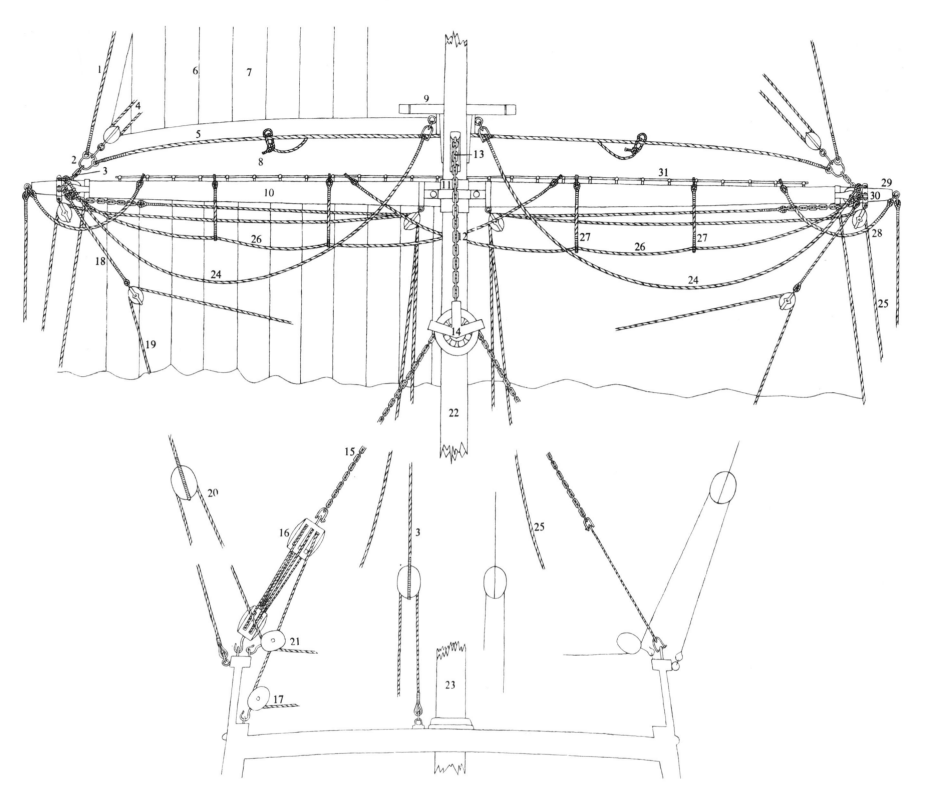

TOPMAST, TOPSAIL, AND TOPGALLANT SAIL WITH RUNNING GEAR

1 Topgallant leech, port side
2 Topgallant clew
3 Topgallant sheet
4 Topgallant clewline
5 Tabling on foot of topgallant sail

6 Flat seam between the cloths of the sail
7 Cloth of canvas, generally 2 feet wide
8 Topgallant buntline
9 Topmast crosstree
10 Upper topsail yard
11 Upper topsail yard parrel

12 Upper topsail yard tie
13 Sheave hole in topmast for the tie
14 Topsail tie gin block
15 Topsail halliard chain span
16 Topsail halliard tackle

17 Topsail halliard lead block
18 Upper topsail brace pendant
19 Upper topsail brace runner
20 Upper topsail brace falls

21 Leading block of upper topsail brace
22 Topmast
23 Lower mast
24 Topsail yard lift
25 Topsail yard downhaul

26 Foot rope of upper topsail yard
27 Stirrups to support foot rope
28 Yardarm horse
29 Yardarm
30 Yardarm band
31 Jack stay to which sail is bent

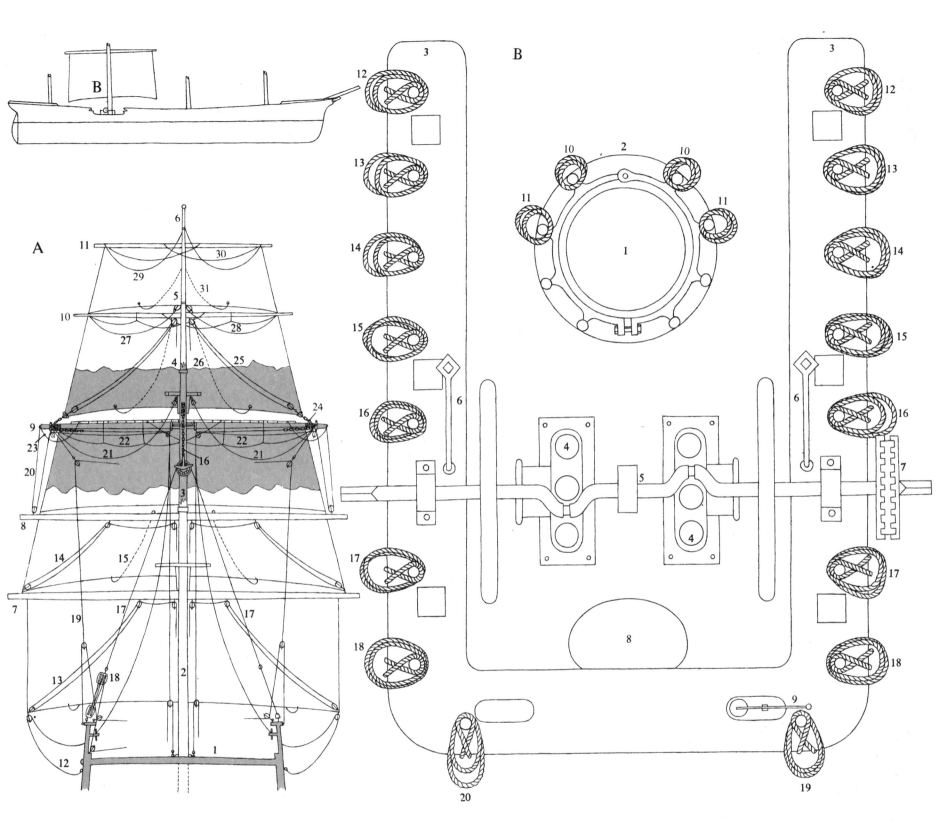

THE SQUARE SAIL

A *Square-rigged mast,*
   seen from aft
1 Deck
2 Lower mast with top
3 Topmast with cross-
   trees
4 Topgallant mast
5 Royal mast
6 Pole
7 Lower yard
8 Lower topsail yard
9 Upper topsail yard
10 Topgallant yard

11 Royal yard
12 Lower sheet
13 Clewgarnet
14 Topsail clewline
15 Lower topsail buntline,
   shown in broken lines
   forward of sail
16 Topsail halliard, tie
17 Topsail halliard,
   spanner
18 Topsail halliard,
   tackle or falls
19 Upper topsail brace
20 Topsail downhaul
21 Topsail lift

22 Upper topsail yard
   footrope
23 Upper topsail yardarm
   horse
24 Topgallant sheet
25 Topgallant clewline
26 Topgallant buntline
27 Topgallant lift
28 Topgallant yard
   footrope
29 Royal lift
30 Royal yard footrope
31 Royal buntline

B *Plan of fife rail at*
   mizzenmast of a big
   sailing ship
1 Section of mast with
   spider hoop
2 Mast coat at deck
3 U-shaped fife rail
   with belaying pins
4 Bilge pumps on deck
5 Pump axle with fly-
   wheels
6 Detachable pump
   cranks stowed on fife
   rail

7 Chain wheel for mes-
   senger from steam
   winch
8 Manhole from deck
   to pump well
9 Fresh water pump
   from tanks below deck
10 Lower topsail sheet
11 Upper topsail sheet
12 Crossjack clewgarnet
13 Inner crossjack bunt-
   lines

14 Outer crossjack bunt-
   lines
15 Crossjack lift
16 Mizzen topgallant
   sheet
17 Main lower topgallant
   brace
18 Main upper top-
   gallant brace
19 Jigger topmast staysail
   downhaul
20 Jigger topgallant staysail downhaul

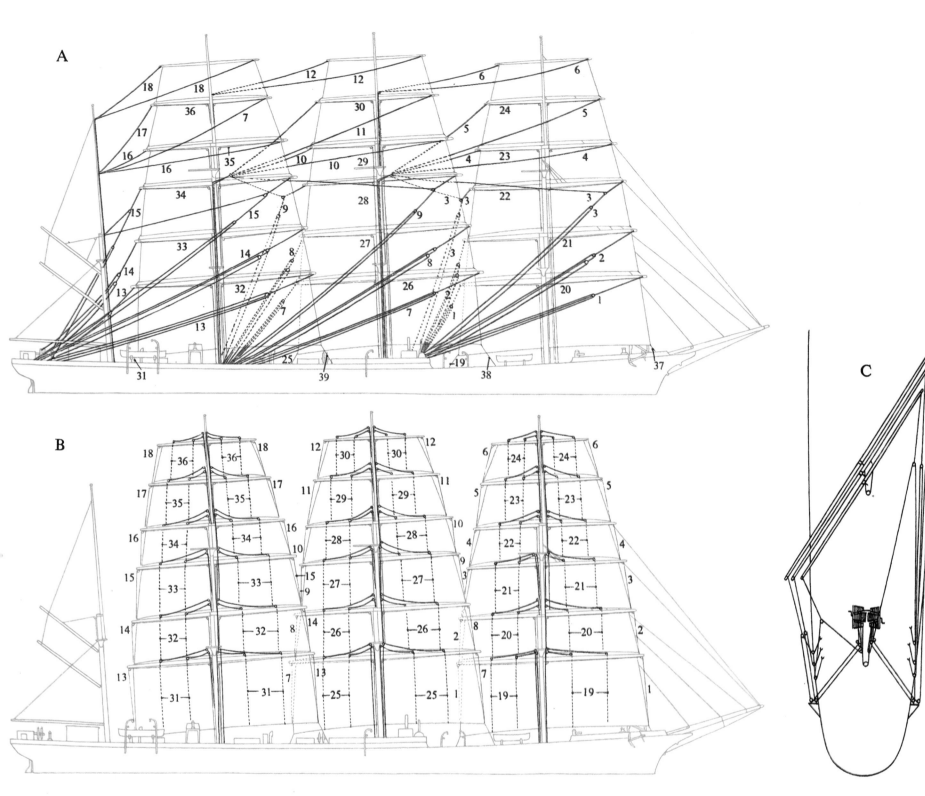

RUNNING RIGGING OF THE SQUARE SAILS OF A FOUR-MASTED BARK

A *Braces and sheets*
1 Fore brace
2 Fore lower topsail brace
3 Fore upper topsail brace
4 Fore lower topgallant brace
5 Fore upper topgallant brace
6 Fore royal brace
7 Main brace
8 Main lower topsail brace

9 Main upper topsail brace
10 Main lower topgallant brace
11 Main upper topgallant brace
12 Main royal brace
13 Crossjack brace
14 Mizzen lower topsail brace
15 Mizzen upper topsail brace
16 Mizzen lower topgallant brace

17 Mizzen upper topgallant brace
18 Mizzen royal brace
19 Fore sheet
20 Fore lower topsail sheet
21 Fore upper topsail sheet
22 Fore lower topgallant sheet
23 Fore upper topgallant sheet
24 Fore royal sheet

25 Main sheet
26 Main lower topsail sheet
27 Main upper topsail sheet
28 Main lower topgallant sheet
29 Main upper topgallant sheet
30 Main royal sheet
31 Crossjack sheet
32 Mizzen lower topsail sheet

33 Mizzen upper topsail sheet
34 Mizzen lower topgallant sheet
35 Mizzen upper topgallant sheet
36 Mizzen royal sheet
37 Fore tack
38 Main tack
39 Crossjack tack

B *Buntlines, clewlines, and downhauls*
1 Fore clewgarnet
2 Fore lower topsail clewline
3 Fore upper topsail downhaul
4 Fore lower topgallant clewline
5 Fore upper topgallant downhaul
6 Fore royal clewline
7 Main clewgarnet

Continued

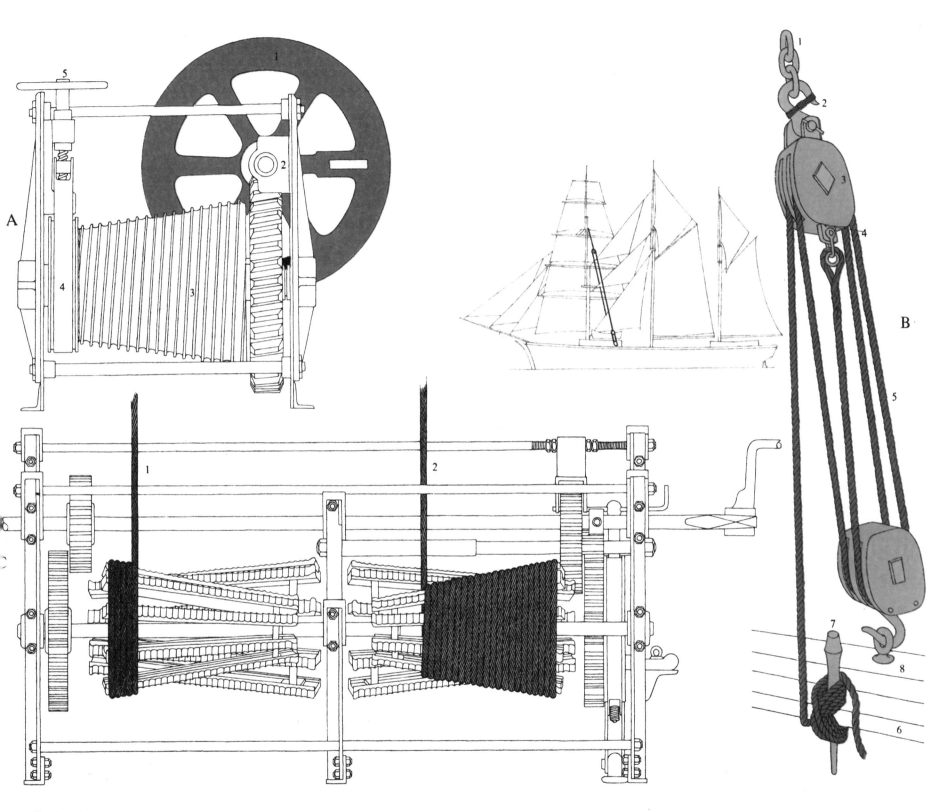

Since this is an outline sketch only, see also page 245

Continued

8 Main lower topsail clewline
9 Main upper topsail downhaul
10 Main lower topgallant clewline
11 Main upper topgallant downhaul
12 Main royal clewline
13 Crossjack clewgarnet
14 Mizzen lower topsail clewline
15 Mizzen upper topsail downhaul

16 Mizzen lower top-gallant clewline
17 Mizzen upper top-gallant downhaul
18 Mizzen royal clewline
19 Fore buntlines
20 Fore lower topsail buntlines
21 Fore upper topsail buntlines
22 Fore lower topgallant buntlines
23 Fore upper topgallant buntlines

24 Fore royal buntlines
25 Main buntlines
26 Main lower topsail buntlines
27 Main upper topsail buntlines
28 Main lower topgallant buntlines
29 Main upper topgallant buntlines
30 Main royal buntlines
31 Crossjack buntlines
32 Mizzen lower topsail buntlines

33 Mizzen upper topsail buntlines
34 Mizzen lower top-gallant buntlines
35 Mizzen upper top-gallant buntlines
36 Mizzen royal buntlines
C Mizzenmast with braces leading to a brace winch at the foot of jiggermast

TOPSAIL HALLIARDS AND WINCHES

A Topsail halliard winch
1 Flywheel with remov-able handle, which was removed after the sail was hoisted so as to be out of the way
2 Worm gear
3 Grooved barrel for the halliard, tapered to in-crease power as the yard ascends
4 Brake

5 Wheel with threaded shaft to control the brake. When the top-sail yard was lowered, the brake was eased off and the flywheel was given a start with a push. This set the barrel revolving; the downward speed was regulated by the brake.
Continued

DOUBLE TOPSAILS

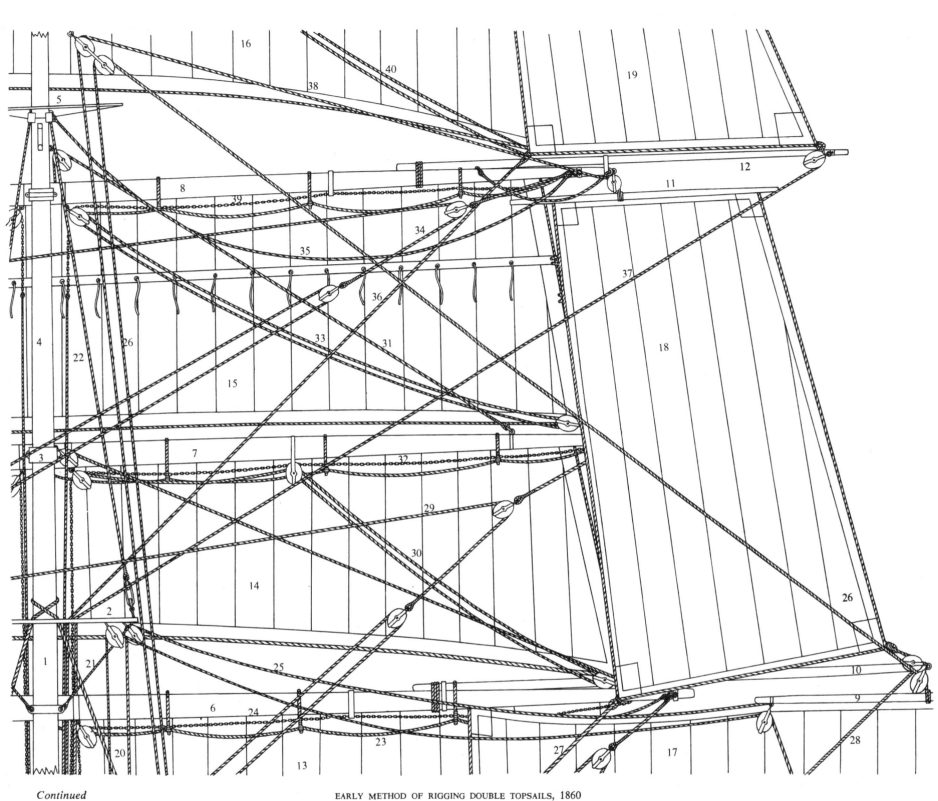

Continued

EARLY METHOD OF RIGGING DOUBLE TOPSAILS, 1860

B *Topsail halliard of a barkentine*

1 End of chain span across the deck
2 Mousing on hook
3 Moving block, double
4 Becket, in one with the straps
5 Fall, two-fold purchase rove to advantage
6 Pin rail
7 Belaying pin
8 Main rail

C *Brace winch invented by Captain J. C. Jarvis*

of Tayport, Scotland. The winch controls the lower brace and the two topsail braces, one winch for each mast. The winch has three axles, each with two barrels, and is so arranged with cogwheels that when the winch is turned, braces on one side pay out as those on the other side wind on.

1 Weather side brace paid out
2 Lee side brace hove in

1 Lower mast, foremast
2 Top
3 Cap
4 Topmast
5 Topmast crosstree
6 Lower foreyard
7 Lower topsail yard
8 Upper topsail yard
9 Lower studding sail yard
10 Topmast studding sail boom
11 Topmast studding sail yard
12 Topgallant studding sail boom
13 Fore course, foresail
14 Lower topsail
15 Upper topsail
16 Topgallant sail
17 Lower studding sail
18 Topmast studding sail
19 Topgallant studding sail
20 Lower rigging or shrouds
21 Futtock shrouds

22 Topmast rigging or shrouds
23 Lower yard footrope
24 Lower topsail sheet of chain
25 Inner lower studding sail halliard
26 Outer lower studding sail halliard
27 Topmast studding sail sheet
28 Topmast studding sail tack
29 Lower topsail brace

30 Lower topsail clewline
31 Lower topsail lift
32 Upper topsail sheet
33 Upper topsail clewline
34 Upper topsail brace
35 Upper topsail lift
36 Topgallant studding sail sheet
37 Topgallant studding sail tack
38 Topmast studding sail halliard
39 Topgallant sheet
40 Topgallant clewline

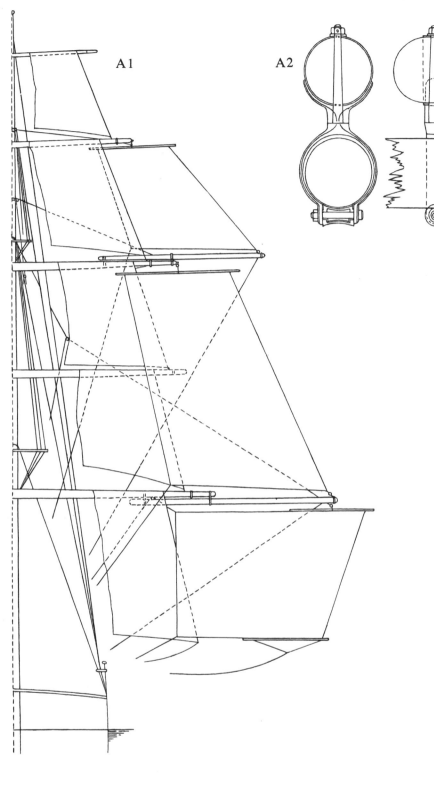

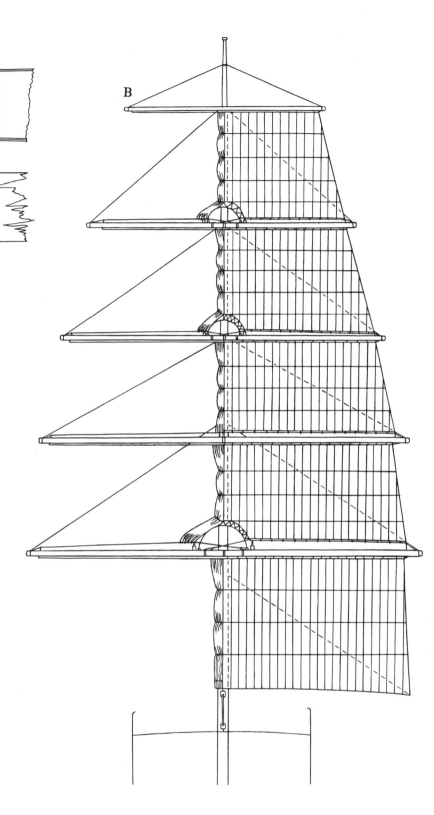

SQUARE SAILS AND STUDDING SAILS

A *Studding sails*
1 Outline sketch showing studding sails and their spars and rigging, looking aft
2 Band on the yardarm for the studding sail boom

B *Square sail by the Rägener system*
Many inventors have tried to improve upon the traditional square rig, which evolved empirically from centuries of experience gained the hard way. None did much to improve the old sailing ship, and this system by Rägener, with trussed yards and sails running on horizontal slides and brailed in to the mast, never got beyond the drawing board.

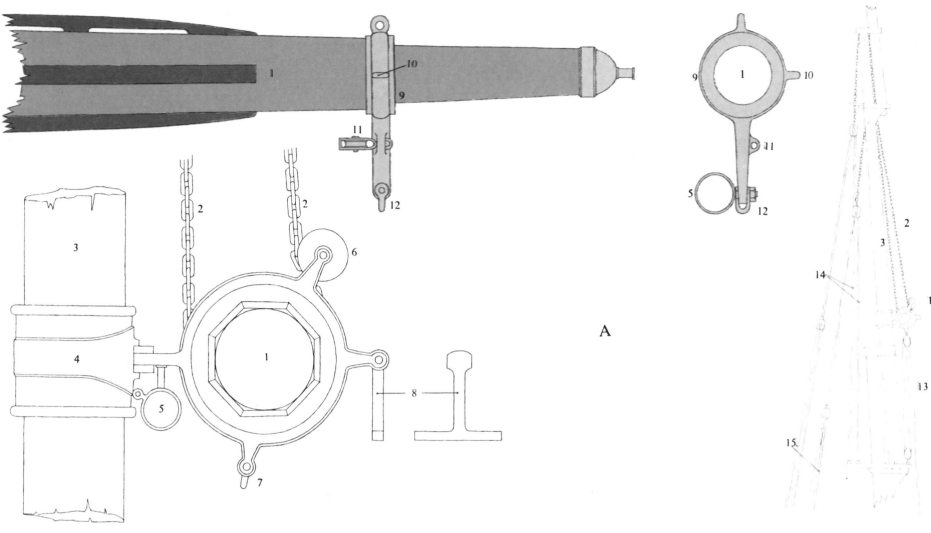

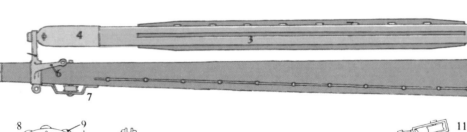

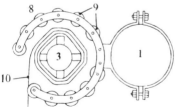

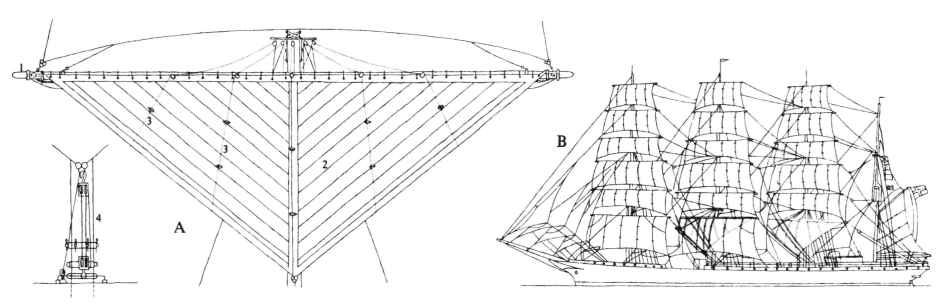

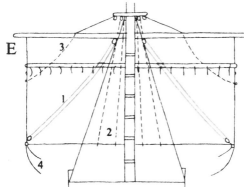

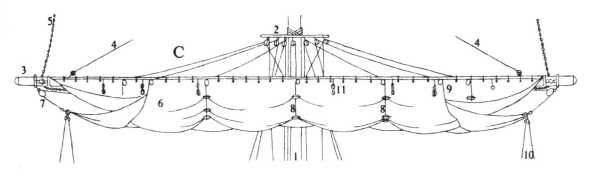

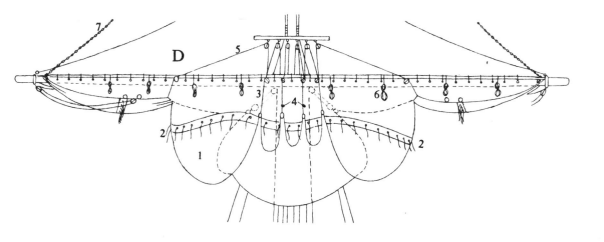

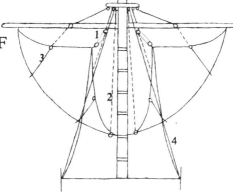

DIFFERENT RIGGING OF LOWER SQUARE SAILS

A *Big square-rigged sailing ships could, sometimes, set a three-cornered mainsail or crossjack. Such a sail could be carried in a gale long after a square sail had to be taken in, but this advantage was counteracted by the fact that the three-cornered sail gave less spread of canvas in a moderate wind. In A the numbers indicate:*

1 Lower yard
2 Three-cornered sail
3 Buntlines
4 Tackle sheet in front of mast

B *A four-masted bark under all sail, setting a three-cornered crossjack, while the mainsail is drawn double showing both a square sail and a three-cornered sail*

C *A course, say, mainsail, clewed up to the yardarm, as seen from forward*

1 Lower mast
2 The top
3 Lower yard
4 Lifts
5 Lower topsail sheet, sail clewed up to the yardarm
6 The sail, say, mainsail
7 Clewgarnets
8 Buntlines
9 Leechlines
10 Tacks and sheets
11 Gaskets

D *A course, mainsail, clewed up in the bunt as seen from forward*

1 The sail
2 Reef band
3 Clewgarnets abaft the sail
4 Buntlines
5 Leechlines
6 Gaskets
7 Lower topsail sheet, sail clewed up in the bunt

E *A mainsail clewed up in the bunt as seen from aft*

1 Clewgarnets
2 Buntlines
3 Leechlines
4 Sheet

F *A mainsail with the clews hauled up as seen from aft*

1 Clewgarnets
2 Buntlines
3 Leechlines
4 Sheets

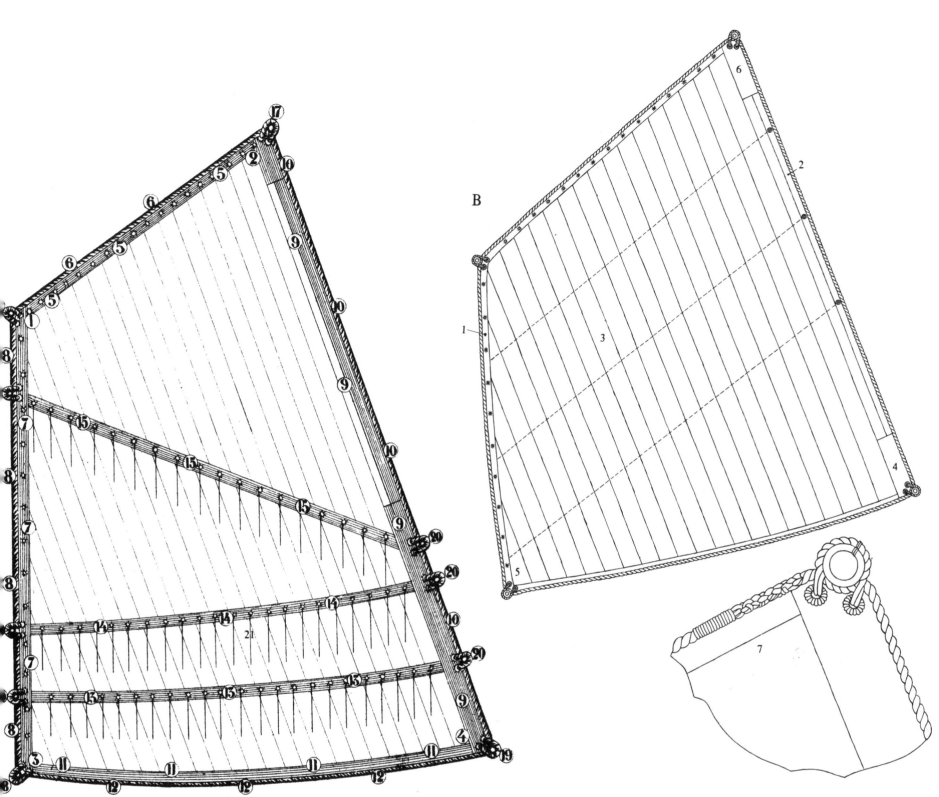

THE GAFF SAIL (FROM PAASCH)

A *Gaff sail*	7 Luff	14 Second reef band	B *A spanker, which sets*
1 Throat	8 Luff rope	15 Balance reef band	*under a standing gaff*
2 Peak	9 Leech	16 Throat cringle	*and brails in to the*
3 Tack	10 Leech rope	17 Peak cringle	*mast, (leeches and crin-*
4 Clew	11 Foot	18 Tack cringle	*gles made as in A)*
5 Head	12 Foot rope	19 Clew cringle	
6 Headrope	13 First reef band	20 Reef cringles	
		21 Reef points	

1 Half a cloth tabling on the luff	4 Sheet patch
2 Folding on the after leech with three holes to take the brails	5 Tack patch
3 Lead of brails across the sail	6 Peak patch
	7 Detail of peak cringle

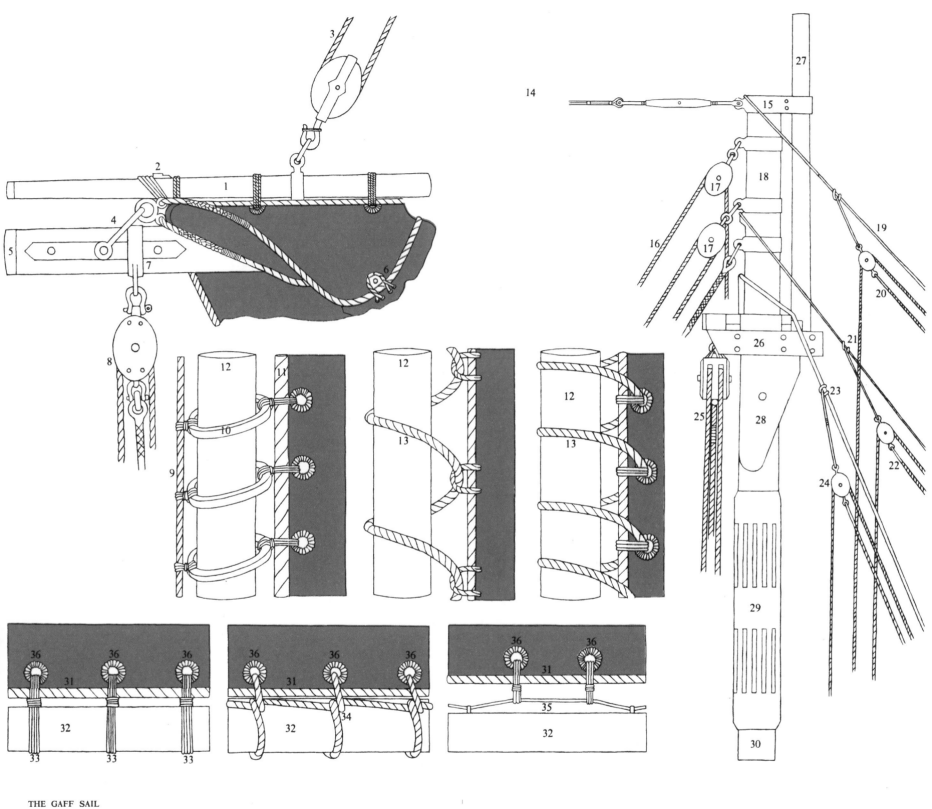

THE GAFF SAIL

1 Gaff	7 Sheet band	13 Spiral lacing	19 Outer jibstay	25 Fore throat halliards	31 Foot of sail
2 Head earing	8 Sheet	14 Mainstay	20 Outer jib halliard	26 Trestletrees	32 Boom
3 Peak halliards	9 Distance line	15 Cap	21 Inner jibstay	27 Topmast	33 Seizings
4 Clew shackle	10 Hoops	16 Fore peak halliards	22 Inner jib halliard	28 Cheeks	34 Marline hitched lacing
5 Boom end	11 Bolt rope on luff	17 Peak halliard block	23 Forestay	29 Mast battens	35 Wire jack stay
6 Reef cringle	of sail	18 Foremast head	24 Fore staysail halliard	30 Foremast	36 Eyelet hole for lacing
	12 Mast				

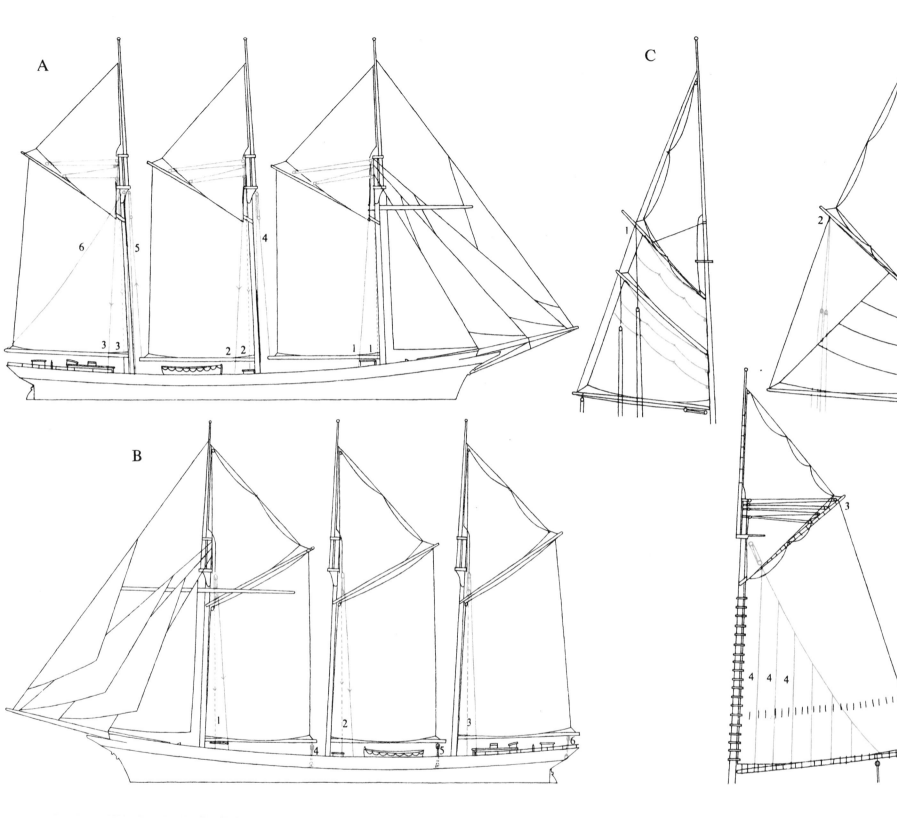

A *The peak halliards and topping lifts of the gaff sails on board a three-masted fore-and-aft schooner*

1 Fore peak halliard
2 Main peak halliard
3 Mizzen peak halliard
4 Fore topping lift
5 Main topping lift
6 Mizzen topping lift

B *The throat halliards and sheets of the gaff sails on board a three-masted fore-and-aft schooner*

1 Fore throat halliard
2 Main throat halliard
3 Mizzen throat halliard
4 Fore sheet
5 Main sheet
6 Mizzen sheet or spanker sheet

C *Different gaff sails*
1 Upper and lower spanker of the five-masted bark *Potosi*
2 Jigger of the four-masted bark *Archibald Russell*

3 Spanker of a big American fore-and-aft schooner. The vertical ropes (4) from the topping lift are called lazy jacks.

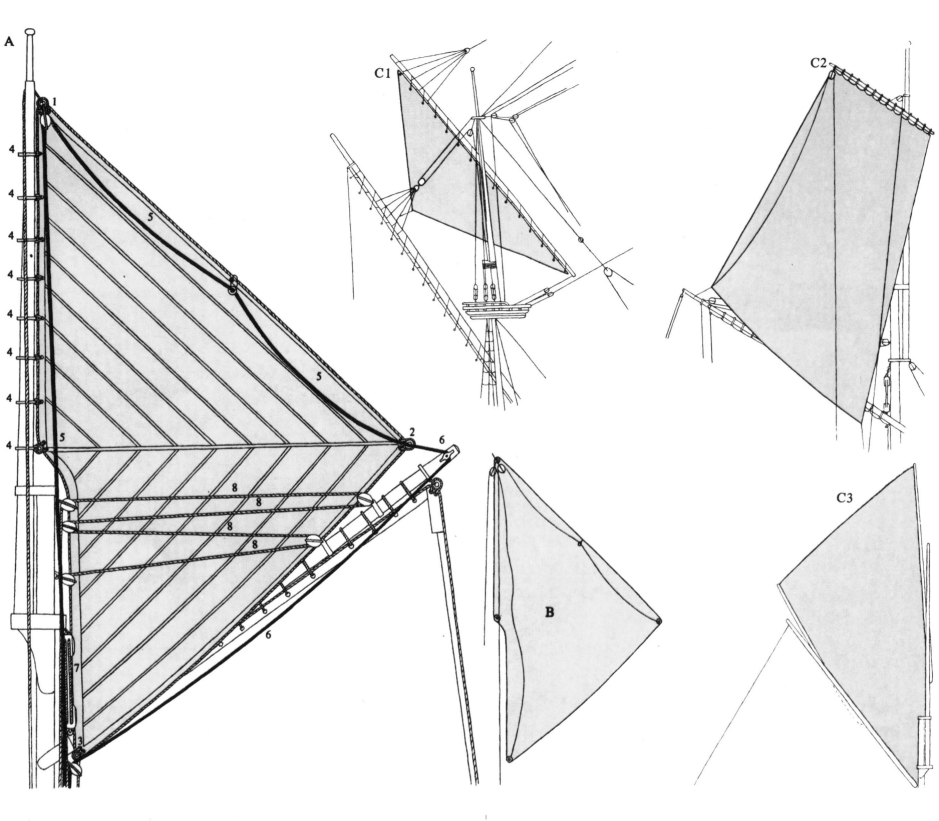

FORE-AND-AFT TOPSAILS

A *Jib-headed gaff topsail*
1 Head
2 Clew
3 Tack
4 Mast hoops
5 Clewline

6 Sheet
7 Throat halliard of
   the gaff sail
8 Peak halliard of
   the gaff sail

The gaff topsail is car-
ried on the lee side of
the peak halliard and
the tack leads down to
deck on the weather
side of the gaff. When
the ship is put about,
one man has to go aloft
and shift the sail over
to the new lee side.

B *Another way of rigging
   the gaff topsail with
   two clewlines*

C *Different types of
   fore-and-aft topsails*
1 Lateen topsail from the
   middle of the 16th
   century

2 Square gaff topsail bent
   to a short yard
3 Jackyard topsail of a
   cutter from the 1890's

STAYSAIL

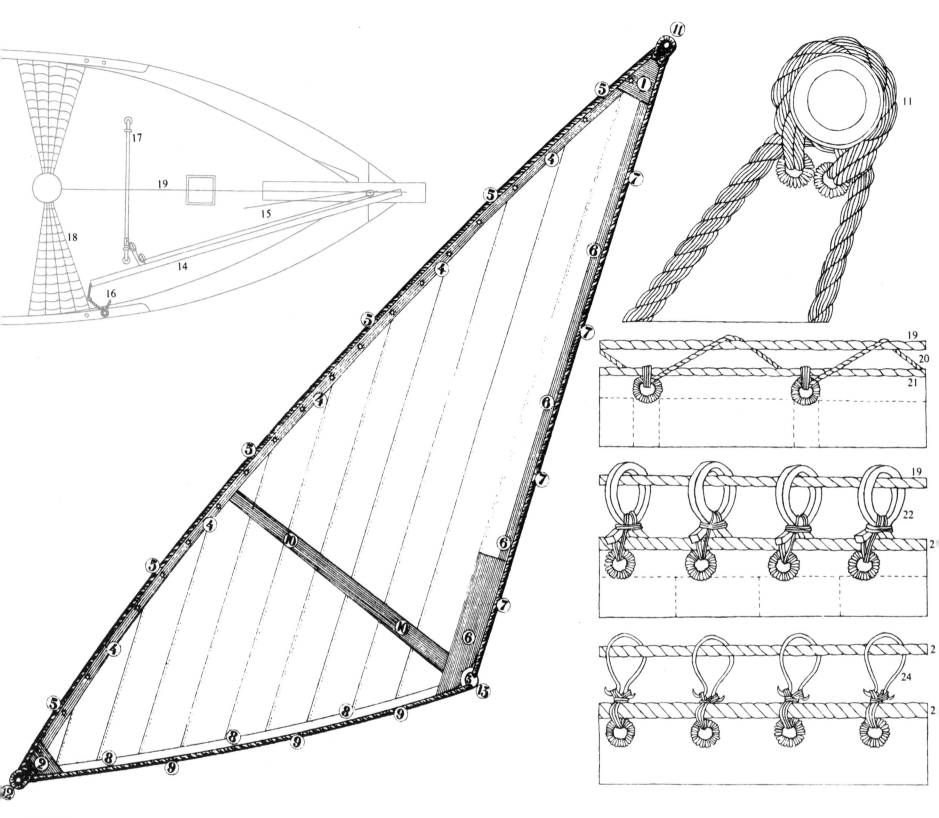

STAYSAIL

1 Head	6 Leech	11 Head cringle	17 Horse	21 Luff rope
2 Tack	7 Leech rope	12 Tack cringle	18 Shrouds	22 Wooden staysail hanks
3 Clew	8 Foot	13 Clew ring	19 Hemp stay	23 Wire stay
4 Luff	9 Foot rope	14 Staysail boom	20 Lacing	24 Iron staysail hanks
5 Luff rope	10 Girth band	15 Fore staysail sheet		
		16 Preventer sheet		

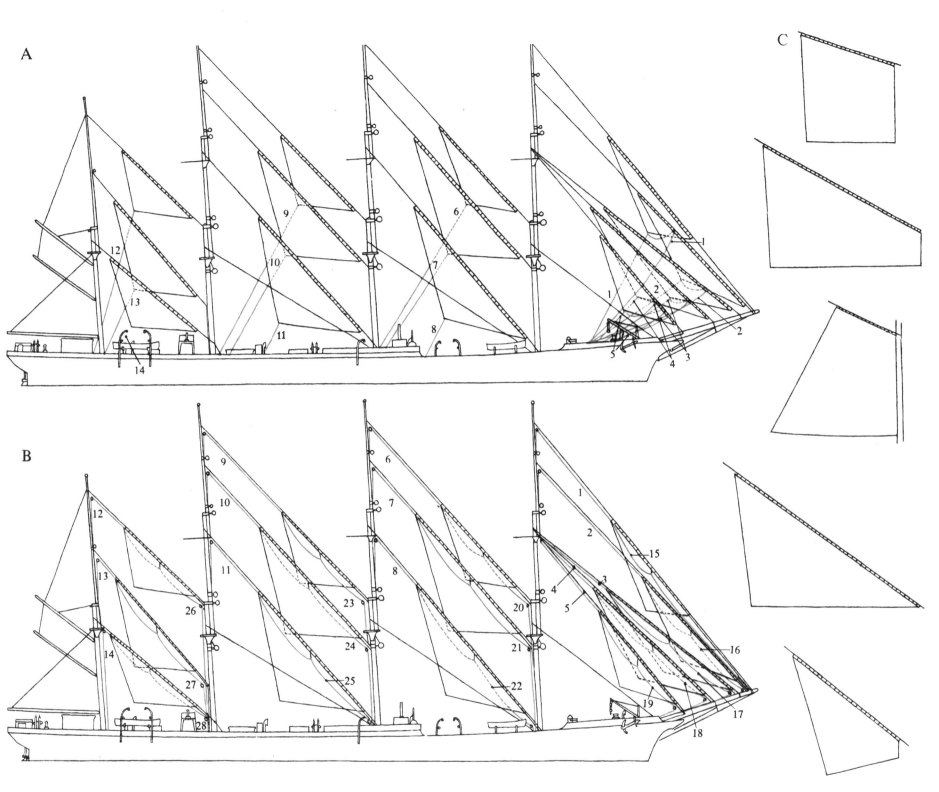

RUNNING GEAR OF STAYSAILS IN A FOUR-MASTED BARK, DIFFERENT TYPES OF STAYSAILS

A *Sheets*
1 Fore royal staysail sheets
2 Flying jib sheets
3 Outer jib sheets
4 Inner jib sheets
5 Fore topmast staysail sheets
6 Main royal staysail sheet
7 Main topgallant staysail sheet
8 Main topmast staysail sheet

9 Mizzen royal staysail sheet
10 Mizzen topgallant staysail sheet
11 Mizzen topmast staysail sheet
12 Jigger topgallant staysail sheet
13 Jigger topmast staysail sheet
14 Jigger staysail sheet

B *Halliards and downhauls*
1 Fore royal staysail halliards
2 Flying jib halliards
3 Outer jib halliards
4 Inner jib halliards
5 Fore topmast staysail halliards
6 Main royal staysail halliards
7 Main topgallant staysail halliards
8 Main topmast staysail halliards

9 Mizzen royal staysail halliards
10 Mizzen topgallant staysail halliards
11 Mizzen topmast staysail halliards
12 Jigger topgallant staysail halliards
13 Jigger topmast staysail halliards
14 Jigger staysail halliards
15 Fore royal staysail downhaul

16 Flying jib downhaul
17 Outer jib downhaul
18 Inner jib downhaul
19 Fore topmast staysail downhaul
20 Main royal staysail downhaul
21 Main topgallant staysail downhaul
22 Main topmast staysail downhaul
23 Mizzen royal staysail downhaul

24 Mizzen topgallant staysail downhaul
25 Mizzen topmast staysail downhaul
26 Jigger topgallant staysail downhaul
27 Jigger topmast staysail downhaul
28 Jigger staysail downhaul

C *Different shapes of staysails*

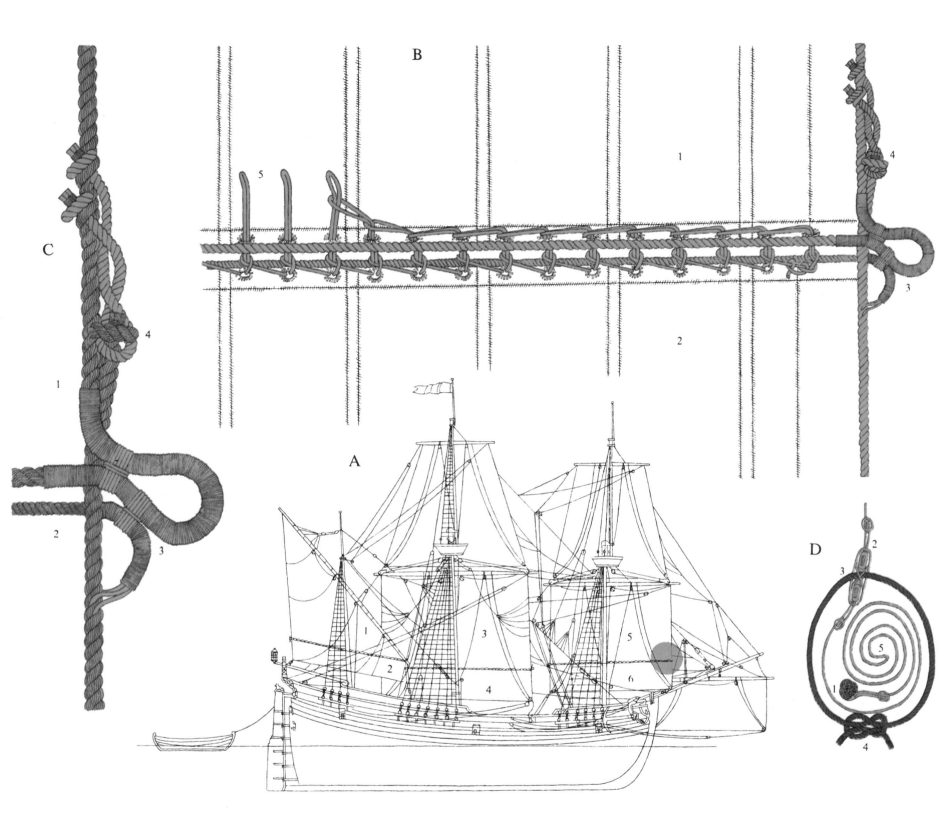

A *A merchant ship from the first half of the 17th century. Additional sails, called bonnets, are laced to the foot of her courses and lateen mizzen. Sail area can be reduced by unlacing the bonnets.*

1 Mizzen
2 Mizzen bonnet
3 Mainsail
4 Main bonnet
5 Foresail
6 Fore bonnet

B *The bonnets were laced to the sails in such a way as to make the lacing spill itself once it was started; this made quick work of shortening sail*

1 Lower sail
2 Bonnet
3 The clew of the sail seized to the earing of the bonnet
4 The leech rope of the bonnet, ending in a wall knot and stropped to the leech of the sail
5 Lacing of head of bonnet to foot of sail is made to spill once its stop is let go

C *Enlargement of clew of sail, showing details*

D *Sectional view of a reefed sail*
1 Foot of sail
2 Reef band
3 Reef point
4 Reef point knotted around reef with a reef knot
5 Rolled-up canvas in reef

120

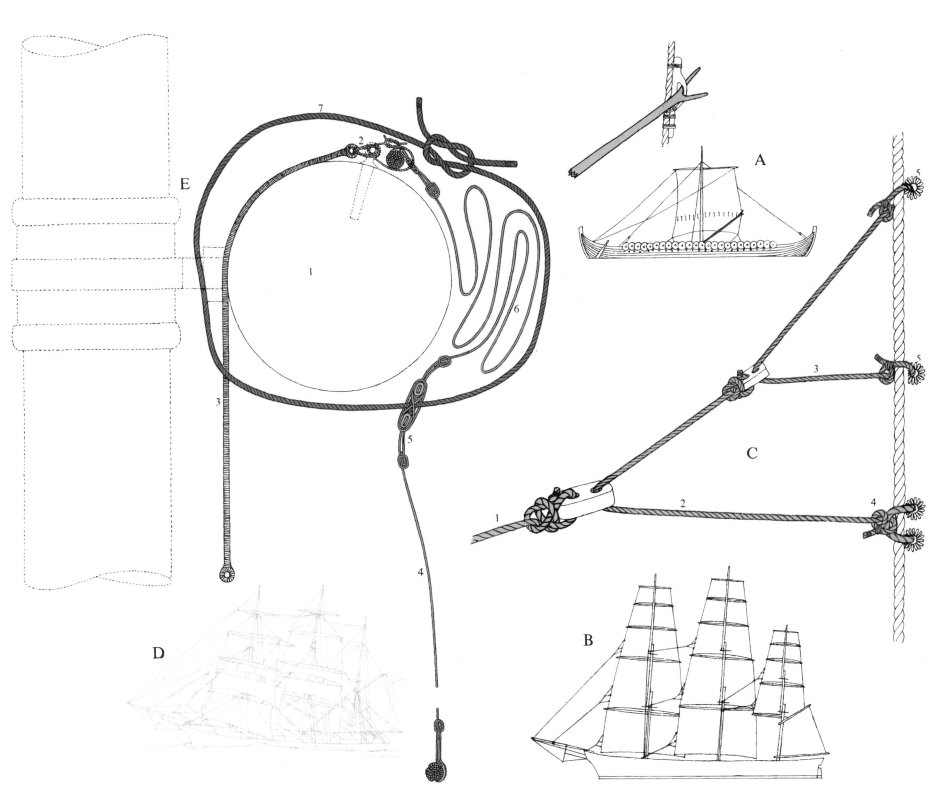

SAIL DETAILS

A *Norse Viking ship beating with a spar, known as a beatas, to hold the weather leech instead of a bowline; detail showing the spar's connection to sail*

B *Outline drawing of an American clipper close hauled on the port tack, with her weather bowlines picked out on her courses, topsails, and topgallant sails*

C *Detail of a bowline bridle*
1 Bowline hitched to the dead block with a bowline
2 Long bridle
3 Short bridle
4 Bowline cringle in sail
5 Eyelet-holes in sail for short bridle

D *Bark with double topsails, sailing by the wind under reefed upper topsails, lower topsails, and foresail*

E *Section of a yard showing a reefed sail*
1 Yard
2 Jack stay
3 Stirrup
4 Sail below the reef
5 Reef band
6 Reefed part of sail
7 Reef point tied around yard and sail with a reef knot

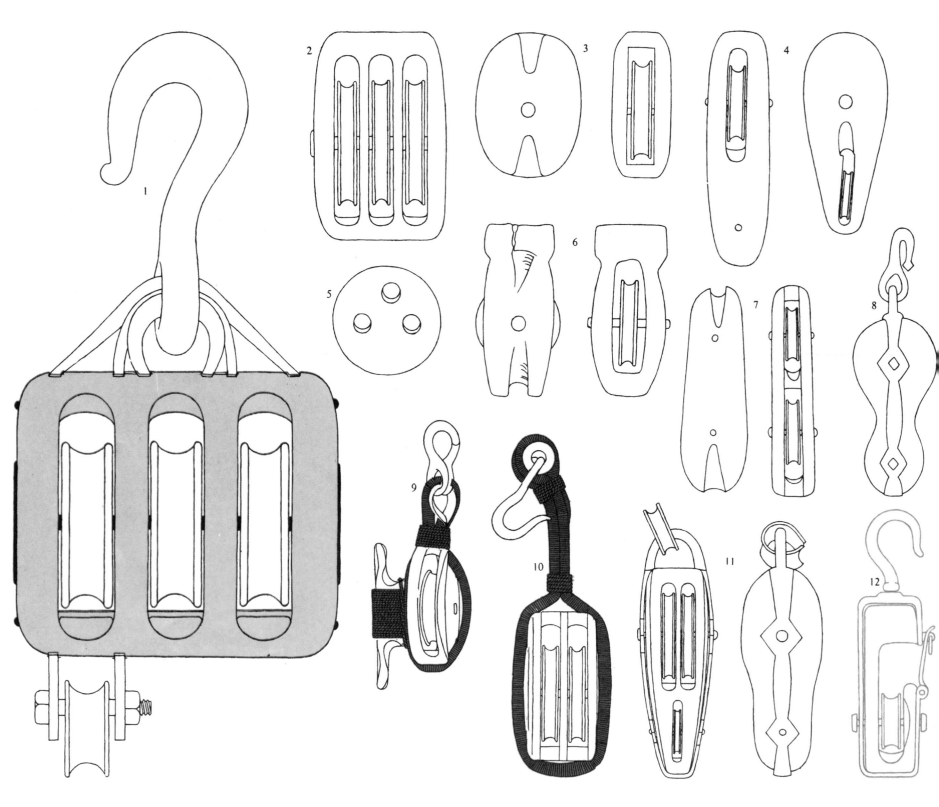

BLOCKS OF DIFFERENT TYPES

1 Large modern triple block, with internal straps and side hook; parts of the straps go through the block and form the becket for the standing part of the fall

2 Triple block for a hemp strop, 19th century

3 Single block, side view and front view, for a hemp strop, 18th century

4 Dutch style yardarm sheet block for topsail sheet and lower lift, front view and side view, 17th century

5 Deadeye, 19th century

6 Clewgarnet block, side view and front view; this block has been turned on a lathe; medieval or 16th century

7 Fiddleblock, side view and front view, with two sheaves, 18th or 19th century

8 Fiddleblock, with external strap and hook, 19th century

9 Wire-stropped sheet block, with clip hooks and a cleat for the sheet, so as to make the sheet block travel on a horse, 20th century

10 Double block with a double strop and hook, for masthead pendant, 19th century

11 Triple fiddleblock, with external strap and thimble for splicing the pendant, 19th century

12 Snatch block, with external straps and a swivel hook, 19th century

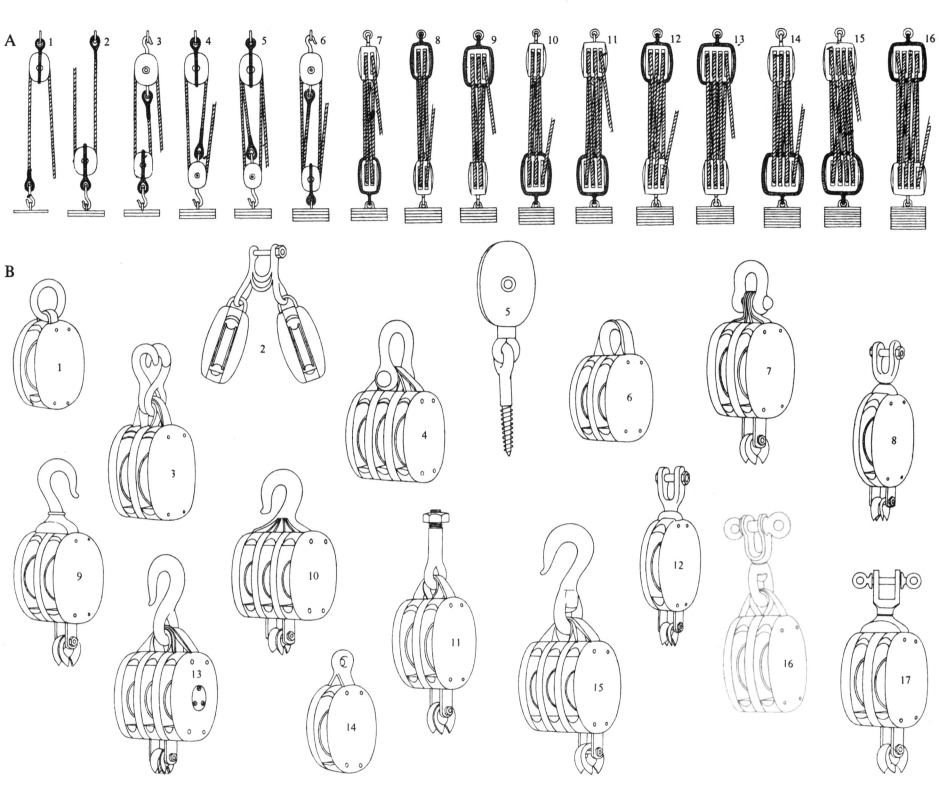

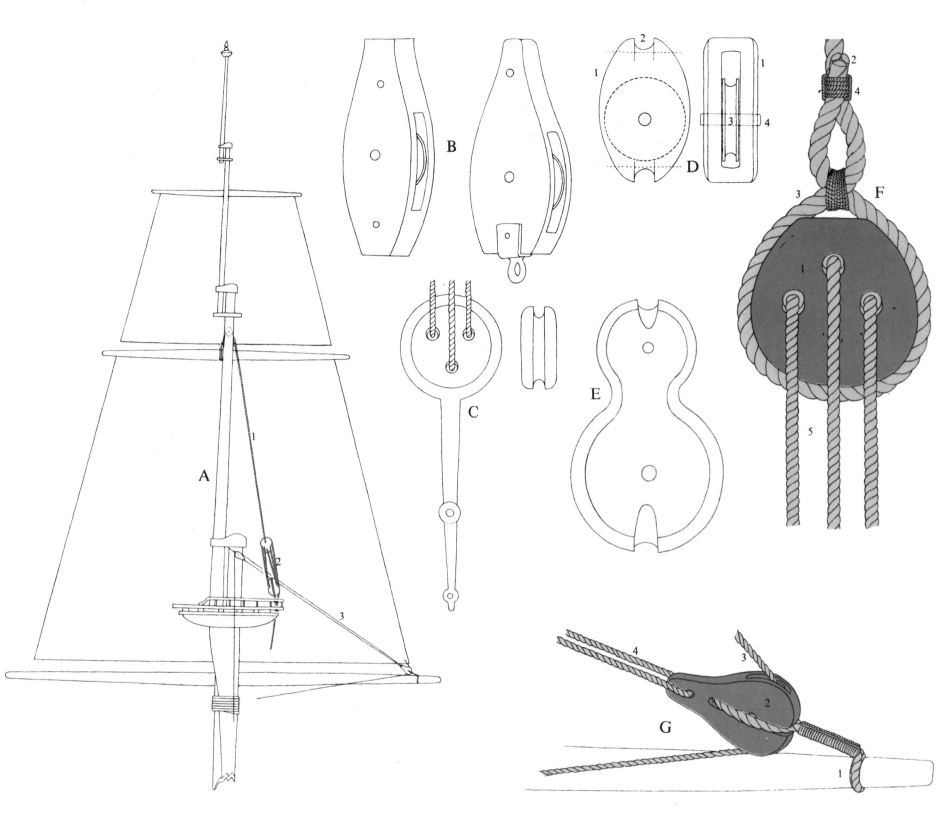

SOME OLD RIGGING DETAILS

A *Topsail halliard, end of 17th century*
1 Tie
2 Tackle
3 Lower lift

B *Wooden blocks without strops*
C *Chain plate with dead-eye*

D *Block for hemp strop*
1 Shell
2 Score for the strop
3 Sheave
4 Pin

E *Fiddleblock with one sheave smaller than the other*

F *Deadeye, turned in a shroud*
1 Deadeye
2 Shroud
3 Throat-seizing
4 End-seizing
5 Lanyard

G *Lower yardarm with topsail sheet block*
1 Lower yardarm
2 Topsail sheet block
3 Topsail sheet
4 Lower lift

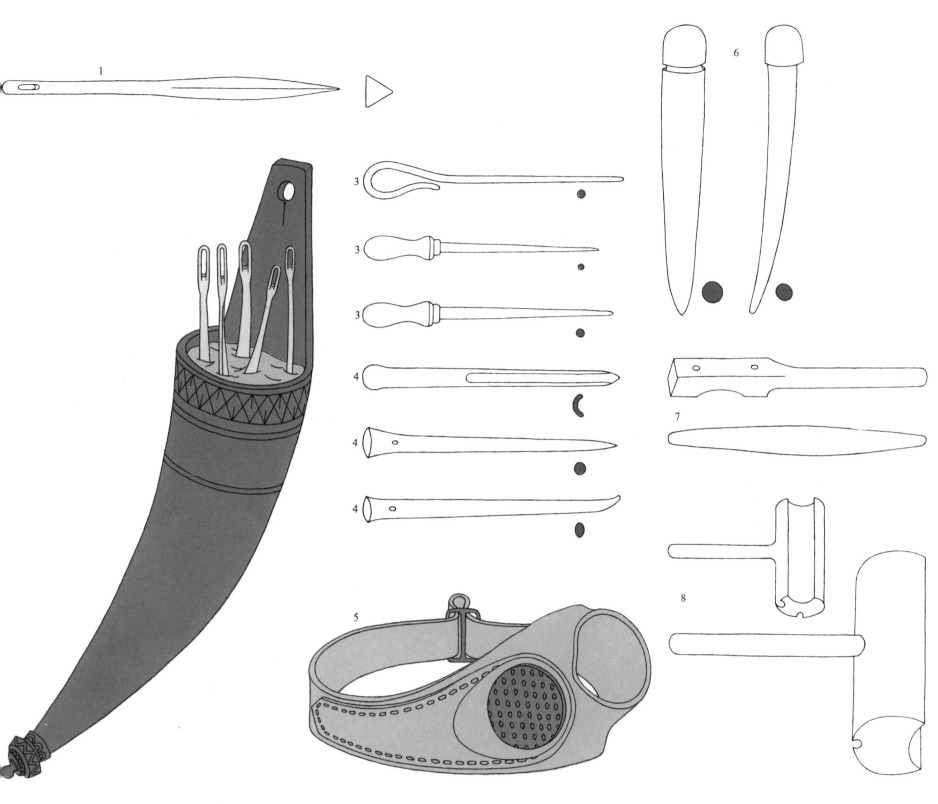

TOOLS FOR SAIL-MAKING AND RIGGING WORK

1 Big sail needle, roping
  needle
2 Carved bullock's horn
  with tallow for holding
  needles

3 Prickers for small
  work
4 Marlinespikes for
  splicing wire

5 Sail-maker's palm
6 Splicing fids
7 Turning fids or
  heavers
8 Serving mallets

SAILING SHIPS

OLD TYPES OF SAILING SHIPS

1 Egyptian sea-going
   ship, about 1500 B.C.
2 Roman trader, about
   A.D. 200
3 Viking longship,
   A.D. 900
4 Norman ship from the
   13th century

5 Hulk of the Hanseatic
   League, about 1470
6 Spanish caravel, about
   1490
7 Spanish ship, nao,
   about 1490

8 English carrack, about
   1500
9 Swedish kravel,
   galleon, 1550
10 North European
   boeier, 1560
11 West European
   galleon, 1590
12 Dutch flute, 1640

OLD TYPES OF SAILING SHIPS

13 Dutch pinnace, middle of 17th century

14 Swedish packet, 1690

15 72-gun ship, 1746

16 Merchantman, 1770

17 Hooker, second half of 18th century

18 Algerian chebec, 18th century

19 Swedish krayer, second half of 18th century

20 Swedish East Indiaman, 1786

21 Swedish snow, 1783

22 Swedish bark, 1792

23 Baltimore clipper, 1820

ETHNOGRAPHICAL BOAT TYPES

SOME ETHNOGRAPHICAL BOAT TYPES

1 Reed-boat from Lake Titicaca, South America
2 Boat from Lake Victoria
3 Koster boat from west coast of Sweden
4 Portuguese muleta
5 Small fishing boat from west coast of Sweden
6 Outrigger canoe from the South Pacific
7 Piragua from Tahiti
8 Norwegian jacht
9 Boat from East Pakistan
10 Boat from Kimari, India
11 Sloop from archipelago off Stockholm
12 Tartan, trading craft from western Mediterranean
13 Dutch barge
14 Boat from the Göta River, West Sweden
15 Fishing boat from the Åland Islands, Finland
16 Danish revenue cutter
17 Norfolk wherry
18 Turkish caique
19 Humber keel, Yorkshire

SOME ETHNOGRAPHICAL BOAT TYPES

20 Dutch koff
21 Boat from Bahia, Brazil
22 Bilancella, Italian
   fishing craft
23 Bovo, Sicilian coaster
24 Arabian dhow
25 Egyptian markab

26 Paduakan, coasting
   craft from Celebes
27 Scow schooner, New
   Zealand
28 Thames barge
29 Ketch, Åland Islands,
   Finland

30 Junk, Amoy, South
   China
31 Velocera, Sicilian,
   lateen-rigged
   barkentine
32 Old barge, Lake of
   Vänern, Sweden

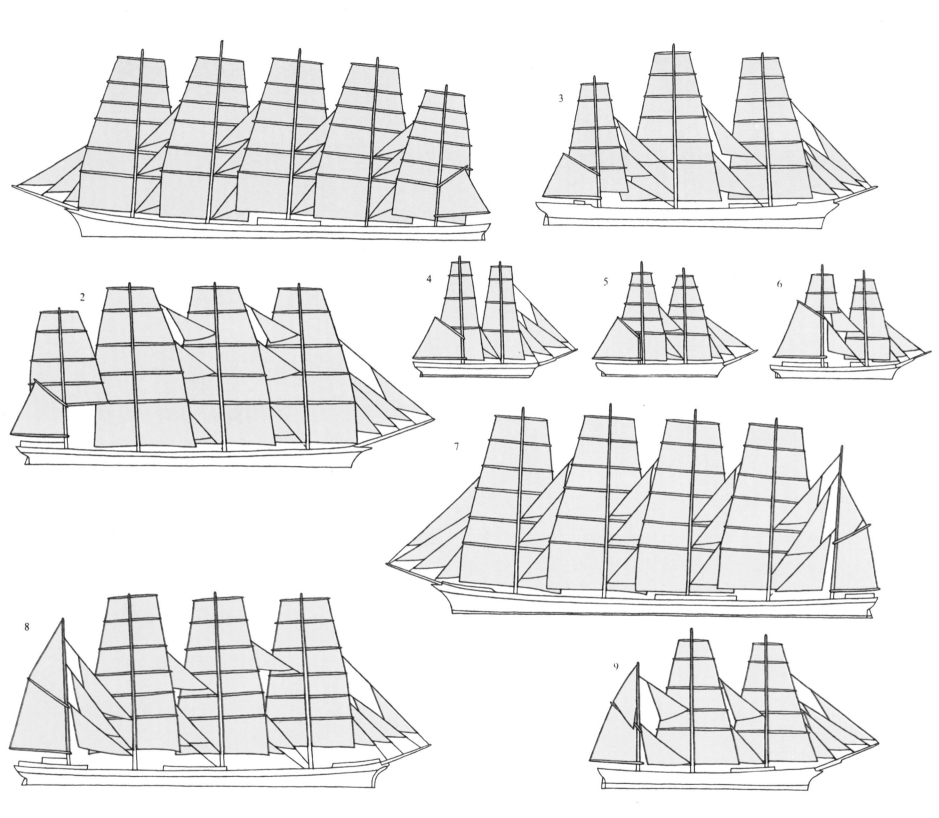

DIFFERENT RIGS

1 Five-masted ship
2 Four-masted ship
3 Ship
4 Brig
5 Snow

6 Main topsail brigantine
7 Five-masted bark
8 Four-masted bark
9 Bark

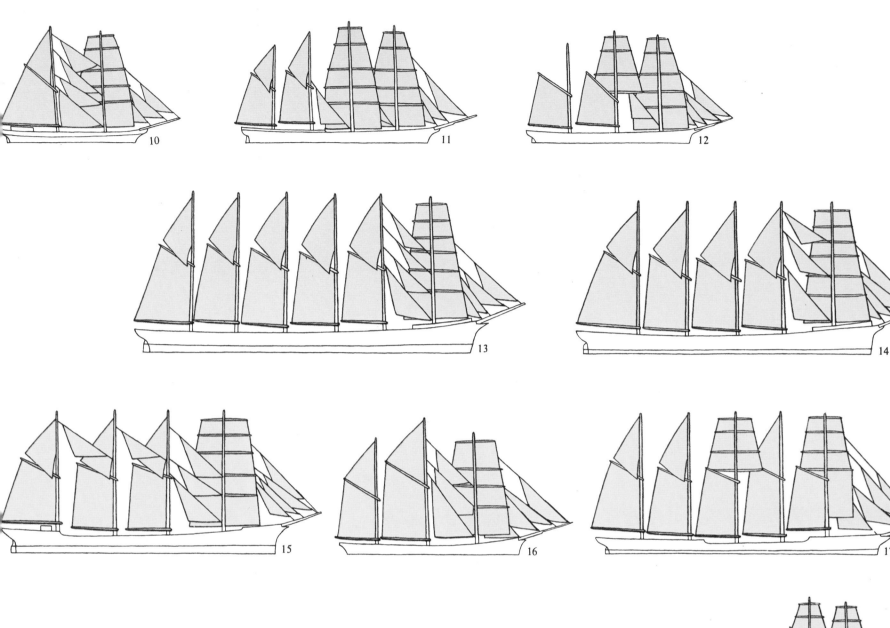

10 Brigantine or hermaph-
    rodite brig
11 Four-masted jackass
    bark
12 Jackass bark

13 Six-masted barkentine
14 Five-masted barkentine
15 Four-masted
    barkentine

16 Barkentine
17 Five-masted two-
    topsail schooner
18 Four-masted topsail
    schooner

19 Three-masted topsail
    schooner
20 Topsail schooner
21 Main-topsail schooner
    or two-topsail schooner

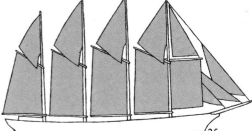

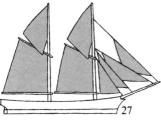

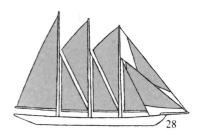

DIFFERENT RIGS

22 Seven-masted fore-and-
aft schooner
*The only seven-masted
schooner ever built was
the American schooner
THOMAS W. LAWSON
built at Quincy, Mass.,
1902. According to a*
*letter from the captain
the masts were named as
follows: Fore, Main,
Mizzen, Number 4,
Number 5, Number 6
and Spanker. This letter
is kept in Peabody
Museum, Salem, Mass.*

23 Six-masted fore-and-
aft schooner
24 Five-masted fore-and-
aft schooner
25 Four-masted fore-and-
aft schooner rigged
with a flying foresail
26 Three-masted fore-and-
aft schooner

27 Two-masted fore-and-
aft schooner
28 Three-masted staysail
schooner
29 Two-masted staysail
schooner

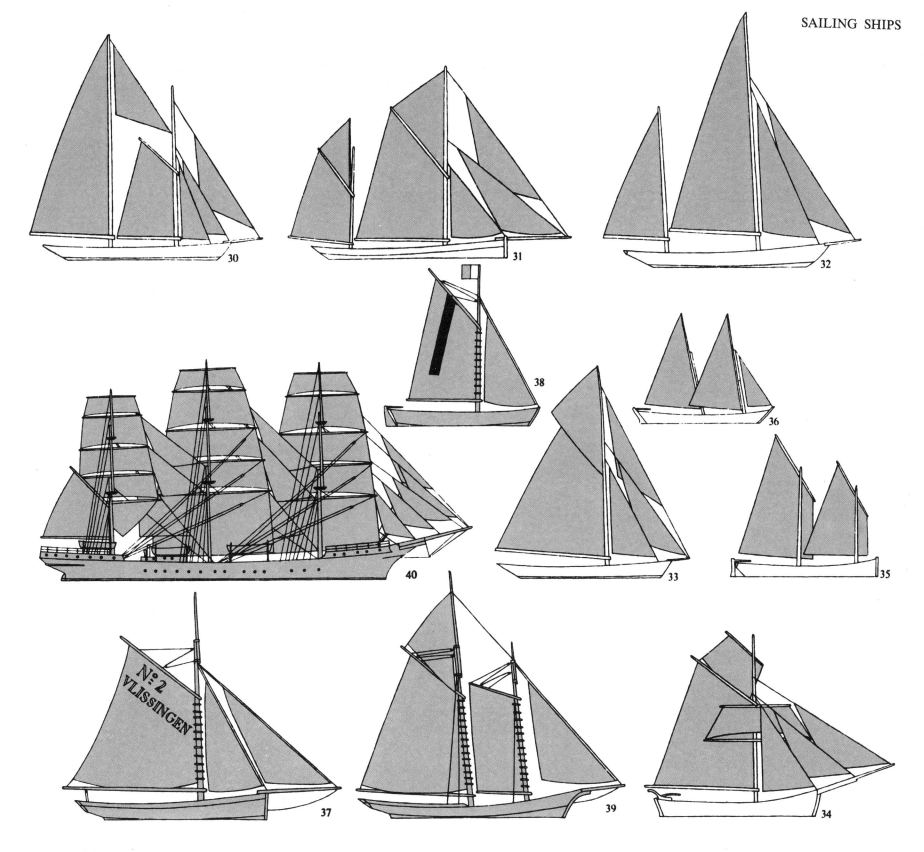

DIFFERENT RIGS AND AUXILIARY SAILING VESSELS

30 Two-masted schooner
    with Bermuda
    mainsail
31 Ketch
32 Bermuda-rigged ketch
33 Gaff-rigged cutter

34 Baltic sloop
35 Launch rigged with
    dipping lugsails
36 Gunter-rigged gig

37 Dutch pilot cutter, 1880's
38 Old Swedish sailing pilot
    cutter
39 New York pilot schooner
40 Training ship, *Denmark*,
    three-masted full-rigged
    ship

FLAGS

FIVE FLAGS

A *Sweden*
1 In the second half of the 16th century the present Swedish flag was not yet in use. Instead Swedish men-of-war flew a blue-and-white striped flag.
   The pennant at the masthead, however, carried the three Swedish crowns.
2 The three-tongued blue flag of the fleet of the army, 1761-1813

3 The ensign of 1658, from the oldest preserved Swedish flag, now in Rijksmuseum, Amsterdam
4 Merchant flag, 1815-1844, with the canton of the Swedish-Norwegian Union
5 The ensign with the canton of the Union, 1844-1905
6 Merchant flag, after 1905

B *Great Britain*
1 Union flag
2 Cross of St. George
3 Cross of St. Andrew
4 Cross of St. Patrick
5 Merchant flag (red ensign)

C *Denmark*
   According to a legend, the Danish flag fell from the sky in front of the army in 1219 and lead the army to victory. It is probably the oldest flag in the world, and has been Denmark's colors since the 14th century.

D *United States of America*
1 The U.S. flag of today. The stars represent the 50 states and the stripes the original 13 states.
2 The 13 stars of 1777
3 1795
4 1818
5 1846
6 1848
7 1912
   No official design for placement of the stars existed before 1912

E *Australia*
   The five stars in the field are the principal stars in the Southern Cross constellation. The large star below the canton is the symbolic "Commonwealth Star"
1 National flag
2 Merchant flag

A1

2

3

4

5

6

S
7

A
8

9

10

11

12

13

14

S
15

16

V N
17

B

C

D

F L
18

S
19

G E
20

FLAGS

A *House flags from sailing ship days*
1 The Hanseatic League, Lübeck (the Middle Ages)
2 The East India Company, London
3 Black Ball Line, New York (1816)
4 Enoch Train White Diamond Line, Boston (1820's)
5 Grinnell, Minturn & Co., New York, Swallow Tail Line for Liverpool

6 Grinnell, Minturn & Co., New York, Swallow Tail Line for London
7 Arthur Sewall, Bath, Me.
8 Alaska Packers Association, San Francisco
9 Money Wigram & Sons, London
10 George Thompson & Co., Aberdeen White Star Line, Aberdeen
11 John Willis & Son, London
12 Devitt & Moore, London

13 John Hardie & Co., Glasgow
14 Thomas Law & Co., Shire Line, Glasgow
15 John Stewart & Co., London
16 Andrew Weir & Co., Bank Line, Glasgow
17 Soc. Anon. Des Voiliers Nantais, Nantes
18 Ferdinand Laeisz, Hamburg
19 S. O. Stray & Co., Kristiansand
20 Gustaf Erikson, Mariehamn

B *Other house marks: Black Ball Packet* Besides flags, proud owners often had marks on the sails similar to the funnel marks of today. The Black Ball Line, New York, carried a black ball on the fore topsail, which was visible from far away.

C *Flags of a merchant ship*
1 Jack, often a small house flag or coat of arms, only flown in port

2 When in port abroad: the color of the country. In ports at home: when loading, the color of the country where bound, or when discharging, the color of the country from which the ship has arrived
3 Code flag, the Blue Peter, if vessel is to proceed to sea
4 Mail flag, if vessel carries mail

5 House flag
6 National colors, when in port
7 National colors, when at sea, if ship is fitted with an ensign gaff on the mainmast

D *Flags of man-of-war*
1 Union Jack
2 Naval flag
3 Commander's flag or pennant

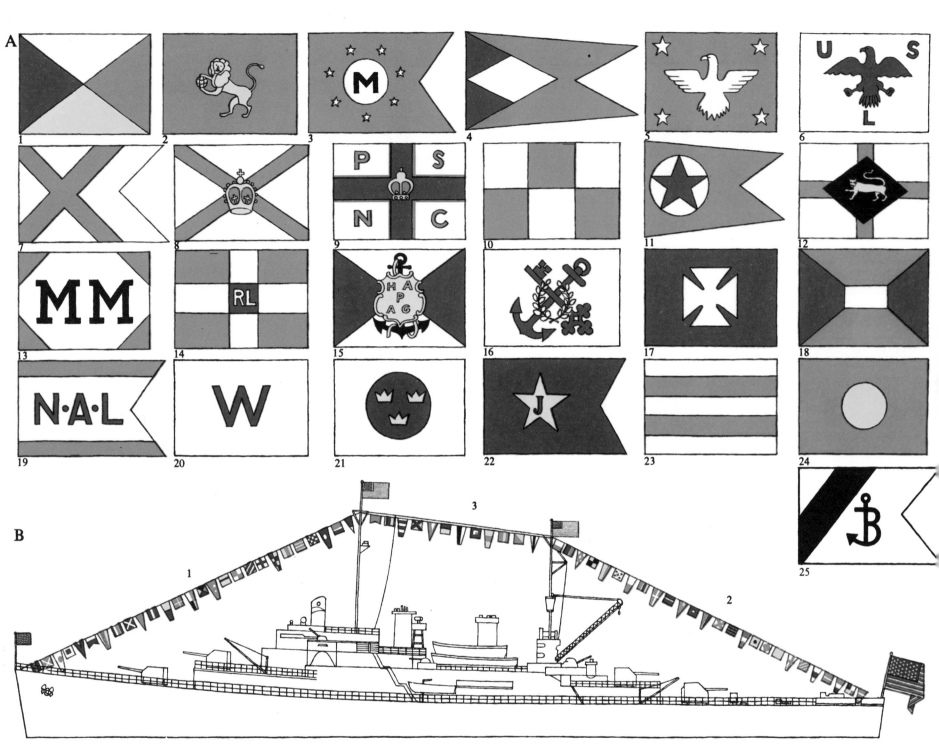

A *Later house flags*
1 P & O Steam and Nav. Co., London, 1834
2 Cunard Steamship Co., Liverpool, 1840
3 Matson Nav. Co., San Francisco
4 United Fruit Co., Boston, New York
5 American President Line, San Francisco
6 United States Lines, New York
7 British India Co., London

8 Royal Mail Steam Packet Co., London
9 Pacific Steam Nav. Co., Liverpool
10 Canadian Pacific Railways Co., London
11 Blue Star Line, London
12 British Tankers Co., Ltd., London
13 Cie de Messageries Maritimes, Paris
14 Rotterdamsche Lloyd, Rotterdam. This original flag was later changed with a crown over the "RL".

15 Hamburg American Line, Hamburg
16 Norddeutscher Lloyd, Bremen
17 Det Forenede Dampskibselskab, Copenhagen
18 J. Lauritzen, Copenhagen
19 Norwegian American Line, Oslo
20 Wilhelm Wilhelmsen, Oslo
21 Swedish American Line, Gothenburg
22 Johnson Line, Stockholm

23 Nippon Yusen Kaisha, Tokyo
24 China Merchant Nav. Co., Hong Kong

B *How to dress a ship Dressing a ship means displaying national ensigns from the flag-staff and each masthead. Full dressing also calls for a rainbow of signal flags and pennants. The order of flags in the US Navy is shown above.*

1 Main down. Beginning at Ensign Staff: 3, L, p2, 4, p7, X, Church pennant, 0,

In the Royal British Navy, the order is:
1 Fore down. Beginning at jack staff: E, Q, Desig, G, p3, Z, Negat, W, p9, 7, p4, R, p8, P, p4, i, p1, T, p7, 6, Corpen, 8, p2, X, Preparative, H, Code, 5, Starboard, X, p0, F, Church pennant, Division, Form, O, Sub Division.
2 Main down. Beginning at Ensign Staff: 3, L, p2, 4, p7, X, Church pennant, 0,

Interrogative, B, p0, V, p4, K, pQ, N, Code, J, Form, R, Turn, M, Corpen, P, p7, 3, p3, 2, Desig, 5, p8, 9, Speed Flag.
3 Fore to Main: Station, Y, Third Substitute, U, First Substitute, D, Fourth Substitute, 3, Emergency, 1, Third Substitute, L, Emergency, 7, Second Substitute, Squadron, First Substitute, C.

137

SIGNALS CODE

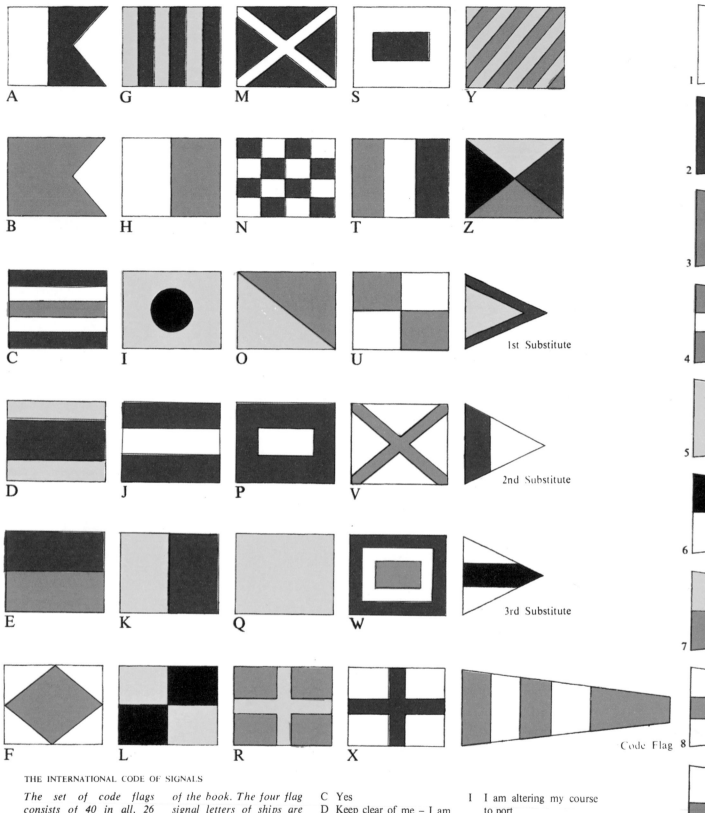

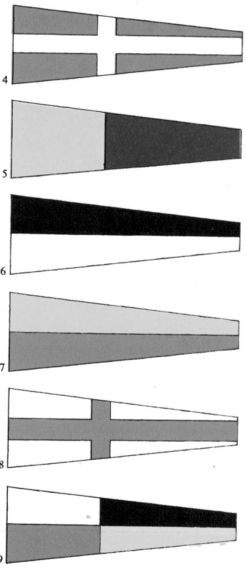

1st Substitute

2nd Substitute

3rd Substitute

Code Flag

THE INTERNATIONAL CODE OF SIGNALS

The set of code flags consists of 40 in all, 26 alphabetical flags, 10 numeral pennants, 3 Substitutes, and the code pennant. Signals are made in one-, two-, three-, and four-letter flag hoists, arranged in alphabetical order, as are also the chief words of their corresponding phrases, so that the coding and decoding can usually be done in the same section of the book. The four flag signal letters of ships are given in a separate book entitled The Mercantile Navy List and also in another book called Signal Letters of British Ships.

Single-letter signals are either for emergencies or in everyday use:

A I have a diver down; keep well clear at slow speed

B I am taking in, or discharging, or carrying dangerous goods

C Yes

D Keep clear of me – I am maneuvering with difficulty

E I am altering my course to starboard

F I am disabled – communicate with me

G I require a pilot. When made by fishing vessels on fishing grounds it means "I am handling nets"

H I have a pilot on board

I I am altering my course to port

J I am on fire and have dangerous cargo on board: keep well clear of me

K I wish to communicate with you

L You should stop your vessel instantly

M My vessel is stopped and making no way through the water

N No

Continued

138

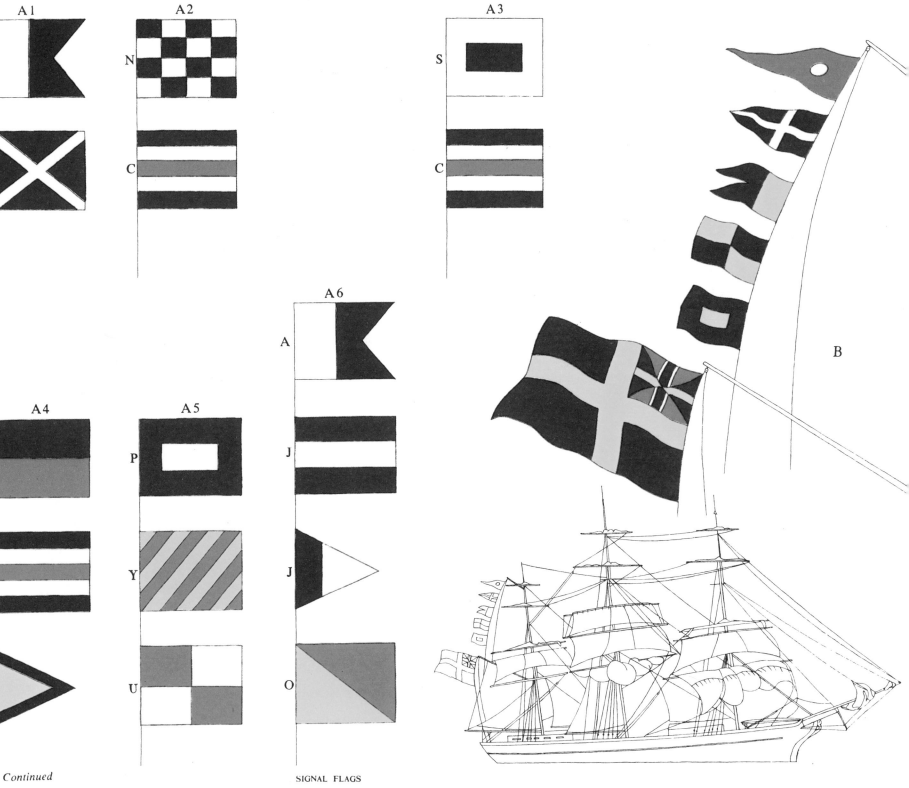

A 1
A
M

A 2
N
C

A 3
S
C

A 4
E
C
E

A 5
P
Y
U

A 6
A
J
J
O

B

SIGNAL FLAGS

Continued

O Man overboard

P *In harbour*. All persons should report on board as the vessel is about to proceed to sea. *At sea*. It may be used by fishing vessels to mean: "My nets have got caught on an obstruction"

Q My vessel is healthy – I request a free pratique

R The way is off my ship you may feel your way past me

S My engines are going full speed astern

T Keep clear of me; I am engaged in pair trawling

U You are standing into danger

V I require assistance

W I require medical assistance

X Stop carrying out your intentions and watch for my signals

Y I am dragging my anchor

Z I require a tug. When made by fishing vessels on fishing grounds it means "I am handling nets"

A *The international signal code*
  Selection of two-letter signals

1 AM–Have you a doctor?

2 NC – I am in distress and require immediate assistance

3 SC – I am under way. SC1 – I am ready to get under way. SC2 – I shall get under way as soon as the weather permits

A selection of three-letter signals

4 ECE – What course are you steering? *(When 1st flag is to be repeated, it is indicated by the 1st Substitute)*

5 PYU – Good voyage!

Example of a four-letter signal

6 AJJO – Liverpool (When the 2nd flag is to be repeated, it is indicated by the 2nd Substitute)

B *Earlier signal systems During a few decades in the middle of the 19th century. Marryat's code was in use before the Commercial Code became universal. The number in Marryat's Code of the Swedish three-masted ship Indiaman of Gävle, 1856, is shown above the ship.*

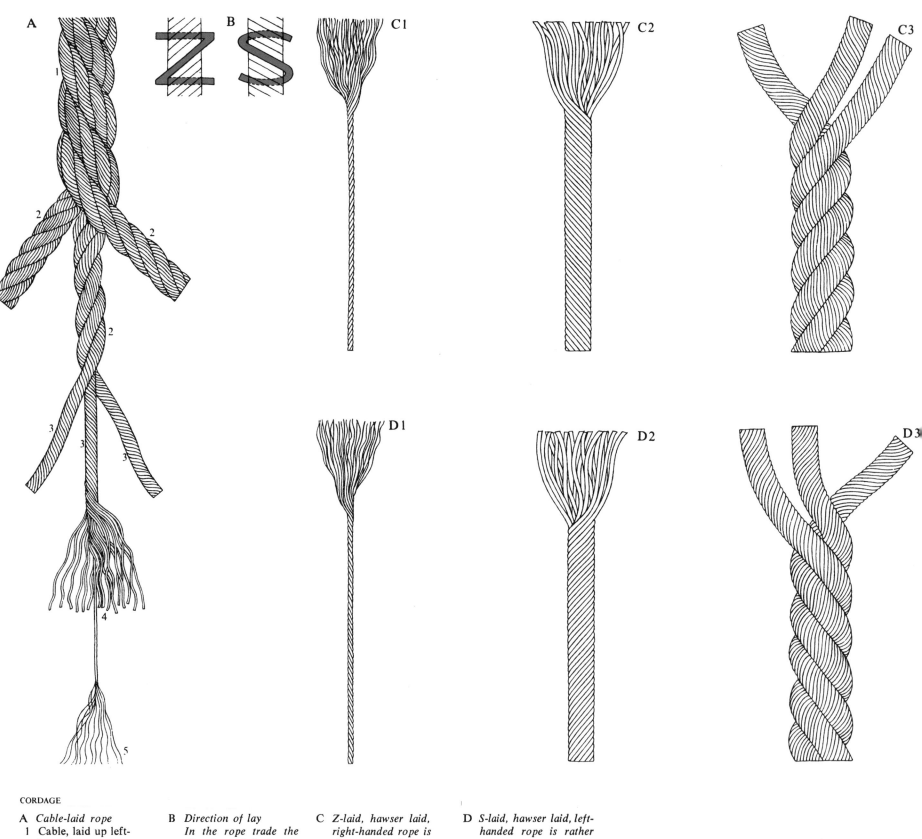

A *Cable-laid rope*
1 Cable, laid up left-handed
2 Hawser, laid up right-handed
3 Strands
4 Yarn
5 Fiber

B *Direction of lay*
In the rope trade the directions of the lay are described as Z-twist and S-twist, in accordance with the figure they make. Z-twist is also called right-hand lay and S-twist is called left-hand lay.

C *Z-laid, hawser laid, right-handed rope is the most used*
1 Z-spun yarn
2 S-twisted strand
3 Z-laid rope

D *S-laid, hawser laid, left-handed rope is rather uncommon*
1 S-spun yarn
2 Z-twisted strand
3 S-laid rope

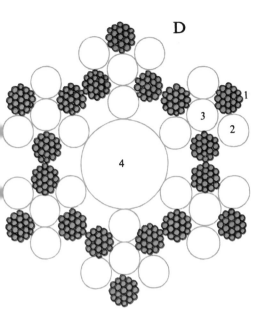

D

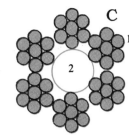

C

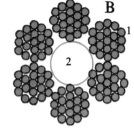

B

A

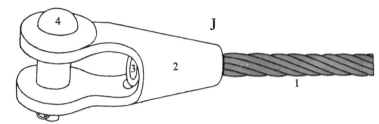

J

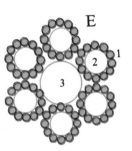

E

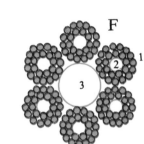

F

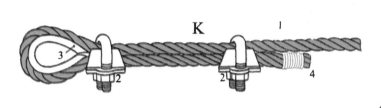

K

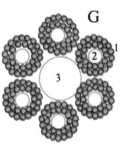

G

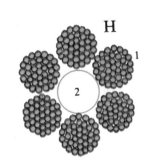

H

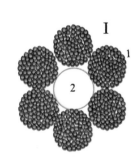

I

WIRES

A *Regular lay, right lay steel wire rope*
1 Left-handed twisted strand
2 Heart of hemp
3 Steel wires
4 Hemp or jute core

B *Standard hoisting wire rope, 6×19+1*
1 Strand of 19 steel wires
2 Heart of hemp

C *Standing rigging wire rope, 6×7+1*
1 Strand of 7 steel wires
2 Heart of hemp

D *Hemp-clad wire rope, 6×(3+4)+1*
1 Wire rope
2 Hemp string
3 Jute core
4 Heart of hemp

E *Running wire rope, 6×12+7*
1 Wire
2 Jute core
3 Heart of hemp

F *Mooring line and hawser, 6×24+7*
1 Steel wire
2 Jute core
3 Heart of hemp

G *Mooring line and hawser, 6×30+7*
1 Steel wire
2 Jute core
3 Heart of hemp

H *Tiller wire rope, 6×37+1*
1 Galvanized steel or bronze wire strand
2 Heart of hemp

I *Tiller wire rope, 6×61+1*
1 Strand (like H)
2 Heart of hemp

J *Open wire-end socket*
1 Wire rope
2 Socket
3 End spread and soldered
4 Bolt with cotter pin

K *Temporary wire rope eye*
1 Wire rope
2 Wire rope bulldog grips
3 Thimble
4 Whipping

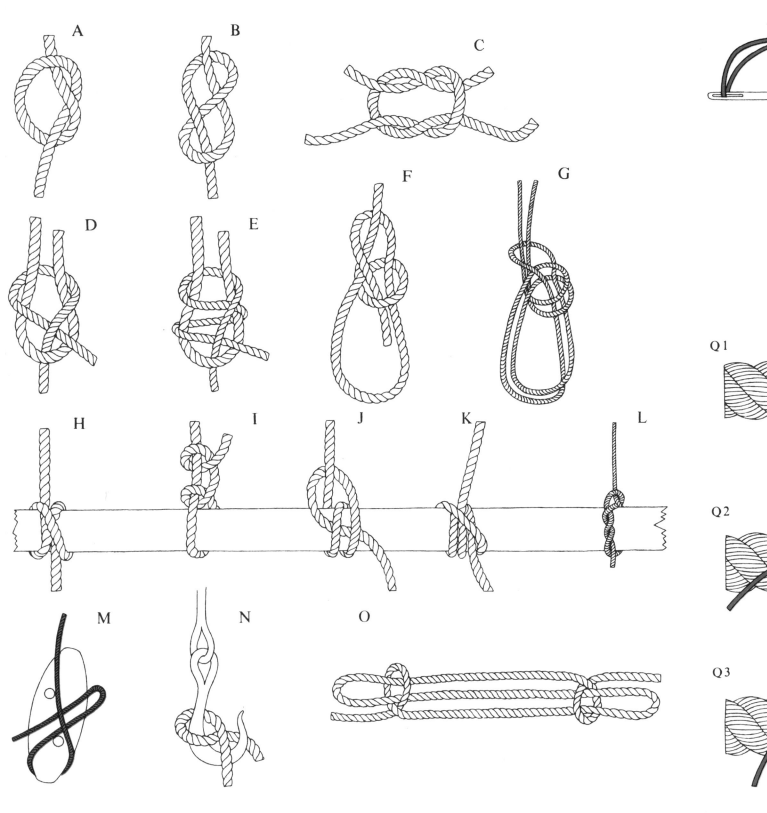

KNOTS AND WHIPPINGS

A Overhand knot	E Double sheet bend, variation	J Fisherman's bend	O Sheepshank
B Figure of eight knot, Flemish knot	F Bowline	K Rolling hitch	P Palm and needle whipping
C Square knot, reef knot	G Bowline on the bight	L Timber hitch	Q Common whipping
D Sheet bend	H Clove hitch	M Slippery hitch	
	I Two half-hitches	N Blackwall hitch	

A

B1

C1

2

D

SPLICES

When splicing cordage the strands are tucked against the lay. Each strand is taken over the strand on its left and then under the next one.

A *Short splice, ropes put together before beginning to splice*

B *Long splice*

1 The ropes laid up before beginning to splice

2 Way of knotting the strands

3 Way of tucking the strands

C *Eye splice*

1 Way of placing the strand before commencing the splice

2 Way of tucking the two first strands

D *Eye splice on a wire rope, one tuck made on each strand.*

When splicing wire rope each strand is generally tucked around the same strand all the time, in the same direction, as the single wires are laid.

Columbus' stately ship
can no longer serve as
the introductory note
for the up-to-date
chapter on propulsion.
Instead, a rough print
of the cylinder top
in a diesel motor has
been used.

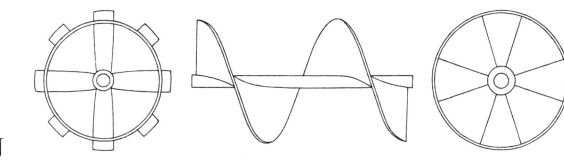

PROPULSION

BY TAGE BLUM

The first primitive craft, hollowed-out tree trunks or skin-covered boats built on light frames, were propelled by a paddle which was held with both hands and had no support by the gunwale. If there were many paddles on each side a considerable speed could undoubtedly be obtained. Even quite large ships have been paddled, which is apparent from many Egyptian reproductions. The "Hjortspring boat" in the National Museum in Copenhagen is a good example of a ship which had been built for propulsion by paddles. The invention of the oar with a fixed support on the gunwale was a very great advancement. The "Nydam boat" (Gottorp Castle) was an effective and fast "rowing ship" of slender shape and with twenty-eight oars. In Scandinavia the sail came into use early, and even though the Norsemen's Viking ships and longships were very easily rowed, sail was always used when making long voyages.

It was different in the Mediterranean, where the rowing vessel had a unique development. Here, they were not content with one line of oars or one man to an oar, but built vessels with two, three, and possibly more tiers of oars banked over each other. Probably the largest vessels employed several men to an oar. They were named biremes, triremes, quadriremes, quinquiremes, and so on even to one huge "40." Of these, the trireme was the best (170 oarsmen, maximum speed 8—9 knots). To give some idea of its efficiency, it was not until the time of Napoleon III that there was a faster postal service by steamship over the Mediterranean than that which the triremes maintained during Roman times. A factor should, however, be pointed out: while it was an honor to row an oar in a Viking ship, it was the slaves who rowed the Mediterranean galleys.

The idea of using paddle wheels appeared comparatively early. Appius Claudius is said to have experimented with hand-driven paddle wheels as early as the year 263 B.C. During the course of time, the idea appeared again and "walking drivers" by horses and oxen were tried. About the year 1200 mention is made of Chinese naval battles, where the warships were driven by slaves at capstans. As far as pure muscle power was concerned, the oar was undoubtedly the most effective means of propulsion. From the Middle Ages we have several illustrations of paddle-wheel ships, and in 1543 we hear of Blasco Garay's ship, which was tested in the harbor of Barcelona. But here also the paddle wheel was activated by man-power. A stronger source of propulsion was needed before mechanically driven vessels would have any practical use. Steam became the source of power that solved the problem. The name of James Watt will always be associated with the first practically applicable steam engine, where the movement of the piston was changed into a rotary motion. Watt was an instrument maker and was born in 1736. It cannot be said that he invented the steam engine, as Thomas Newcomen's atmospheric engine was already in existence, but Watt improved Newcomen's engine. It had been a clumsy device; now it was a really usable engine which could be used where a rotating shaft was required. Watt invented the condenser

and made an engine where the piston was operated by the steam pressure and not, as in Newcomen's engine, where the steam was only used to lift the piston while the atmospheric pressure above it pushed it down. Hence the name "atmospheric engine."

Now the steam engine began to be used in ships. The first name in this connection was Denis Papin, the inventor of "Papin's Pot." In the year 1707 Papin is said to have sailed down the Fulda river in a steamboat from Kassel to the Weser. Here, his boat was destroyed by the boatmen who had a monopoly of navigation on the Weser. It is doubtful if this boat was anything other than a hand-powered paddle boat. In the year 1736 the Englishman Jonathan Hull obtained a patent on a steam tugboat, but there is doubt if it ever came into being. In 1776 the Marquis Claude de Jouffroy built a steamboat in which the engine drove paddle feet. In 1783 he built a larger, paddle-wheel boat, which forced the current on the Saône river as witnessed by many spectators. In 1788—1789 the Scotsman William Symington built two less successful steamboats; all of these experiments, however, were of no significance.

About the same time, in 1785, in America, the clockmakers, John Fitch and Henry Voigt, built a steam engine in a boat which had twelve oars. This experiment was successful, and with his third boat Fitch carried on a regular passenger service on the Delaware river between Philadelphia and Trenton, a distance of thirty miles. Fitch, however, never received any recognition. It was Robert Fulton who succeeded commercially and reaped riches and fame. Originally he was an artist, but with technical interests. About this time, in 1801, William Symington built the steam tugboat, Charlotte Dundas, which in many ways was before its time. Its engine differed from others by having a horizontal cylinder, with the piston rod, crosshead, guides, and connecting rod acting directly on the crankshaft. It was direct-acting as compared with the beam engine. The paddle wheel was placed in the stern and was fitted with wheel rims. The helm was situated on the foredeck. Fulton studied this boat, and in 1802 built a steamboat in France. The machinery was from Boulton and Watt. At a trial on the Seine he succeeded in winning the confidence of the American Ambassador in Paris, Robert Livingston, and in 1806 he returned to America. Here, he built the paddle steamer Clermont, with an engine from Boulton and Watt, and in 1807 he made his historic and successful voyage up the Hudson river. Even if Fulton was not the inventor of the steamship, it was he who made the first steamship which had any practical value. The Clermont will always be considered a milestone in the development of the steamship. In spite of its successful voyages in 1802 it was not the Charlotte Dundas that opened a new era. Instead, it was forbidden the use of the Clyde canal for fear it would damage its banks. Henceforth, all steamship traffic in Great Britain was stopped until years later. In America, under more favorable circumstances, development of steamships on the big rivers was rapid. Five years after the Clermont's

journey there were fifty steamships in regular service. The high speeds attained by these paddle steamers are rather surprising: for example, the fastest ship at that time, the Daniel Drew of 1860, was able to maintain an average speed of 22 knots. However, these were large ships! For instance, the New World was 380 feet long, had a paddle wheel of 46 feet in diameter, and had no less than 680 berths.

Not until 1812 did the building of steamships begin in Europe. This was when Henry Bell launched the Comet, a ship with a length of 40 feet and a beam of 10½ feet. The engine was a single cylinder unit of 3—4 horsepower and the speed was only 4—5 knots. It differed from other paddle steamers by having two wheels on each side. The whole engine installation was much more primitive than that of the Charlotte Dundas, but, in spite of this, the Comet became the model for practical steamship service in England.

At first, steamships were looked upon as only suitable for river and coastal traffic; possibilities for development were a lot greater in America with its large waterways. It is therefore notable that it was an American steamship that first crossed the Atlantic. On May 26, 1819, the Savannah left Savannah, Georgia, and arrived at Liverpool twenty-five days later. Savannah was a full-rigged ship, fitted with a 90 horsepower engine that drove the wheel shaft directly. The paddle wheels were sixteen feet in diameter and were fitted with chains instead of wheel rims, so that the paddle wheels could be folded up when the sails were in use. From the logbook it can be seen that the steam engine was used for eighteen days of the voyage, while only the sails were used during the remaining seven days. The Savannah's dimensions were: length 100 feet; beam 27 feet 9 inches; draft 14 feet. The vessel held seventy-five tons of coal and three-thousand cubic feet of wood bunkers.

The ships mentioned up to now, with the exception of the Charlotte Dundas and the Savannah, were all fitted with beam engines on which the piston rod was joined to one end of a center pivoted rocker beam and the crankshaft to the other end. There were many variations of the beam engine: engines with the beam above, and engines with the beam below; also the "grasshopper engines," with the beam pivoted at one end. In Europe a low-location beam was mostly used, as this gave a low center of gravity. Paddle wheels, in the beginning, had fixed paddles, but these were inefficient. Soon, movable paddles came into being. These paddles could, by means of a series of rods, operated by a cam, stand almost vertical during the whole time they were under water (Morgan's patent paddle wheel).

As early as about 1770 the French scientist, Daniel Bernoulli, had suggested the propeller as a means of propulsion. There were both corkscrew and windmill types. In 1836 the Englishman, E. P. Smith, made a propeller that resembled a corkscrew, while the Swede, John Ericsson, experimented with a propeller that resembled the sails of a windmill. Smith's propeller had a pitch of $1^{1/2}$-3 turns to start with, but during one of the test runs part of it was knocked off and it was then found that it was much more effective. John Ericsson, who was born in 1803 and died in 1889, built a successful propeller-driven boat, the *Francis B. Ogden*, which was demonstrated on the Thames in 1837. His idea, however, was not popularly received, so he left for America where he quickly met with great success. Among the early propeller ships, Samuel Owen's *The Witch of Stockholm*, 1816, should be mentioned.

The engines used in paddle steamers were much too slow to drive propellers, and attempts were made to increase the speed by means of gears or chain transmission (*S/S Great Britain*, 1839), but these gearings did not solve the problem. Although the propeller had many advantages over the paddle wheel it was a long time before the propeller became a real success. The majority preferred the paddle steamer for passenger traffic and were responsible for the building of the last of the large paddle steamers: *Persia* (1855) and *Scotia* (1862). Especially interesting was the tug of war carried out by the British Navy between H.M.S. *Rattler* (propeller) and the equally large and powerful H.M.S. *Alecto* (paddle wheel). It was a great victory for the propeller.

A unique change was represented by the gigantic ship *Great Eastern* (trials, 1859) which was equipped with both propeller (24 feet in diameter) and paddle wheels (56 feet in diameter, each weighing 92 tons). Commercially, the ship was a failure, but even so, it will always be looked upon as a milestone in the history of shipbuilding.

The first boilers were very primitive, with an external firebox and often with large flat surfaces. These potboilers could not stand high pressures. They were then developed into boilers with internal fireboxes, and then into fire tubes boilers with combustion chambers and several fire tubes. This increased the heating area and used the fuel more effectively. Five tube boilers (the Scotch boilers) became the commenest type in merchant ships about 1900 and later. Development continued with water tube boilers, where the water (as opposed to the fire tube boilers) is contained inside the tubes and the furnace and combustion gases are outside. Water tube boilers contain less water than fire tube boilers. Steam can be raised much more quickly with a water tube boiler than with a Scotch boiler. They became even more economical with the introduction of the superheater, artificial draft created by fans, preheating of the water, and so on. The engine went through a comparable development, to direct-acting vertical steam engines with chankshaft placed under the cylinders. The expansion of steam became more efficient with the use of a three-cylinder engine with high, medium and low pressure cylinders. The triple-expansion engine became the most usual type in the merchant navy.

A really powerful engine had been developed in the shape of the reciprocating steam engine, but it was, however, of rather complicated construction. It was, therefore, obvious that an engine where the energy was directly transformed into rotation had to be built.

As far back as two-thousand years ago, Hero of Alexandria described such a machine. It was the famous Hero steam ball, which was a complete reactive turbine. In 1629 the Italian, Johann Branca, described a machine where a jet of steam drove a bladed wheel This was also a turubine, an active turbine. Both were only curiosities, and it was to make centuries before the first usable turbine was designed by the Swede, de Laval. De Laval's turbine was an active one where the expansion of the steam took place in a stationary turbine casing. This is called an equal pressure tur-

bine because the steam acts directly on the rotor. With high rotor speed, about 30,000 r.p.m., and consequently, great centrifugal force, it was difficult to transmit the power to slower rotating shafts. It was necessary to expand steam pressure through several stages. This brings us to multistage turbines and such inventors as Zoelly, Curtis, and Parsons, who used several rotors on the same shaft but separated them with stationary guide blade rings.

The most important figure in the development of the steam turbine as a marine-power palnt was Sir Charles Parsons, who built the first turbine-powered ship, the steam-yacht *Turbinia* , powered by a 2,000s.h.p. turbine., which drove a propeller approximately 1,800 r.p.m. The first trials were a disappointment: a speed of $19^{3/4}$ knots at 1,780 r.p.m. The trouble was that at such high revolutions caviation occured at the propeller, a problem of which little was then known.

In 1893, the *Turbinia's* power plant was rebuilt with three turbines, each driving its own shaft, and with a total of nine propellers. With this change came success: a maximum speed of up to 34 knots — a rather incredible speeed at that time. The Admiralty, however, showed no interest in it. This led to Parsons' historical demonstration, in 1897, at the naval review at Spithead. Parsons sailed at a speed of over 30 knots past the warships at anchor. A naval vessel was sent out to stop the unwelcome visitor, but the speed of the *Turbinia* only made tha naval ship look ridiculous. This demonstration resulted in an order for the first turbine-powered destroyer, H.M.S. *Viper*. The steam turbine had many advantages compared with the reciprocating engine, such as no vibration and less space required for the same amount of power. Nevertheless, while direct drive was used, trouble with propeller caviation was encountered. This trouble was not overcome until gears, which could transmit high power, were developed. Naval ships, as well as large passenger ships, where vibration had to be kept to a minimum, quickly changed to steam turbines.

Just before the steam engine and the steam turbine reached the peak of their development a new source of power appeared: the diesel engine. Even the best steam plant is still an external combustion engine in which the fuel's energy is converted into dynamic energy through an intermediate means. If an engine could be made where the actual combustion took place inside the cylinder, greater power for the same amount of fuel could be attained. It was this which Rudolf Diesel (1858 — 1913) did when he invented the engine which now bears his name all over the world. Diesel soon decided to make such an internal combustion engine. In 1893 he described in a treatise the theory and construction of an internal combustion engine, and this put him in contact with two well-known concerns of Krupp and M.A.N., which then did everything to complete the task. The first usable diesel engine was completed in 1897. Its main principle was the ignition of the fuel itself in the cylinder when highly compressed with air. The temperature rose to about 800°C. During combustion (not explosion), the piston was pushed down the cylinder. The diesel engine used about thirty-five per cent of the energy in the fuel, while the steam engine used only fifteen per cent.

The main contributors to the development of the marine diesel engine were, however, Ivar Knudsen, the Danish director of A/S Burmeister & Wain, and the chief of his diesel engine design department, Dr. H. H. Blacke. From 1897 onward, an engine emerged that could compete with the steam turbine, even for powering supertankers and fast cargo liners. Still, the diesel engine contains many heavy parts to convert reciprocating into rotating movement. There was an obvious need for an engine which directly transferred the energy from combustion gases to a turbine.

This led eventually to the use of nuclear reactors in ships powered by steam turbines. Nuclear fission produces heat which, via an exchanger, generates steam to drive the turbines. While the process seems simple, shielding against radiation is essential. Nuclear fuel was also very expensive — and worldwide environmental concerns became a decisive obstacle to such ships. Opposition to them grew until they were denied entry to harbors.

Instead, large boilers were fired with bunker fuel to create steam. But fuel prices rose so high that the approach proved unprofitable. Diesel engines were revived and, to solve the fuel-price problem, they were adapted to run on oils of ever worse quality, as well as to work more efficiently and produce more power per cylinder. This has succeeded by, for example, increasing the top pressure and the stroke length relative to the cylinder diameter. At the same time, materials have been developed that can withstand the greater pressures and temperatures involved.

Engine manufacturers also try to improve the overall economy of diesel equipment through less frequent servicing and less wear on parts. For instance, the Sulzer rotating piston considerably decreases wear on the cylinder wall and piston rings. Consumption of cylinder oil becomes lower across the engine's lifespan, and lubrication is more effective. In addition, control mechanisms have become more precise by replacing rods and rocker arms with hydraulic valves. Alongside diesel engine development, too, research has been done on gas turbines — primarily for fast boats such as catamarans — since they have the advantage of producing enormous power in relation to their size.

Environmental awareness has furthered efforts to decrease the exhaust pollution from diesel engines. Higher efficiency yields lower specific fuel consumption and, therefore, less discharge of carbon dioxide and sulfur oxides. However, a side-effect is more discharge of nitrogen oxides, and methods of avoiding this have been sought. One is to mix water with the fuel, thus lowering the combustion temperature and the consequent formation of nitrogen oxides. Another goal of research is a catalyzer suitable for marine diesel-oil operation, the difficulty being that diesel engines require a large surplus of air. With the SCR (Selective Catalytic Reduction) catalyzer, nitrogen oxides are converted to pure nitrogen gas and steam with no by-products. Such equipment is now used in about ten ships, with good results.

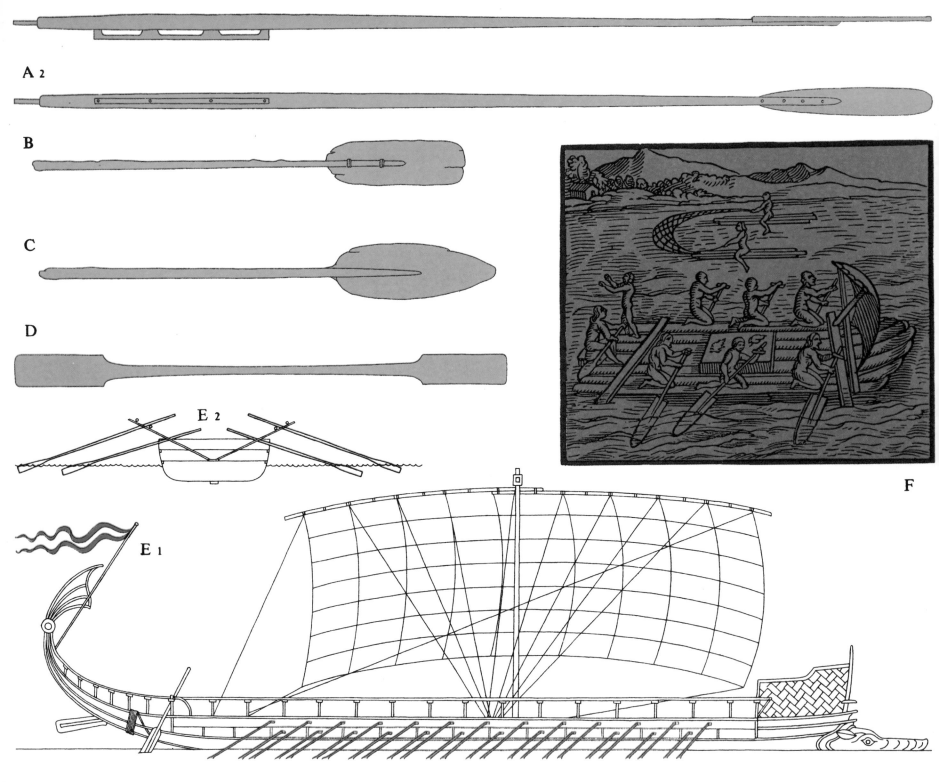

OARS

A *Old galley oar*
Because of their size, these oars were always built with the blade bolted to the shaft. They had handles so that four men could pull each oar.

B *Old Indian paddle*
C *Old Egyptian paddle*
D *Eskimo paddle*

E *Greek warship from 500 B.C.*
1 Drawing from a vase painting
2 Sketch showing the position of oars in a bireme, that is, a boat with two banks of oars on each side

F *Peruvian raft of balsa wood, with sail and paddles (from Benzoni)*

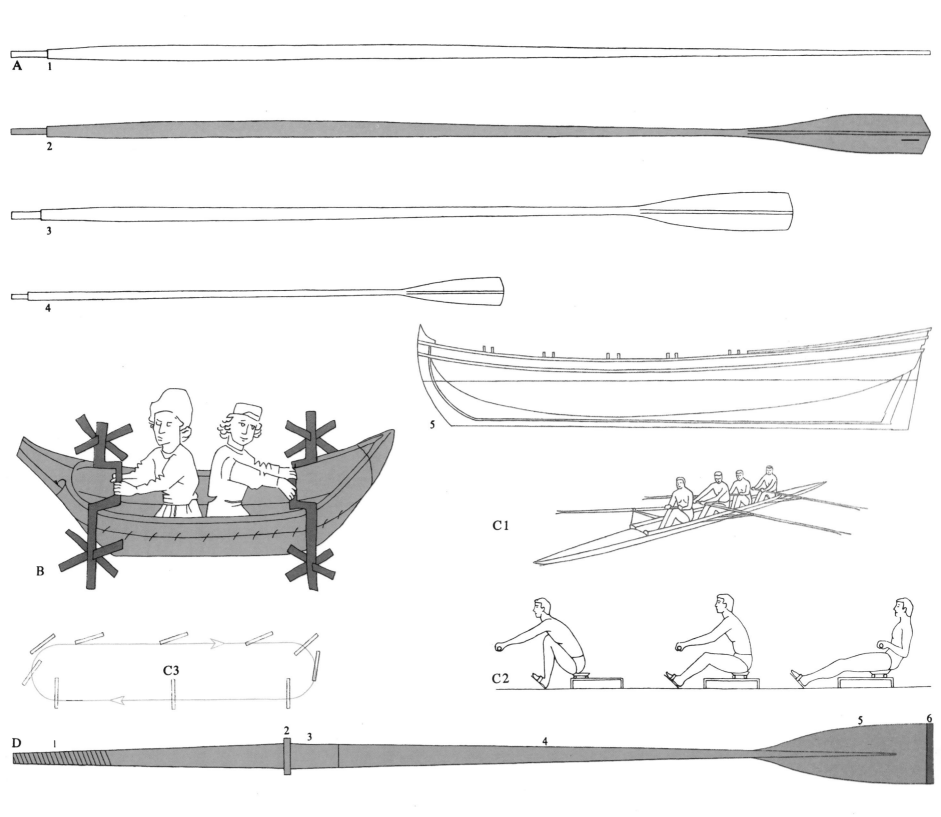

OARS

A *Oars from a book on shipbuilding by Rålamb, Å.C., 1691*

1, 2 The longest oar that can be pulled by one man should not exceed 16½ feet. An oar should never be more than three times the beam of the boat.

3 A handy oar for one man is 14 feet in length

4 When sculling, the oars should not be more than 9 feet and not more than 1½ times the beam of the boat

5 A pulling boat, 20 feet long, pulling ten oars

B *Medieval boat with paddle wheels*

C *Modern competition rowing*

1 Four oars with out-riggers, no coxswain

2 Position of oarsman when pulling

3 The path of the oar blade during a stroke

D *The oar*

1 Grip

2 Loom

3 Leather-covered seat

4 Shaft

5 Blade

6 Copper-banded tip

PADDLE WHEEL

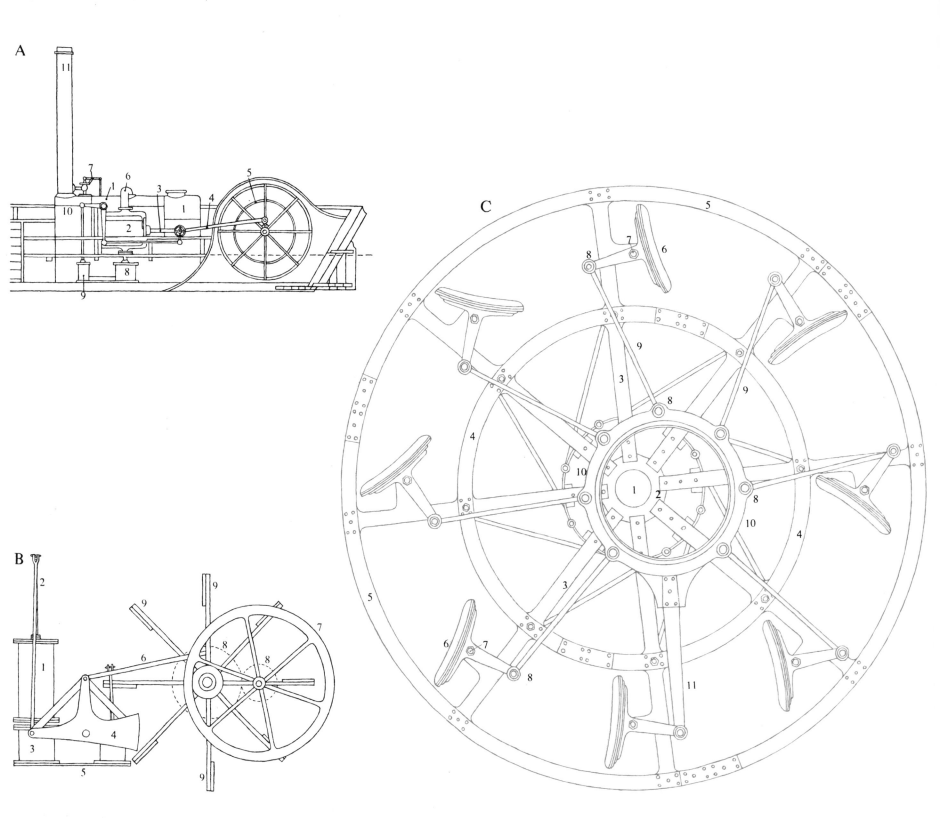

A

B

C

PADDLE WHEEL AND OLD PADDLE ENGINES

A *Symington's direct-drive steamship engine, 1802*	5 Paddle wheel	B *Geared steam engine of the Clermont by Fulton, 1807*	4 Balance	C *Paddle wheel*	6 Paddle
1 Boiler	6 Steampipe		5 Bearing	1 Paddle shaft	7 Wrist pin
2 Cylinder	7 Safety valve	1 Cylinder	6 Connecting rod	2 Hub	8 Limbs
3 Piston rod	8 Condenser	2 Piston rod	7 Flywheel	3 Spoke	9 Drag link
4 Connecting rod	9 Pump	3 Condenser	8 Gear	4 Inner rim	10 Eccentric strap
	10 Smoke box		9 Paddle wheel	5 Outer rim	11 King rod
	11 Funnel				

PADDLE WHEEL ENGINE AND OLD PROPELLERS

A Propeller development	B Triple-expansion paddle wheel engine	4 Connecting rod	10 Oil cup	16 Tail rod	21 Double-bar link
1 1785		5 Eccentric	11 HP-cylinder steam inlet	17 LP-cylinder	22 Cooling water, inlet
2 1800	1 Foundation	6 Eccentric strap	12 LP-cylinder exhaust pipe	18 LP-cylinder steam inlet	23 Cooling water, outlet
3 1812	2 Crank shaft	7 Oil cup	13 Reversing lever	19 Valve-spindle guide	24 Condenser
4 1840	3 Turning gear	8 Connecting rod	14 Throttle valve wheel	20 Link operating bar	25 Pipe to vacuum pump
5 1860		9 Eccentric rods	15 Throttle valve wheel		26 Tank top plating
					27 Bottom plating
					28 Plate floor

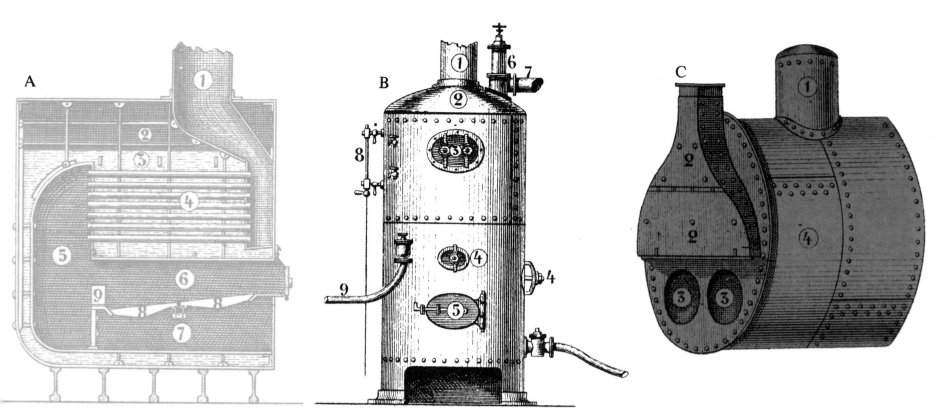

A

B

C

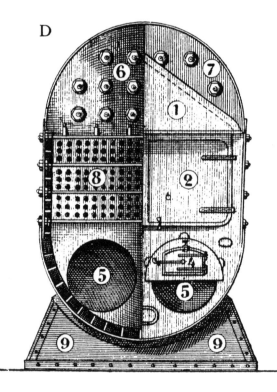

D

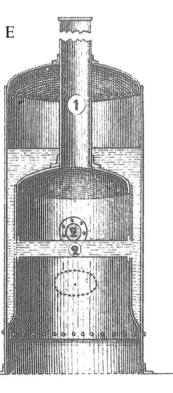

E

F

VARIOUS TYPES OF OLDER BOILERS

A *Rectangular or*
 box boiler
1 Uptake
2 Steam space
3 Water level
4 Boiler tubes
5 Combustion chamber
6 Furnace
7 Ash pit
8 Furnace bars
9 Furnace bridge

B *Vertical donkey boiler*
1 Donkey funnel
2 Crown of donkey
 boiler
3 Manhole door
4 Sludge hole doors
5 Furnace door
6 Safety valve
7 Steam pipe
8 Gauge glass
9 Feed pipe

C *Cylindrical boiler*
 (Scotch type)
1 Dome
2 Uptake and smoke box
3 Furnaces
4 Shell of boiler

D *Oval donkey boiler*
1 Uptake and smoke box
2 Smoke box door
3 Furnace front
4 Furnace door
5 Furnace and ash pit
6 Back plate
7 Front plate
8 Back tube-plate
9 Boiler bearer

E *Water tube donkey*
 boiler
1 Funnel
2 Water tubes

F *Double-ended boiler*
1 Steam space
2 Water level
3 Boiler stays
4 Boiler tubes
5 Combustion chamber
6 Furnaces
7 Ash pits

A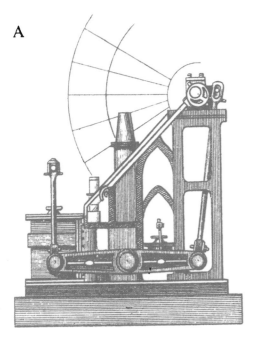

B

C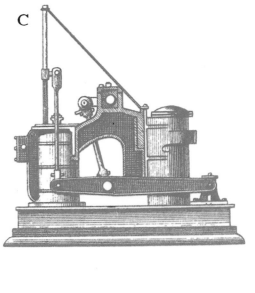

D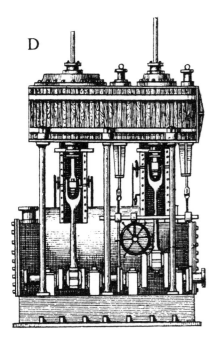

E

F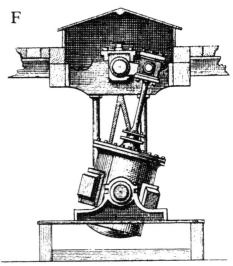

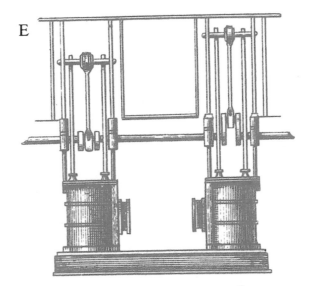

G

H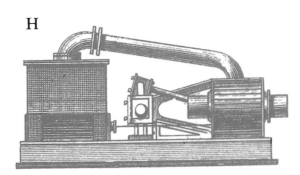

VARIOUS KINDS OF OLDER STEAM ENGINES

A *Side lever engine*
B *Overhead beam engine*
C *Grasshopper engine*
D *Inverted vertical reciprocating compound engine*
E *Steeple engine*
F *Oscillating engine*
G *Diagonal engine*
H *Horizontal (trunk) engine*

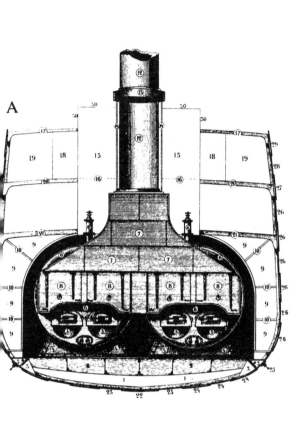

A

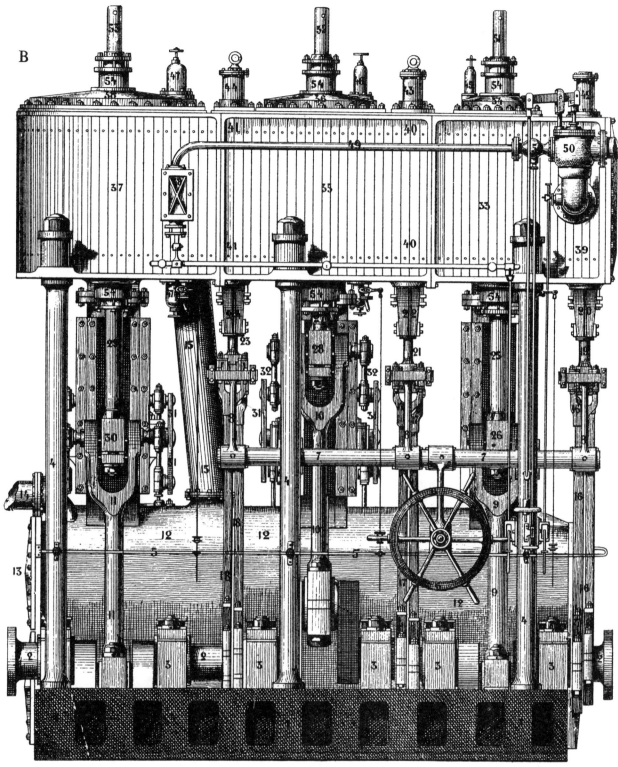

B

ENGINE AND BOILER, 1880

A *Midship section of a steamer, showing boiler room*
1 Floor
2 Water ballast in double bottom
3 Brackets
4 Boiler bearers
5 Ash pits
6 Front tube plates
7 Smoke box, uptake
8 Smoke box doors
9 Side coal bunkers

10 Bunker stays
11 Safety valves
12 Funnel
13 Funnel cape
14 Air casing of funnel
15 Fidley
16 Fidley gratings
17 Bridge deck beam
18 Alley-way, in bridge-house
19 Officer's room
20 Upper deck beam

21 Lower deck beam
22 Flat plate keel
23 Garboard strakes
24 Bottom plating
25 Bilge keel
26 Side plating
27 Sheer strake
28 Side plating of bridge
29 Sheer strake of bridge
30 Fidley top

B *Triple-expansion engine*
1 Bedplate
2 Crank shaft
3 Main bearings
4 Cylinder columns
5 Hand rail
6 Reversing wheel
7 Weigh shaft
8 Weigh shaft arms
9 High-pressure connecting rod
10 Intermediate-pressure connecting rod
11 Low-pressure connecting rod

12 Condenser
13 Condenser head
14 Circulating-pump discharge pipe
15 Exhaust pipe
16, 17, 18 Eccentric rods
19, 21, 23 Valve spindles
20, 22, 24 Valve spindle guides
25, 27, 29 Piston rods
26, 28, 30 Piston rod crossheads
31 Pump levers
32 Pump links

33 High-pressure cylinder
34, 36, 38 Cylinder covers
35 Intermediate cylinder
37 Low-pressure cylinder
39, 40, 41 Valve casings
42, 43, 44 Balance cylinders
45, 46, 47 Escape valves
48 Starting valve
49 Starting valve pipe
50 Throttle
51, 52, 53 Tail rods
54 Stuffing boxes

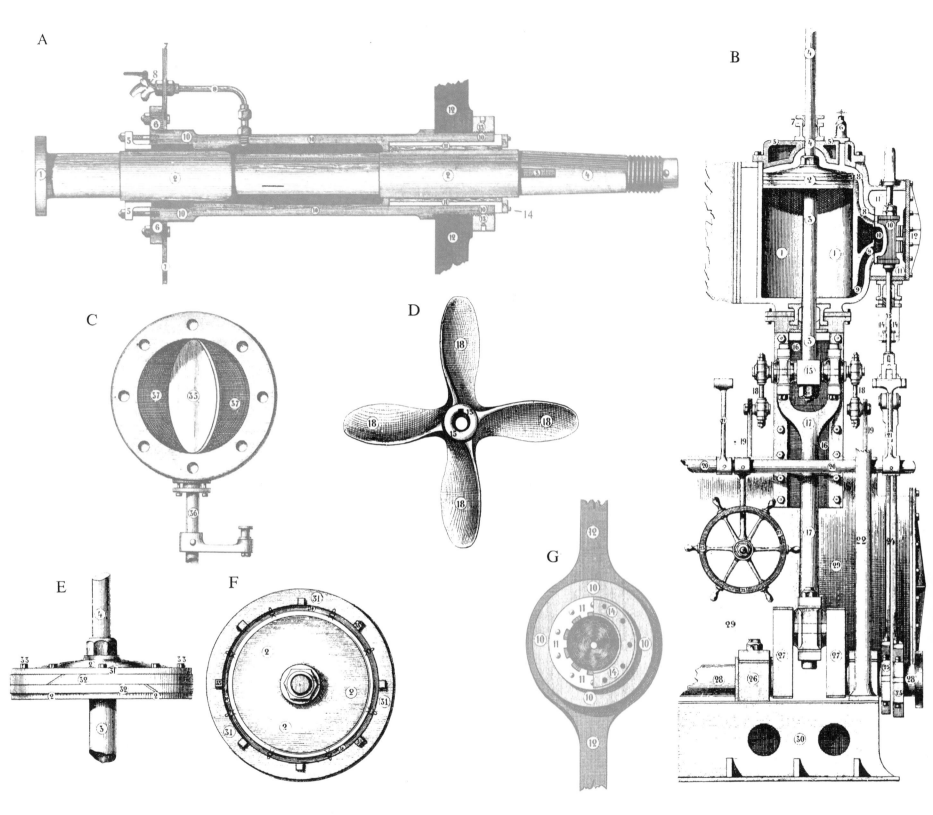

OLD STEAM ENGINE AND ANCILLARY DETAILS, FROM AN OLD DRAWING

A *Propeller tail shaft*
1 Coupling flange
2 Sleeve
3 Keyway
4 Tail end
5 Stuffing-box gland
6 Stern tube flange
7 Stuffing-box bulkhead
8 Tunnel cock
9 Water pipe
10 Stern tube
11 Stern tube bushing

12 Stern post
13 Stern tube nut
14 Guard ring
B *Piston steam engine*
1 Cylinder
2 Piston
3 Piston rod
4 Tail rod
5 Cylinder cover
6 Escape valve
7 Stuffing box
8 Steam ports
9 Steam ports

10 Slide valve
11 Slide valve casing
12 Slide valve casing door
13 Slide valve rod
14 Valve rod guide
15 Piston rod crosshead
16 Crosshead guide
17 Connecting rod
18 Pump links
19 Pump levers
20 Weigh shaft
21 Weigh shaft arms

22 Cylinder column
23 Reversing wheel
24 Eccentric rods
25 Eccentric straps
26 Main bearing
27 Crank web
28 Crank shaft
29 Condenser
30 Bedplates
C *Throttle valve*
35 Throttle valve
36 Throttle valve spindle
37 Steam pipe

D *Propeller*
15 Propeller hub
18 Propeller blades
E *Piston*
2 Piston
3 Piston rod
4 Tail rod
31 Junk ring
32 Packing rings
33 Junk ring bolts

F *Piston, seen from above*
2 Piston
31 Junk ring
33 Junk ring bolts
34 Guard ring tail
G *Propeller shaft, end view*
10 Stern tube
11 Stern tube bushing
12 Stern post
14 Guard ring

A

B

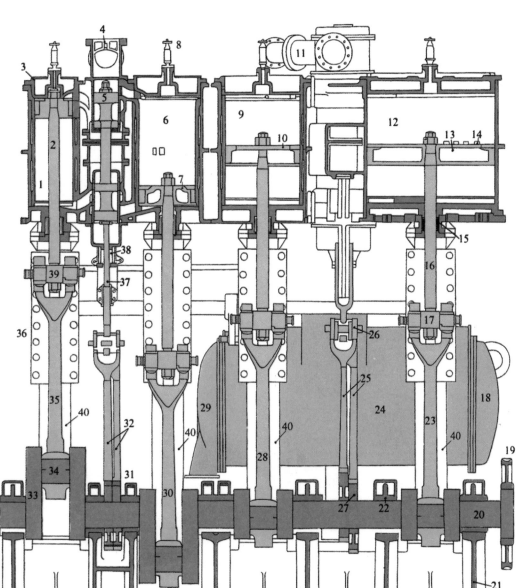

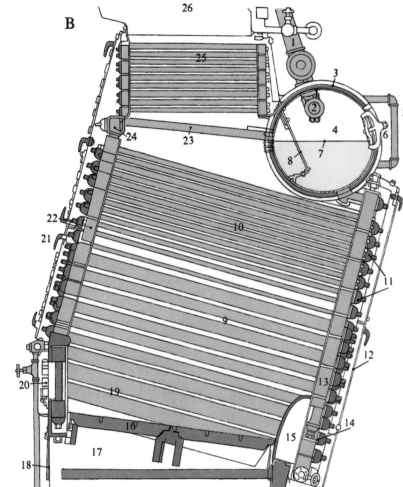

MODERN BOILER AND ENGINE

A *Quadruple steam engine, starboard engine of a twin-screw steamer*	10 Piston	21 Bedplate	30 1st IP-connecting rod
1 HP-cylinder	11 Steam line from turbocompressor	22 Main bearing	31 Eccentrics and straps
2 Piston rod	12 LP-cylinder	23 LP-connecting rod	32 Eccentric rods
3 Cylinder cover	13 Piston	24 Condenser	33 Crank web
4 Steam line to intermediate reheater	14 Extraction steam ports	25 Eccentric rods	34 Crank pin
5 Piston valve	15 Piston rod box	26 Double-bar link	35 HP-connecting rod
6 1st IP-cylinder	16 Piston rod	27 Eccentrics and straps	36 Crosshead guide plates
7 Piston	17 Crosshead	28 2nd IP-connecting rod	37 Valve spindle
8 Safety valve	18 Condenser head	29 Condenser head	38 Stuffing-box
9 2nd IP-cylinder	19 Turning gear		39 Crosshead
	20 Crank shaft		40 Engine frame

B *Water-tube boiler, header boiler*	13 Rear header		
1 Steam outlet	14 Mud drum		
2 Dry pipe	15 Furnace bridge		
3 Steam drum	16 Furnace-bars (-grate)		
4 Steam space	17 Ash pit		
5 Feed-water pipe	18 Ash pit door		
6 Manhole	19 Furnace		
7 Water level	20 Furnace door		
8 Steam collecting baffle	21 Locking handle		
9 1st tube bank	22 Front header		
10 2nd tube bank	23 Return tubes		
11 Hand hole plates	24 Cross box		
12 Boiler casing	25 Economizer		
	26 Uptake		

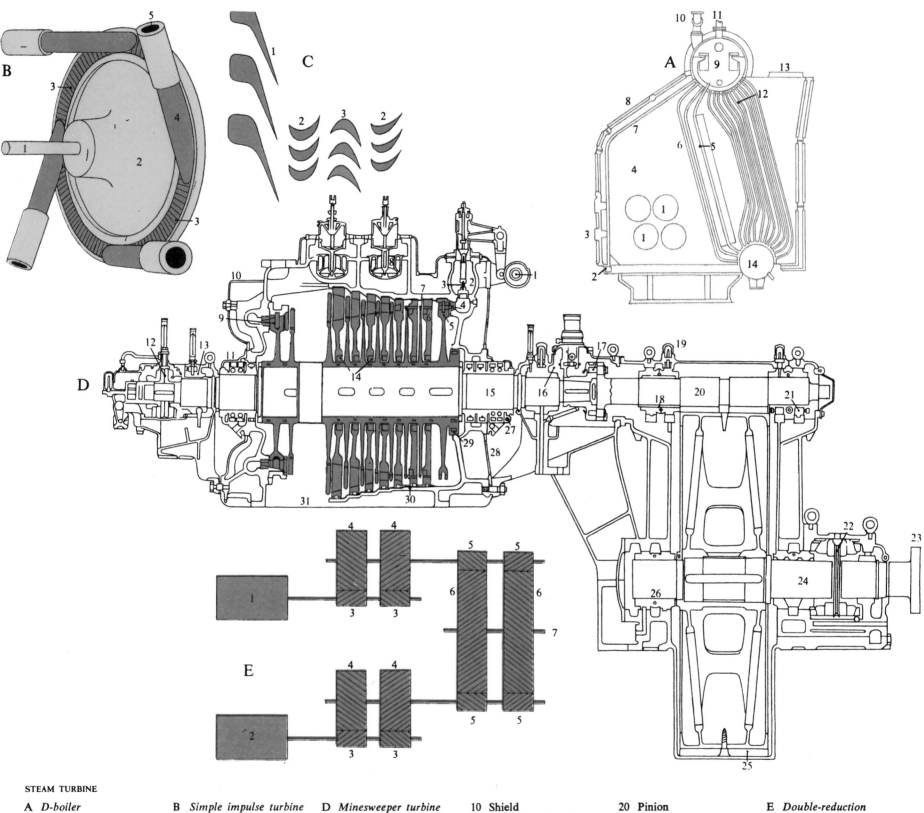

STEAM TURBINE

A *D-boiler*
1 Oil burner
2 Wall header
3 Furnace peepholes
4 Furnace
5 Superheater tubes
6 Furnace tubes
7 Water wall
8 Boiler casing
9 Steam drum
10 Steam outlet
11 Relief valve
12 Boiler generating tubes
13 Uptake
14 Water drum

B *Simple impulse turbine*
1 Shaft
2 Blade wheel
3 Blading
4 Laval nozzle
5 Steam supply

C *Velocity stage (Curtis)*
1 Nozzle block
2 Moving blades
3 Fixed blades

D *Minesweeper turbine*
1 Cam shaft
2 Steam inlet
3 Nozzle control valve
  or throttle valve
4 Nozzle block
5 Velocity stage (Curtis)
6 Diaphragm
7 Wheel
8 By-pass valve
9 Astern turbine
  elements

10 Shield
11 Steam-sealed packing
12 Thrust bearing
13 Bearing
14 Shaft packings
15 Turbine shaft
16 Bearing
17 Coupling
18 Bearing
19 Sight glass

20 Pinion
21 Gear
22 Thrust bearing
23 Line shaft flange
24 Shaft
25 Gear
26 Bearing
27 Turbine gland
28 Shield
29 Shaft packing
30 Casing
31 Foundation

E *Double-reduction gear*
1 HP-turbine
2 LP-turbine
3 1st reduction pinion
4 1st reduction gear
5 2nd reduction pinion
6 2nd reduction gear
  (main gear)
7 To propeller shaft

ENGINE-ROOM TELEGRAPH

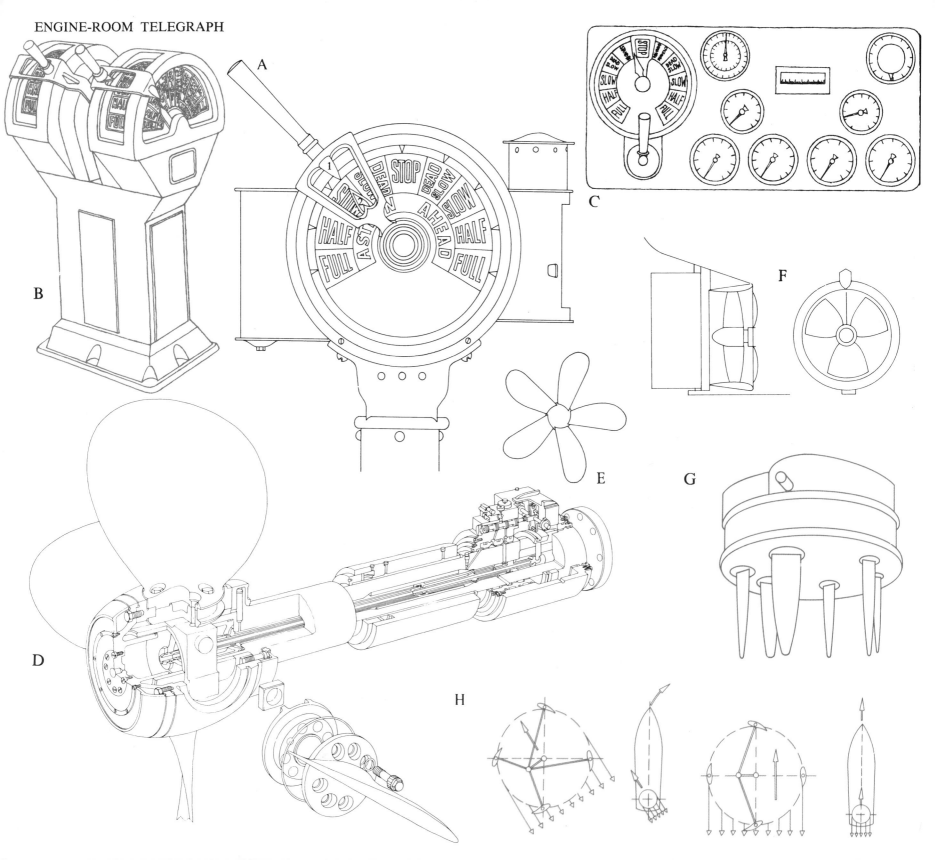

ENGINE-ROOM TELEGRAPH AND MODERN PROPELLERS

Orders are transmitted from the bridge to the engine room by means of a wire and chain telegraph on the bridge and another in the engine room, so that orders from the bridge can be repeated in the engine room for confirmation: In a twin-screw ship there is one telegraph for each engine.

A *Wire-operated telegraph*
1 When the lever is moved to, say, STOP on the bridge telegraph the pointer on the engine room telegraph moves to that same position. The engineer then replies by moving the lever of his telegraph to STOP. By so doing, the correspond-ing pointer on the bridge (2) moves to STOP, thus indicating that the order has been understood and is being executed.

B *Electrical telegraph for a twin-screw vessel, worked on this same principle but by electricity*

C *Control panel of the engine room, with the engine room telegraph shown on the left on the panel*

D *Controllable pitch propeller (Kamewa propeller). By changing the angle of the propeller blades the propelling power and the thrusting direction* can be altered without changing the shaft-revolutions or shifting the gear from forwards to backwards

E *Five-bladed propeller. Widely used in larger ships. A five-bladed propeller of a 300,000 tons tanker has a weight of approx. 50 tons and a diameter of about 9 m (29 ft).*

F *Nozzle-propeller*

G *Cycloidal propeller with rotating blades, called the Voith-Schneider propeller (in the U.S.A., the Kirsten-Boeing propeller).*

H *The principle behind the functioning of the Voith-Schneider propeller*

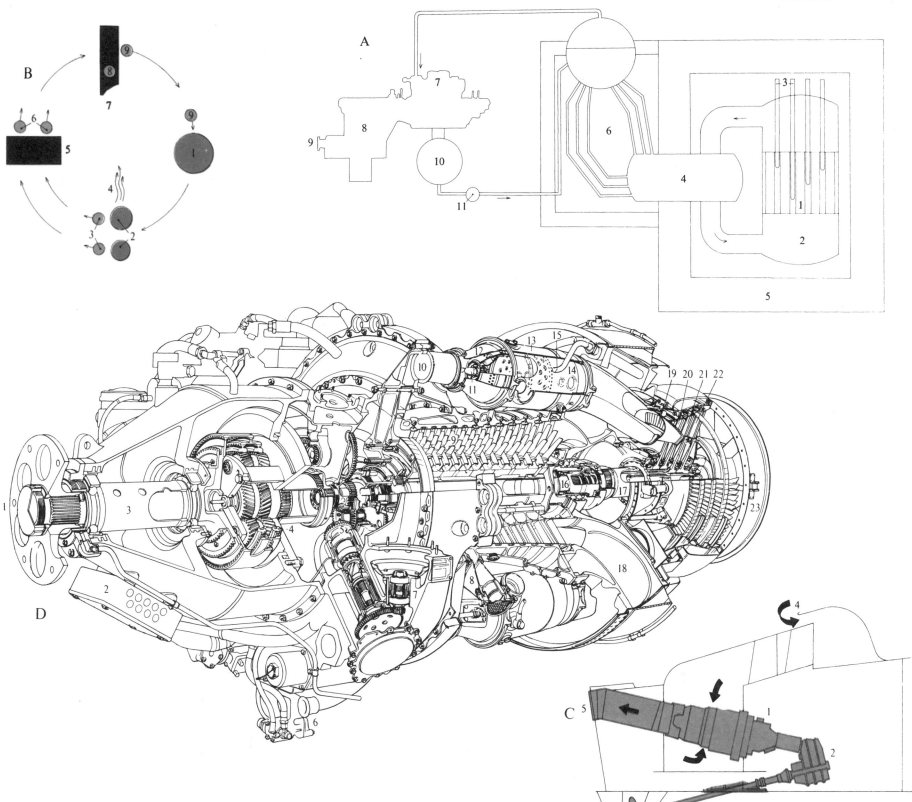

GAS-TURBINE AND NUCLEAR POWER

A *Nuclear ship plant*
1 Nuclear fuel elements
2 Heated fluid
3 Control rods
4 Heat exchanger
5 Lead radiation shielding
6 Boiler
7 Steam turbine
8 Gear
9 Driving shaft
10 Condenser
11 Feedwater pump

B *Principle of atomic fission*
1 Uranium atomic nucleus
2 Nucleus fragments
3 High speed neutrons
4 Heat energy
5 Moderator
6 Low speed neutrons
7 Control rod
8 Absorbed neutron
9 Low speed neutron on its way to split atomic nucleus

C *Engine room installation, SPICA torpedo boat*
1 Three Proteus gas-turbines
2 Reduction gearbox
3 C.p. propeller
4 Air intake
5 Exhaust

D *Marine gas-turbine (Rolls Royce Marine Proteus). This turbine engine has a maximum power rating of 4250 bhp, and features the compactness and light weight that has made the gas-turbine the competitive engine for units that crave immediate and high power output in a small size. The first ship powered by a gas-turbine was the British motor gunboat 2009, launched in 1948.*

1 Power output shaft coupling flange
2 Electrical services junction box
3 Power output shaft
4 Internal gear rings
5 Starter bevel gear
6 Fuel drain unit
7 Starter bevel gear unit
8 Blow-off valve unit
9 Compressor rotor blades
10 Compressor air delivery unit
11 Burner
12 Expansion chamber
13 Combustion chamber casing
14 Flame tube
15 Cooling air supply pipe for compressor turbine
16 Power turbine coupling shaft
17 Compressor turbine shaft
18 Air intake duct
19–22 1st-4th stage rotor
23 Exhaust annulus

STEAMERS

EARLY STEAMERS

1 *Pyroscape*, built by Marquis Claude de Jouffrouy d' Abbans, 1783.

2 *Charlotte Dundas*, built for the Forth and Clyde Canal in 1802.

3 *Clermont*, built in 1807 by Robert Fulton for the Hudson River between New York and Albany.

4 *Comet*, built in 1812 by James Watt for service on the Clyde.

5 *The Witch of Stockholm*, built by Samuel Owens in 1816.

6 *Savannah*, built in 1818. As the first steamship she crossed the Atlantic in 1819. It is worth mentioning that she used her engine for only short periods during the voyage.

7 *Great Western*, built in 1838. First steamer in transatlantic service.

8 *Rob. F. Stockton*, built in 1839. The first iron hulled vessel to cross the Atlantic.

9 *Hamburger Paquet*, built in Gothenburg in 1858.

10 *Great Eastern*, built in 1858, length 692 ft., displacement 27,400 tons, speed 15 knots, crew 400, passengers 4,000. In her time she was the biggest ship in the world, and was not surpassed in size until 1899.

EARLY STEAMERS

11 Side-wheeler *Natchez*. Until 1870 the fastest boat on the Mississippi River.

12 A paddle steamer from 1873.

13 The passenger steamer, *Odin*, built in 1875.

14 The tank steamer *Gluckauf*, built in 1886 in Great Britain for German owners. The first modern tanker.

15 The passenger vessel, *Deutschland*, built in 1900, length about 670 ft., speed 24 knots.

16 Turret deck steamer from 1907.

17 *Mauretania*, 1913, 33,000 gross tons register, speed 25.8 knots, length about 760 ft.

MERCHANT AND PASSENGER SHIPS

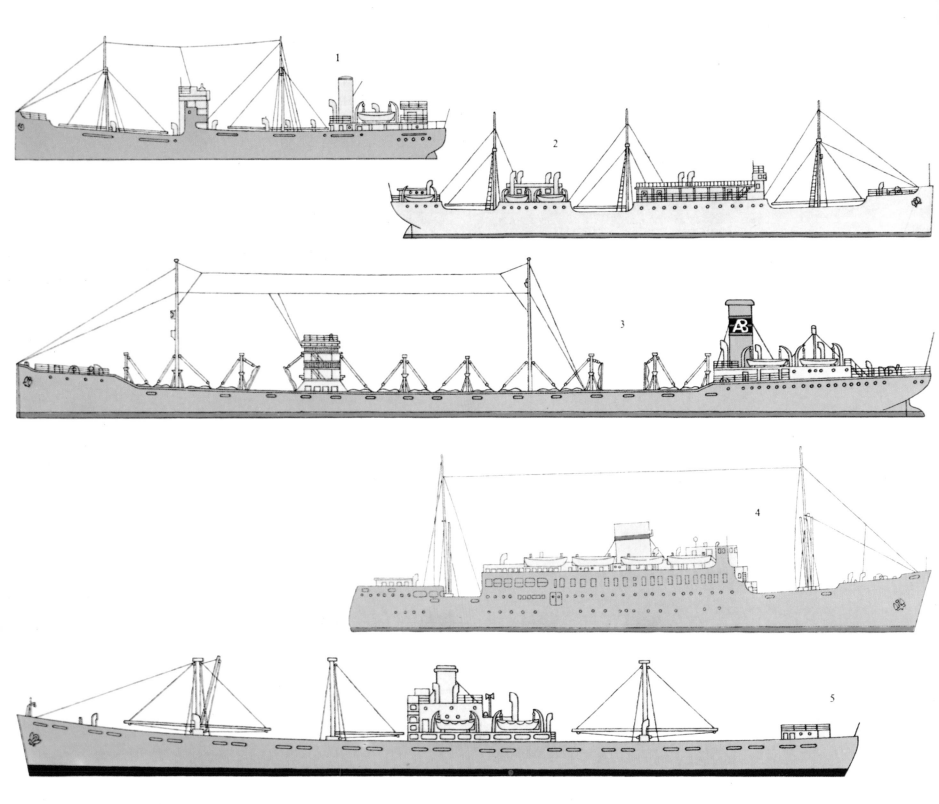

MERCHANT AND PASSENGER SHIPS

1 British collier, a ship that chiefly carries North Country coal to London

2 *Selandia*. The first ocean-going cargo diesel motorship in the world, built in Denmark in 1911

3 *Amerikaland*. Swedish ore-carrying vessel, built in 1925 for service between South and North America, 22,800 tons dwt.

4 Passenger ship used on short sea routes, for instance, the cross Channel service, about 3,000 gross tons

5 U.S. Liberty standard vessel, displacement 14,000 tons

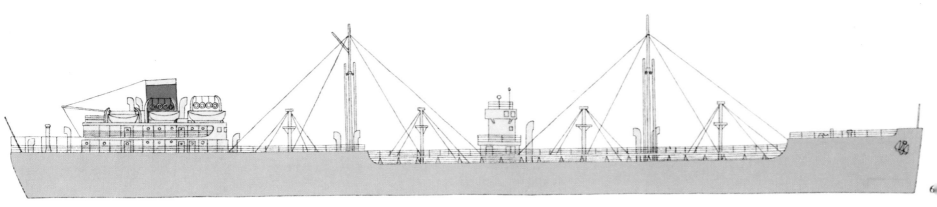

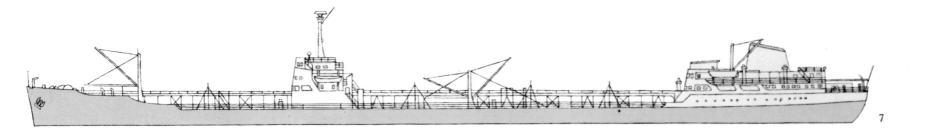

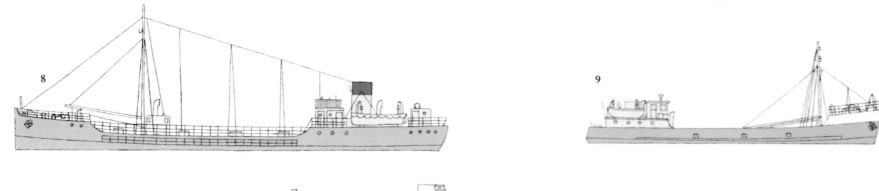

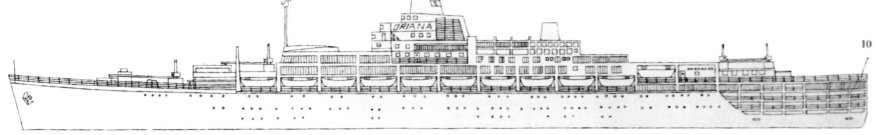

MERCHANT AND PASSENGER SHIPS

6 Ore tanker, 1950
7 Motor tanker of 40,000
  tons dwt, speed 16¹/₂
  knots. (At the time she
  was built, 1958, she was
  the largest motor tanker
  in the world)
8 A coastal tanker of about
  800 tons dwt.

9 A small Dutch motor coaster
10 Oriana. Turbine
   passenger vessel,
   40,000 gross tons

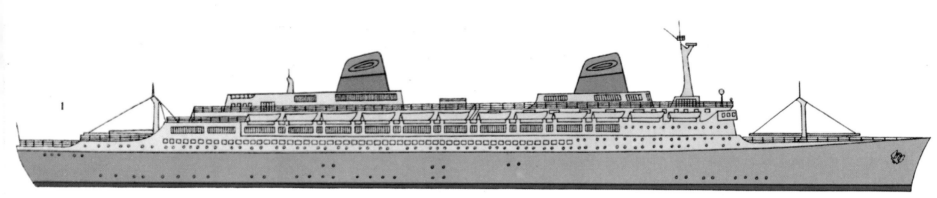

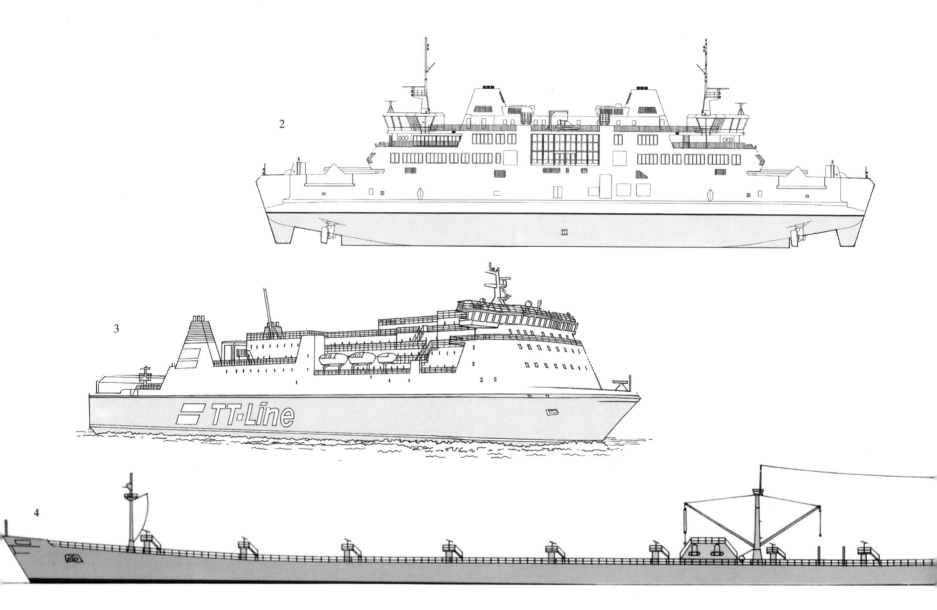

SOME MODERN SHIPS

1 Passenger liner *France*. Gross tonnage 66,000, length 315 m, breadth 33 m, 2,044 passengers, service speed 30 knots

2 Passenger, train and car ferry, *Aurora af Helsingborg*, delivered 1992. L 110.2 m, B 28.2 m, speed 15 knots. Can carry at once 9 railroad wagons, 80 automobiles and 1,250 passengers

3 Ro/ro and passenger ferry *Robin Hood*, delivered 1995. L 179.7 m, B 27.2 m, speed 19.5 knots, 317 passengers

4 Supertanker of 495,000 tons. L 387.9 m, B 67.1 m, D 25.6 m, speed 16.1 knots. Total tank capacity 600,000 cubic metres

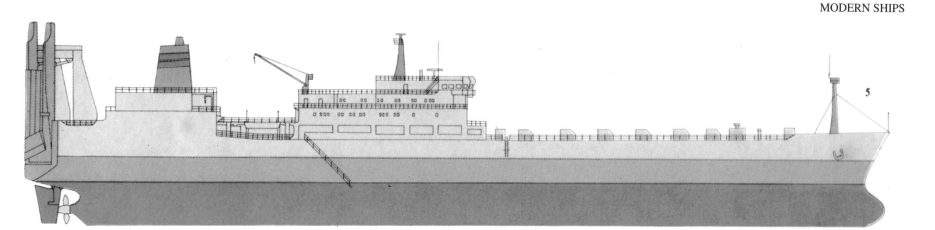

5

6

7

8

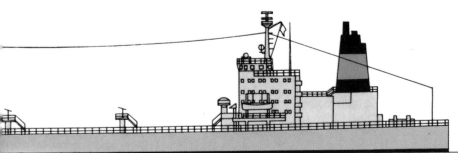

SOME MODERN SHIPS

5 The world's first heavy cargo ship with gas-turbine power, *Iron Monarch*, a ro/ro vessel carrying steel products, launched in Australia in 1973. L 179.3 m, B 24.9 m, D 9.14 m. Displacement 14,453 tons. Speed 20 knots

6 The passenger ferry *Colorseacat*, built in 1991, plies between Fredrikshamn (Denmark) and either Gothenburg (Sweden) or Langesund (Norway). L 73.6 m, B 26.3 m, speed 37 knots. It can take 450 passengers and 80 cars.

7 Italian hydrofoil boat. Such vessels do regular short-range service all over the world.

8 Passenger ferry *Stena Danica* (Stena Line), in traffic between Sweden and Denmark. Built 1983, rebuilt 1995. L 155 m, B 28 m, D 6.32 m. Capacity 550 cars or 100 15-m trailers, and 2,300 passengers. Speed 19 knots

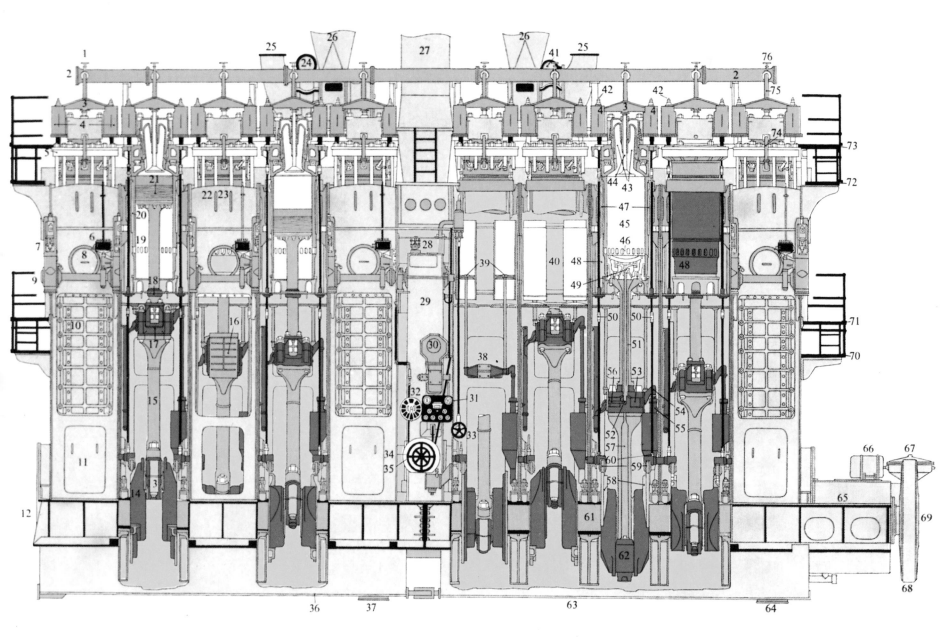

LONGITUDINAL VIEW OF A 10-CYLINDER, TURBOCHARGED 2-STROKE, CROSSHEAD, DIRECT DRIVE, PROPULSION DIESEL ENGINE

 1 Fore end cylinder
 2 Overhead cooling
    water pipe
 3 Exhaust gas valve yoke
 4 Encased valve springs
 5 Cylinder cover
 6 Cylinder lubricator
 7 Fuel injection pump
 8 Air receiver access
 9 Cam shaft
10 Door to crosshead
    guide
11 Crankcase access door
12 Fore end of crankshaft

13 Crank pin bearing
14 Crank web
15 Connecting rod
16 Crosshead shoe
17 Crosshead bearing
18 Piston rod stuffing box
19 Scavenging ports
20 Cylinder liner
21 Working piston with
    rings
22 Fuel valve
23 Indicator valve
24 Forward turbocharger
25 Air compressor intake

26 Gas turbine outlet to
    boiler
27 Turbocharger by-pass
    pipe
28 Chain transmission
    stretcher
29 Chain transmission
    casing
30 Over-speed governor
31 Gauge board
32 Engine room telegraph
33 Master starting air
    valve wheel
34 Maneuvering
    hand-wheel

35 Telegraph reply wheel
36 Forward oil pan
37 Oil pan drain
38 Scavenging air pumps
    connecting arms
39 Scavenging air double-
    acting pumps
40 Scavenging air receiver
41 Aft turbocharger
42 Top end of valve
    drag links
43 Exhaust gas pipe
44 Exhaust gas valve

45 Cylinder in position
    for scavenging
46 Scavenging ports
47 Water cooling jacket
48 Scavenging air receiver
49 Oil cooling channels
50 Valve drag links
51 Piston rod oil cooling
    pipes
52 Crosshead pin
53 Cooling oil entrance
54 Telescope arm
55 Telescope pipe
56 Cooling oil drain

57 Connecting rod
    lubricating pipe
58 Exhaust valve cam
    segment
59 Cam rollers
60 Exhaust valve levers
61 Crankshaft journal and
    main bearing
62 Crank pin and con-
    necting rod bearing
63 Aft oil pan
64 Oil pan drain
65 Propeller thrust
    bearing
66 Electric turning motor

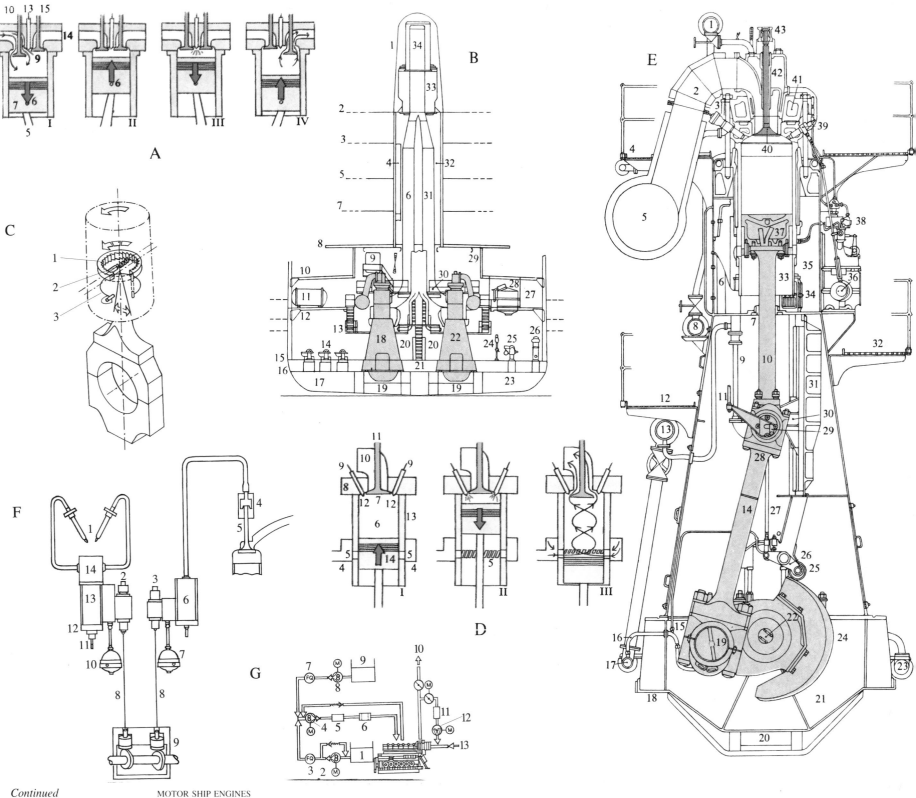

Continued

C *Sulzer's rotating pistons*
1 Gear ring
2 Back stop
3 Spring

D *Two-stroke diesel engine principle*
I Compression stroke
II Power stroke
III Scavenging
4 Scavenging air- receiver
5 Scavenging ports
6 Combustion chamber
7 Exhaust gas valve
8 Cylinder cover
9 Fuel pipe
10 Exhaust manifold
11 Valve spindle
12 Fuel valve
13 Cylinder liner
14 Piston

E *Cross-section of a two-stroke crosshead direct-drive propulsion diesel engine*
1 Overhead cooling-water pipe
2 Exhaust pipe
3 Starting air valve
4 Top platform
5 Exhaust receiver
6 Suction valves
7 Piston rod stuffing box
8 Bottom cooling-water pipe
9 Piston cooling-oil telescopic pipe
10 Piston rod
11 Scavenging air pump connecting arm
12 Lower platform (starboard side)
13 Lubricating and cooling-oil main pipe
14 Connecting rod

15 Crank end bearing
16 Main-bearing lubricant pipe
17 Main lubricant pipe
18 Bedplate
19 Crank pin
20 Cast steel saddles
21 Crankcase
22 Crankshaft
23 Lubricating and cooling-oil return pipe
24 Exhaust-valve cam segment
25 Cam roller
26 Exhaust-valve lever
27 Exhaust-valve pull rod
28 Crosshead bearing
29 Crosshead pin
30 Crosshead shoe
31 Crosshead guide
32 Lower platform (port side)
33 Scavenging air compression chamber

34 Scavenging air delivery system
35 Scavenging air receiver
36 Camshaft
37 Oil-cooled working piston
38 Fuel-injection pump
39 Fuel valve
40 Exhaust gas valve
41 Water-cooled cylinder cover
42 Cooling water
43 Exhaust-gas valve yoke

F *Example of improved engine control with hydraulic assistance*
1 Fuel valves
2 Electronic control unit for fuel valves
3 Electronic control unit for exhauster
4 Hydraulic piston with damper for exhauster
5 Exhaust valve
6 Servo pump for exhauster
7 Accumulator vessel
8 Mechanical reserve control
9 Camshaft
10 Accumulator vessel
11 Index axle
12 Limiter
13 Servo pump for the fuel pump
14 Fuel pump
15 Fuel pipe

G *Example of a system which lowers the NO_x number*
1 Fuel
2 Fuel pump
3 Flow meter
4 Booster pump
5 Homogenizer
6 Filter
7 Flow meter
8 Water pump
9 Water
10 Exhaust gases
11 Heat exchanger
12 Fan
13 Combustion air

FISHING

BY GERHARD TIMMERMANN

It is not known when man began to collect living creatures from the sea as part of his food. Probably this was first done with bare hands, as it still is in some places today. The earliest fishing equipment yet discovered is from the Old Stone Age in Europe (20,000-8,000 B.C.) and consists of small spears or harpoons that were hand-thrown. In tropical regions, some people continue to fish with a bow and arrow, or with blow-guns that shoot darts. Various kinds of toothed spears have also been common.

Catching fish with bait can be traced far back in time, as fish hooks made of stone and bone have been found that date from Europe's New Stone Age (8,000-3,000 B.C.). It is also likely that wooden twigs were sharpened at both ends and baited, to be taken by the fish and then pulled with a line. The fishing rod has been gradually developed in many forms for different types of fishing.

Hooks are adapted to the fish's size. For catching large fish such as shark and tuna, hooks up to 40 cm (16 inches) are used. Since World War II, tuna have also been caught by leading electricity through the hook, which stuns the fish and makes it easier to board.

From the 17th century onward, long-line fishing with hooks has been done at the Grand Banks off Newfoundland, by the French-Canadian inhabitants as well as by Portuguese and Americans. The lines would be set out during the morning by men in small dory boats, operating from a schooner. After a few hours they were taken up and the catch was brought back to the depot ship. Cod, halibut and other species were cleaned and salted on board, some fish being wind-dried. This fishing had great economic significance to Catholic countries, where only fish and vegetables may be eaten at times of fasting.

In the late 20th century, hook fishing has become highly automated, with ships specially built for the purpose, using up to 20-30,000 hooks per day. Another important kind of fishing gear is equipment to enclose a catch. The most frequent examples are cages and traps provided with bait. Further types exploit the fish's natural behaviour when migrating along coasts and feeding in waterways. This is illustrated by fyke nets and bottom-nets which are not baited. Originally, such gear was made of woven or tied plants, including bamboo that is easy to shape. Modern devices are constructed with steel and plastic covered in net.

The oldest depictions of enclosing structures appear in Egyptian reliefs from the Fifth Dynasty, around 3000 B.C. Fishermen have relied on the currents in rivers and streams, too, for guiding the catch into their gear. Even the movements of tidal water could be helpful. A bottom-net, which has an extending arm and ends in a catching section, is used primarily for fish that swim in coastal waters. The Roman historian Pliny (23-70 A.D.) described how walls were made of branches and placed along the German coast during the ebb tide.

In general, fishing nets are either floated at the surface or anchored on the bottom. Although most common in coastal and lake fishing, they are also familiar at sea. Nets were used already in the Stone Age, occurring in Egyptian reliefs of the Fourth Dynasty. Today, manufactured from synthetic materials, they have great strength and durability in spite of their thin threads.

To catch cod and flatfish, nets are laid on the bottom. When fishing for salmon or mackerel, they are hung from floats at the surface. Fishermen may tie nets together in a series over two kilometres long. The nets can drift freely with the wind and current, while supervised from the fishing vessel.

During the 15th century, the Dutch started to fish for herring in the North Sea with drift nets. Often the catch was salted into barrels on board, for preservation and subsequent transport. The merchants who supplied the fishermen with salt and barrels played a key role. They also had a well-developed network for marketing the fish. Much of the herring catch in southern Scandinavia was distributed by traders of the North German Hansa League.

Other nations followed into the North Sea, and soon after 1600 the English organized fishing companies which, however, could not compete with the Dutch. With the advent of steam power in the 19th century, lively fishing with herring nets was done by "drifter" boats from England and Scotland. German vessels also took part in the herring harvests of these waters.

The first boats were made of hollowed-out tree trunks, according to evidence as early as 6000 B.C. During the course of time, this method of boat-building developed into clinker-built boats. In the Mediterranean area, the raft was probably the boat's origin, as shown by reliefs in Egypt about 3000 B.C. Yet in some countries where wood is scarce – Greenland, Ireland, Wales – boats have always been built of bone or wood frames with animal hides stretched over them. The carvel method of construction, with planks laid edge to edge, arose in the Mediterranean and, after improvements in Northern Europe, has spread around the world.

Fishing vessels were driven only by sails until nearly 1900. The Dutch, French and Germans used round-bellied boats, later replaced by slender luggers. From England came the fast-sailing cutter, which served for many kinds of fishing. At the beginning of our century, ever bigger ships – mostly of steel – were built for fishing and powered with steam, then diesel, engines. Materials like aluminum and plastic have been added, chiefly to build smaller boats.

The quality of unsalted fish became much better when the boats' holds began to carry crushed ice, in which the catch was packed. Another technique was to equip the hold with wells through which sea water flowed, keeping the fish alive until the boat reached shore. In recent decades, the ships have been increasingly specialized. A stern trawler, which retrieves the net at the rear, drops the catch below deck, where it is cleaned and iced in containers. A further step is taken by the factory trawler with on-board cleaning, filleting, freezing and packaging of fish.

Herring often move in huge shoals from the ocean depths toward land. To catch them from the shore, small seine nets have been laid out with boats and drawn in by hand. At sea, a ring net is laid by two boats that sail away from each other

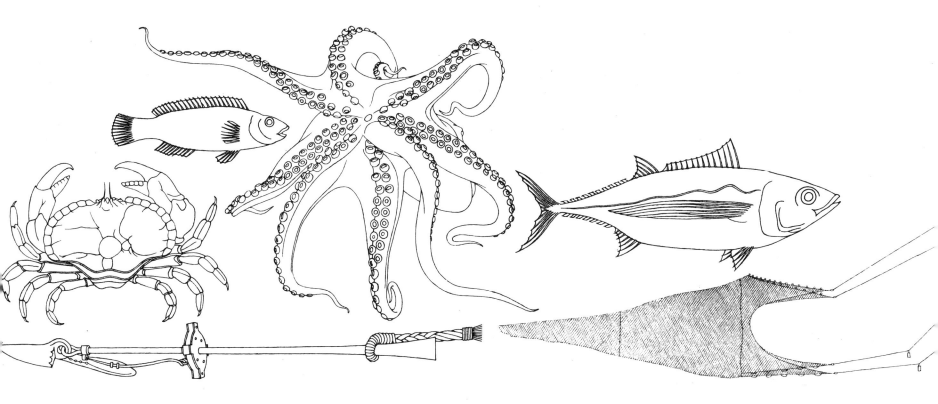

in a semicircle and finally come together. A purse seine has a rope or wire along its bottom edge, which can be pulled to close the net around the fish.

Seine nets have grown continually in size since World War II. The heaviest work involves taking in the net. Development of the block and tackle has led to mechanization of the boarding process. The net is still pulled shut at the bottom with its wire controlled by a separate winch. Now, though, the catch is no longer lifted aboard in nets, but is pumped directly into ice-cold water in tanks. Enormous, deep ring-nets are handled with blocks and cranes on their ships.

The most important method of fishing, however, is with the trawl. As long ago as the Middle Ages, fishing was done with a beam trawl – a net bag held open by a beam or pole and dragged across the sea bottom. But it was not until the end of the 19th century that trawl fishing acquired real economic value. This was, of course, promoted by the introduction of engines and winches to help in handling the equipment. A trawl is now essentially a bag whose mouth is kept open by an arm at each side attached to an outward shear plane, the otter (or trawl) board. The mouth is heightened by buoyant balls of plastic (formerly glass), and can be raised more by an ascending shear plane, or kite.

Trawls have been refined over the years to catch most kinds of fish. Bottom trawls are made to fish deep for both fish and crustaceans, such as shrimp and crayfish. A floating trawl, towed by one or two ships, is used for pelagic species which inhabit the middle water layers, like herring and mackerel. With a single boat, it is handled in the same way as a bottom trawl but at different depths. With two ships, the trawl's depth is altered by its weighting, the towing wire lengths, and the ships' speed or separation. A beam trawl, smaller but sturdy, is dragged rapidly across the bottom and has a chain mat to frighten up fish in front of the trawl mouth. Its main use is to catch flatfish on hard bottoms.

A Danish seine net resembles a trawl in many respects, but is handled as follows. The ship places an anchored buoy at the fishing site. From there, a sinking rope 1,500-3,000 metres long is laid. Next, the net is set out and the same amount of rope is laid in a long arc, back to the buoy. Then the ropes and net are winched in to the ship. Haddock, cod and flatfish are caught with Danish seines.

Electronics is a factor that has strongly contributed to the fast growth of fishing throughout the world in the late 1900s. Echo sounders were widely adopted during the 1950s, offering wholly new opportunities to locate fish shoals, as well as to observe the character of the bottom. A subsequent innovation was "asdic" sonar, originally developed for submarine hunting – like an echo sounder that searches both in front of the ship and at its sides. To the navigator's assistance came radar and the Decca and Loran systems, which made it easier to find fishing places, wrecks and other impediments on the sea bottom. Even more effective as a navigational aid is the Global Positioning System (GPS), enabling a fisherman to register every location exactly.

Apart from ordinary fishing, man has also hunted the great mammals of the sea – notably seals and whales – for about a thousand years. This was evidently done by Norwegians already in the 10th century. After William Poole in 1583, and William Barents in 1596, reported a vast number of Greenland whales off Spetsbergen during searches for the Northeast Passage, an intensive hunt for whales was started by the British, Dutch, Germans and even Americans. The actual pursuit of whales was carried out from small, strongly built rowboats with crews of 6-8 men. At that time, only the blubber was of interest, the rest of the whale being discarded.

Around 1863, a Norwegian whaler became the first to mount a harpoon gun on a steam vessel. From then onward, it was possible to hunt all sizes of whales, which can grow up to 30 metres long. Gradually the whale catch expanded, and factory ships as big as 30,000 tons processed every part of the whales. Once a hunt ended, the whaling boats towed their quarry to the factory ship.

In the Arctic Sea, hunting is still done for seals as well. Both the skins and the fat are taken to advantage. Such hunting has very old traditions, not least among the Eskimos.

However, the killing of whales and seals has met with increasing opposition from scientists and the public, so its future is uncertain.

Fish know no frontiers, and many stocks wander from the open seas to the coasts. Research on fish has thus naturally become an international activity. The need for coordinated research was recognized a hundred years ago, and in 1902 the International Council for the Exploration of the Sea (ICES) was founded, with its base in Copenhagen. The task of ICES is to organize information provided by the member countries. Each country makes scientific studies of fish, crustaceans and so on. Samples are collected and examined on board the countries' research vessels. Biological, hydrographic, and other data are processed together with fishing statistics. The researchers perform joint calculations of, for example, the size of stocks and how much can safely be taken of their respective species.

These facts are then used by various commissions to determine quotas for different areas. In the Baltic Sea, for instance, the Baltic Fishing Commission decides the quotas of particular species for each country. Fishing in the North Sea is regulated among its border countries, except Norway, by agreements within the European Union. As for fishing throughout the world, its statistics and research are coordinated by the Food and Agriculture Organization (FAO) in Rome.

International developments have also occurred in the law of the sea. Since the late 1970s, coastal countries have established economic zones that extend 200 nautical miles out from land – or to agreed lines between zones when they conflict. No country has an independent right to widen its economic zone beyond this limit. Within the economic zone, its own authorities supervise fishing rules, quotas and the like.

OLD FISHING IMPLEMENTS

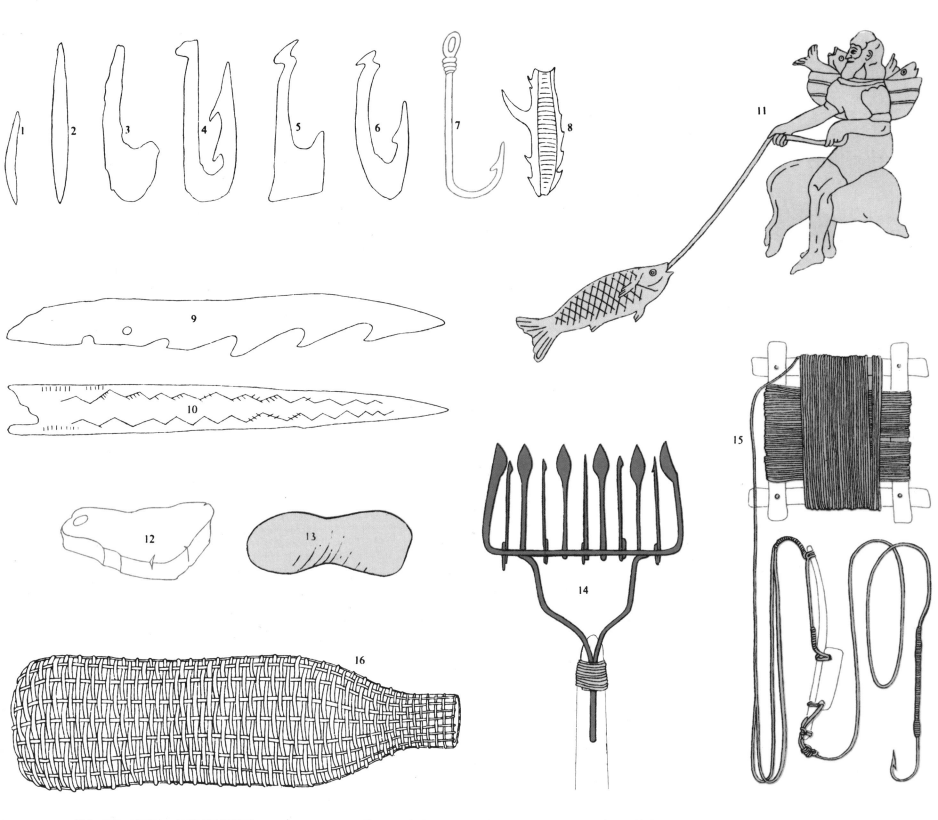

OLD FISHING IMPLEMENTS

1, 2 Primitive bone gorges or bait holders (The slight curving of 1 may possibly be the first step toward the more rounded gorge and, eventually, the bent hook)

3, 4 Bone hooks from the Paleolithic Age in Sweden, *circa* 4000 B.C.

5, 6 Hooks from the Neolithic Age in Sweden, *circa* 2000 B.C.

7 The oldest Mycenaean hook in the British Museum in London

8 Hook ready-made from the spur of an insect, Eurycantha Latro, New Guinea

9 Harpoon from the Paleolithic Age in Sweden, *circa* 4000 B.C.

10 Paleolithic harpoon with ornament; the flukes are worn off

11 Man fishing, sitting astride a blown-up goatskin (From Assyrian sculptures in the British Museum)

12 Carved piece of bark that has been used as a float for a net with coarse meshes

13 Stone sinker belonging to the same net (12 and 13 are finds from the Ancylus period in Finland, *circa* 6000 B.C.)

14 Old grain for spearing eels

15 Hand line, one of the oldest and most practical implements for codfishing

16 Wickerwork creel for catching eels; herring or mackerel spawn were used for bait

TYPES OF FISHING BOATS

1 German heur boat
2 Greek fishing boat
   from Mykonos
3 Open Spanish fishing
   boat (Felucca)
4 Small Norwegian sail-
   ing fishing boat

5 French lugger (chasse
   marée)
6 Line fishing boat,
   Swedish west coast,
   1880
7 German North Sea
   ketch

8 Portuguese barkentine
   for the Grand Banks
9 American Bank
   schooner, 1900
10 French Grand Bank
   schooner
11 British steam trawler
12 Large French motor
   trawler

TYPES OF FISHING BOATS

13 English sailing trawler,
    about 1900
14 Ring-net vessel, 56 m,
    built in Norway in
    1996, with 9 RSW
    tanks, total 775 cubic
    metres
15 Motor trawler, 19.8 m,
    from USA west coast,
    not shelter-decked

16 Swedish west coast
    motor trawler
17 British drift-net steam
    drifter
18 Norwegian motor
    fishing boat
19 German motor trawler
20 Danish coastal motor
    trawler, 15 m
21 British seiner

22 Dutch motor fishing
    boat
23 Fishing boat of older
    type from Öresund
24 Danish motor fishing
    boat, older type
25 Japanese bonito boat
26 Norwegian motor
    fishing boat (Ottring)

TYPES OF FISHING BOATS

27 Motor trawler, 68 m, engine power 3,700 kW. Built in Norway in 1994 for Iceland, it freezes the catch on-board
28 Norwegian sealer
29 French tunny yawl

30 Beam trawler, 44 m, built in Holland. It fishes with a trawl-net on each side via the outrigger beams
31 Modern whaler

32 Beam trawler, seen from front, with both trawls hanging from their beams to pull in the catch
33 Sailing whaler, a three-masted bark, 1850
34 Whaling factory ship

OLD FISHING METHODS AND IMPLEMENTS

A *Mark buoy*
1 Flag
2 Pole
3 Cork float
4 Shackle for buoy line

B *Torch lamp*

C *Trawling for mackerel,*
  about 1880
1 Fishing smack
2 Quarter pole
3 Main pole
4 Bow pole
5 Trawling lines
6 Lead sinkers
7 Snells

D *Shark hook*

E *Whaling harpoon with*
  hinged barb

F *Whaling harpoon*

G *Cod bow net*
1 Cod end
2 Rattan rings
3 Headline
4 Leading net
5 Footrope

A

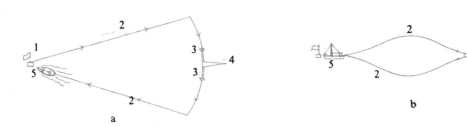

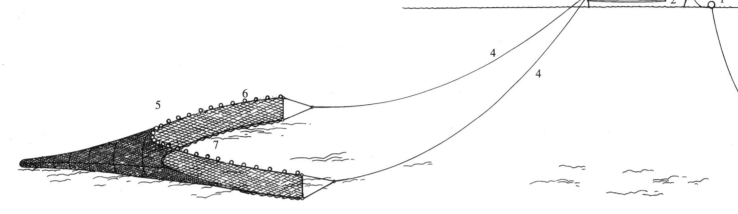

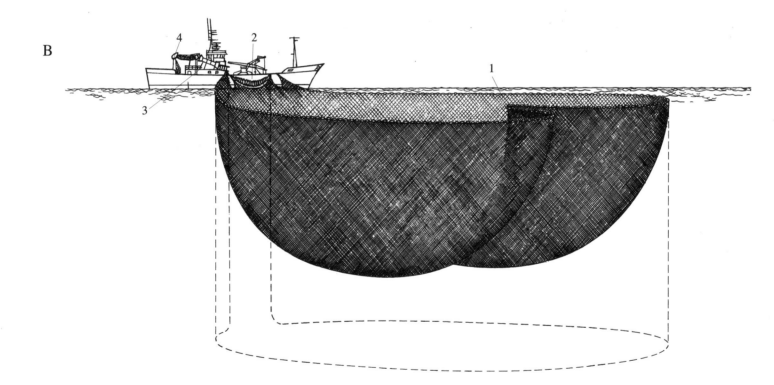

FISHING METHODS

A   *Fishing with seine net
    of Scandinavian type*
a   Setting the seine
b   Hauling the warps
1   Anchor buoy
2   Rope warps
3   Net tails
4   Seine purse cone
5   Seine netter
c   Beginning to hoist the
    seine on board

1   Anchor equipment:
    buoy, wire, anchor
2   Ship with large drums
    under shelter-deck for
    long ropes
3   Hydraulic stern crane
    with block, for taking
    in the seine
4   Long ropes
5   Danish seine net

6   Headline with plastic
    float-balls
7   Footline with chain
    links

B   *Fishing with purse
    seine (here being
    hoisted in)*
1   Headline with floats
2   Footline with large
    heavy rings in which
    the purse seine wire runs
3   Block for hoisting the
    purse seine
4   Crane for stowing the
    seine on after-deck

FISHING METHODS

A *Fishing with nets*
1 At left, drift-net fishing for e.g. mackerel or salmon
2 Mark buoy with flags and radar reflectors
3 Headline with floats
4 Footline with lead-weight sinkers

5 Coastal fishing boat
6 At right, bottom nets
7 Anchor
8 Mark buoy with flags
9 Headline with floats
10 Footline with lead weights or other sinkers

B *Long-line fishing from dories*
1 Norwegian sea-boat (late 19th century)
2 Dory
3 Ground line
4 Snells

C *Long-line fishing for halibut*
1 Buoy
2 Mark buoy
3 Motor fishing boat
4 Buoy rope
5 Anchor
6 Ground line
7 Snells

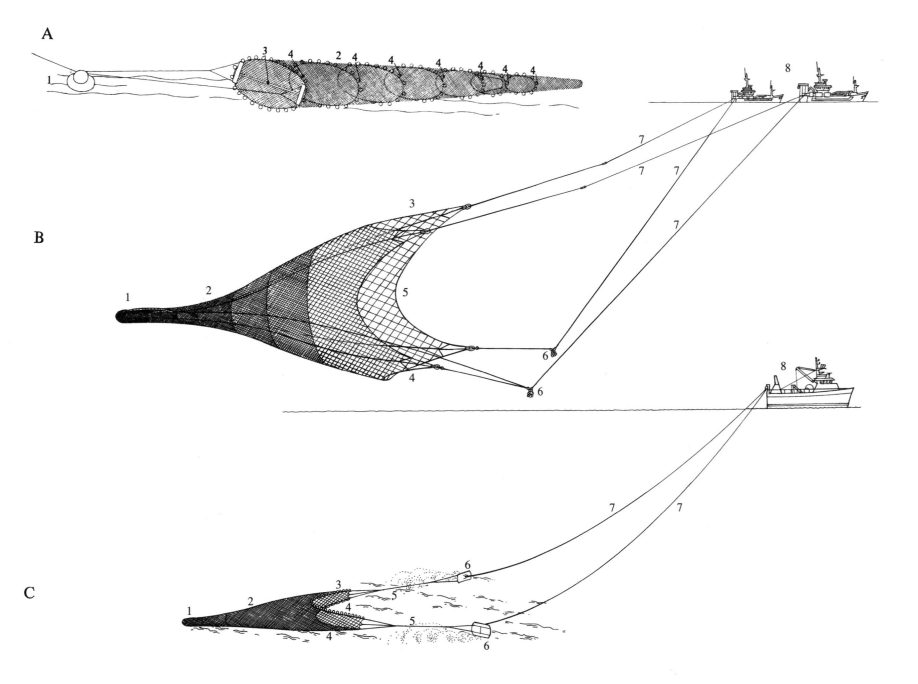

FISHING METHODS

A	Beam trawl, about 1800	B	Modern floating trawl	5	Trawl opening, 30-100 m high, with meshes of 20-40 cm size	C	Bottom trawl	5	Sweep lines
1	Stone weight	1	Hoist, possibly with an attachment to pump the fish on board	6	Weights	1	Hoist	6	Otter boards
2	Belly			7	Towing warps	2	Belly	7	Towing warps
3	Beam	2	Belly, often with outer reinforcement	8	Motor trawlers, trawling in pairs	3	Headline with floats	8	Motor trawler, ca. 20 m long
4	Wooden hoops	3	Headline			4	Footline held down by chain		
		4	Footline						

FISH AND OTHER MARINE CREATURES

1	Seal	8	Bergylt	14	Red snapper
2	Bluefish	9	Ray	15	Conger eel
3	Tunny	10	Greenland whale	16	Great barracuda
4	Albacore	11	Polyprion	17	Dogfish
5	Angler		Americanum	18	Sole
6	Ray's bream	12	Salmon	19	Shark
7	Wrasse	13	Octopus		

FISH AND OTHER MARINE CREATURES

20 Mackerel	27 Sea cat	33 Oyster
21 Turbot	28 Prawn	34 Haddock
22 Cod	29 Halibut	35 Burbot
23 Herring	30 Plaice	36 Ling
24 Whiting	31 Crab	37 Coalfish
25 Brill	32 Hake	38 Sprat
26 Lobster		39 Sardine

The picture of Star
boats in a race, taken
by KEY L. NILSSON,
introduces the chapter
on yachting.

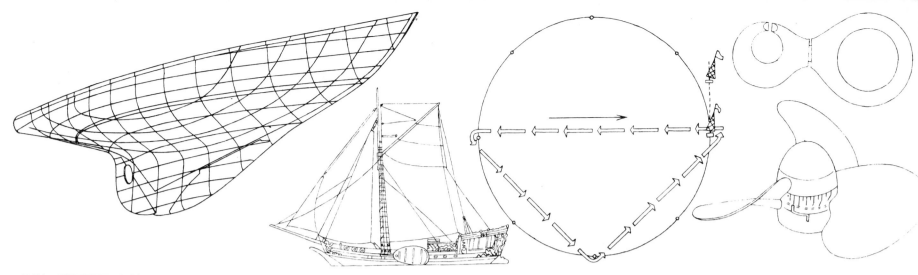

YACHTING

BY GEORGE P. B. NAISH

The word yacht nowadays usually refers to privately owned pleasure craft, used for either racing or cruising. There are still royal or state-owned yachts, but before the 19th century the word normally concerned vessels publicly owned and used for the conveyance of princes, ambassadors, or other great personages from one kingdom to another. The word yacht came into the English language from the Netherlands at the time of the restoration of King Charles II to the throne in 1660. But, of course, ships and boats had been used for purposes of state and for pleasure from earliest times.

Thus, the model of a yacht used on the river Nile by an Egyptian nobleman of the 18th Dynasty, some 1500 years B.C., has been found in a tomb. It is represented as a vessel of a hundred feet in length overall, elaborately decorated and painted, with a deckhouse for a cabin. This yacht was probably used by the nobleman while traveling up and down the Nile valley on business. Egyptian tombs also depict small pleasure craft, which could be towed either from the bank or astern of other vessels. Perhaps Cleopatra's barge, which she used when she first met Antony, should be classed as a yacht. Plutarch tells us that the poop was of gold, the sails of purple, and the oars of silver. In English history we read of King Edgar, who reigned from 959 to 975 A.D., being rowed on the river Dee by a crew of eight lesser kings. But on the whole, in early times people seldom went to sea for pleasure, since there were too many dangers either from storms or from pirates.

The modern pleasure yacht was first developed as a type in Holland, with its maze of rivers and meres, on which, according to the many pictures painted in the seventeenth century, scores of shallow-draft sailing boats, gaily carved and decorated, were raced and shown. There were also large state-owned yachts, and in 1660 one of these, originally built for the East India Company, was bought by the City of Amsterdam for presentation to the restored King of England. Both James I and Charles I had taken a great interest in shipbuilding and naval affairs generally, and Charles II first learned to sail as a boy in a pinnace off the island of Jersey. He had continued to distract himself with sailing during his exile in Holland. The gift yacht from Amsterdam was named the *Mary*, and was a typical Dutch state yacht of a hundred tons, broad in the beam and of shallow draft with lee boards. The stern cabin had a high coach roof and windows. The stern was decorated with the royal arms, surmounted by three poop lanterns, and the figurehead was a unicorn. Eight little guns could be fired from circular gunports, each decorated with carved and gilded port wreaths. The *Mary* was cutter- or yacht-rigged, and carried a boomless mainsail with a long standing gaff, called a half-spreet.

The next year the Dutch gave Charles a smaller yacht, the *Bezan*, having the bezaan rig, well known in Holland, with a boomed mainsail and a short gaff. Charles soon set English shipwrights to building yachts which, for English waters, were an improvement in that they had deeper draft instead of leeboards. The new English royal yachts were much like small warships, but retained the fore-and-aft rig.

When Charles tired of a yacht it was received into the fleet as a dispatch vessel or survey ship. Charles took much pleasure in his yachts for both racing and making trips. His brother James, the Duke of York, as well as certain private gentlemen, followed his example and became owners of yachts. Several private individuals explored the English coast or visited the Continent in the second half of the 17th century.

When Peter the Great, Tsar of Russia, studied shipbuilding in Holland and England, he learned his seamanship in yachts, and the French king, Louis XIV, had yachts built for himself in England. Although yachting for pleasure showed no signs of becoming a popular sport in the 18th century, it managed to hold its own in English waters despite the many long wars. There were river pageants, and in 1775 the Cumberland Fleet or sailing society was founded by the royal Duke of that name, who offered a cup for a regatta between some twenty small yachts of from two to five tons, which was held on the river Thames above London Bridge. The Royal Thames Yacht Club claims descent from this Cumberland Fleet. The Fleet's yachts were distinguished by special pennants and the owners wore smart nautical uniforms.

We find William Hickey sailing in a cutter yacht of fifty tons in 1768: "a heavy dull sailer, but with capital accommodation, having a spacious cabin aft her whole width with sash windows astern."

Greenwich was considered the harbor for royal yachts during the century, and from Greenwich the royal family sailed for Hanover. George III reviewed his fleet at the Nore in 1781, sailing down the Thames with a flotilla of three or four royal yachts. In the National Maritime Museum at Stockholm, the stern and king's cabin of Gustav III's schooner, the *Amphion* built in 1778, is preserved along with its furniture. The King held many councils of war in this cabin, when fighting the Russians in 1790.

The 19th century marked the beginning of yacht racing as a great international sport. In 1815 the peace with France no doubt encouraged the formation in England of the Royal Yacht Squadron, under royal patronage, with its headquarters at Cowes, Isle of Wight, which faced the sheltered waters of the Solent. The members were rich men owning large yachts, which were designed to resemble the brigs and schooners of the royal navy. The members considered, in fact, that one of their duties was to improve the design of sailing ships for the benefit of the royal navy. Mr. Dixon Kemp, a famous writer on yachting subjects, who died in 1899, estimated there were some 50 British yachts afloat in 1800 and as many as 503 in 1850. These yachts averaged some fifty tons apiece; they were mostly cutters with bluff bows and lines which fined off aft, the well-known "cod's head and mackerel's tail" fashion.

In 1851, the American schooner *America* was sailed to Cowes and raced around the Isle of Wight for a cup presented by the Royal Yacht Squadron. The *America* had her dazzling white cotton sails cut to stand flat as boards, in opposition to the very full-cut English flax sails. She also had a light displacement and fine lines fore and aft. She won the cup and her example helped to revolutionize yacht design in European waters. In particular, her long hollow bow was copied.

Racing yachts were now built with deeper and narrower midship sections. The iron ballast was replaced by lead, and this lead began to be put on the keel instead of being interior ballast. A famous and successful yacht was the *Jullanar*, built in 1875, the design concentrating on a short keel, a long water line, and the smallest frictional surface. By the end of the century, the old narrow vessels, with their heavy weight and deep forward section and lean bow water lines, were useless when racing against the new lighter, broader boats. These new racing boats were becoming veritable skimming dishes, until a sensible compromise was effected: then the profile was rounded up forward, and a raking sternpost was built aft so as to cut down the wetted surface.

It was calculated that some 2,000 yachts were in the British Isles by 1881, which amounted to 100,000 tons, an average of 50 tons per yacht. These were built at a cost of about L50 per ton, and had only half the tonnage of sailing yachts. By now, the steam yacht had become popular, and Lord Brassey's auxiliary three-masted schooner, the *Sunbeam*, made a number of world cruises, the first in 1878, which were popularized in the narratives published by Lady Brassey.

By the beginning of the 20th century yachting had become an international sport, as popular in the United States as in the British Isles, and was spreading to the Mediterranean and Baltic and the great sheltered harbors of Australia and New Zealand. Anglo-American yachting rivalry is most well known in the America's Cup races. The first of these was held under the auspices of the New York Yacht Club in 1870.

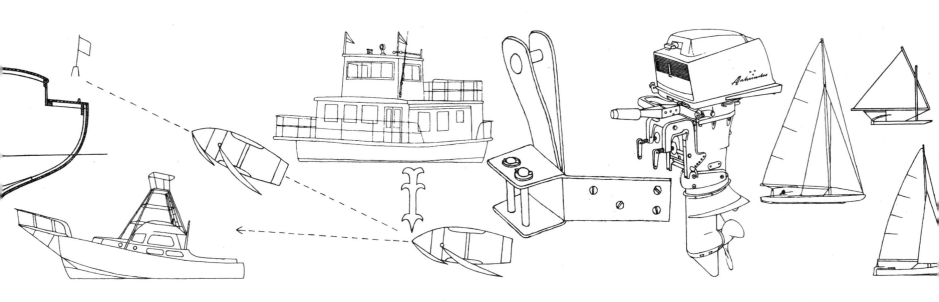

Yachting in America had begun a rapid expansion once the Civil War was over, and in 1866 three rival schooners, the *Vesta*, *Henrietta*, and the *Fleetwing*, raced from Sandy Hook to Cowes Roads, arriving within nine hours of each other, although the *Fleetwing* had six men swept out of her cockpit by a heavy sea. Naturally the great schooners caught the public eye and their doings were recorded in the press.

To many people the word yachting summoned up a picture of a fashionable gathering, for example, Cowes Week, with the roads full of large steam yachts, house parties on board, and fleets of sailing craft racing by day and returning to their moorings each night, so that the owners could attend social gatherings at the various yacht clubs. Serious yacht racing in the big classes had no more keen supporters than King Edward VII and King George V, who owned the famous racing cutter *Britannia*, designed by George Watson, between 1893 and 1935.

The German Kaiser came over to England to race, manning his yachts with English crews. Principally owing to the enthusiasm of King George V, the splendid great "J" Class cutters were raced again after the 1914-1918 war. These large yachts were generally manned by professional crews and became increasingly expensive to run. Therefore, it was not surprising that the trend turned toward building smaller, cheaper yachts, which could be manned and often partially maintained by amateur crews. And at the same time, racing in really small boats proved ever more popular; this popularity has become very obvious since World War II, because it is possible to race the modern dinghy on such small stretches of water as are formed by reservoirs and old gravel pits. It is now quite usual to sight a mass of small white sails earnestly engaged in yacht racing although they are far from the open sea.

Today over 115 countries belong to the International Sailing Federation (ISAF). There are 55 recognized international classes, including the well-known Norwegian-built 12-metre "Dragon" and the 14-foot international racing dinghy. Among the popular classes for both racing and long-distance voyaging are the "Folkboat", an extremely successful Swedish design, and the "Vertue" from an English shipyard.

While yacht racing is more likely to figure in the newspapers, cruising yachts have certainly existed since the 17th century, when we find an English naval officer fitting out his ship's boat and proceeding up the Channel with his dog for crew and company. He armed his boat with a swivel gun against pirates, and fired this off as a salute when entering Rye harbor in the early morning, so that the townsfolk man-

ned their defenses under the impression that the man and dog were themselves marauders. Since then, cruising yachtsmen have included many odd characters, such as men who chose to sail single-handed, sometimes crossing oceans, sometimes exploring difficult coastlines. One of the most famous was Captain Joshua Slocum, who sailed alone around the world in the *Spray* during 1896-98. He was a citizen of the United States who built his own ship in Fairhaven, Massachusetts, by carefully copying an old hull pulled up into a field. Captain Voss made his venturesome voyages in a converted Indian dugout canoe, looking for heavy weather so that he could try out a sea anchor and the effects of pouring oil on troubled waters. Frank Cowper wrote of enchanting sailing tours, combining near-fiction and detailed sailing directions for the coasts of the United Kingdom and Brittany. McMullen sailed heavy luggers up and down the English Channel, "single-handed", for when his wife sailed with him he did not care to count her as his crew. Rob Roy MacGregor not only popularized a type of canoe but built himself a small yawl and wrote a narrative which inspired others to follow his example. These men were on the scene in the closing years of the 19th century, and their example has proved infectious.

Dr. Claud Worth was one of the first of the amateur yachtsmen who turned his scientific training (for he was an eye specialist) toward inquiry into the proper design for yachts and the best materials from which to build them, the proper fastenings and all the details of the fittings connected with the rigging, the ground tackle – everything, in fact, upon which the safety of the yacht at sea depended. Dr. Worth wanted an ocean-going cruising yacht.

The rapid increase of interest in ocean racing and the problems raised by it has also had an important and beneficial effect on the sport as a whole. The object has been to produce small yachts intended to race on the open sea in all weather. Early successes – the first Fastnet Race was held in 1925 – went to converted pilot cutters.

The typical Bristol Channel pilot cutter had a large beam and draft, with interior ballast only, and was developed to establish sea-kindliness and the ability to keep the sea in all weather. As these cutters had to be worked with a small crew, the mast was stepped well aft, which required a large fore staysail, perhaps the easiest sail in the ship to handle. In a breeze, these cutters were fast and weatherly, yet often wet because of over-ballasting. But they were very slow in light weather, so that when the specially designed light displacement ocean racers were built, the heavy old pilot cutters soon went out of business as ocean racers. The new

ocean racers had all their ballast in the keel, many suits of headsails, such as genoas and spinnakers, and beautifully cut Bermudan mainsails, which did away with the weight of the gaff aloft. However, the influence of the older pilot cutters is still great on cruising yachts, a famous example being the *Dyarchy*, built in Sweden in 1939 to the design of Laurent Giles and partners. Nowadays, some small yachts with amateur crews will be racing across oceans, while others, perhaps crewed by a man and his wife, will be circumnavigating the world. The sport is on the increase and the meres and rivers of Holland are as busy with small craft as they were in the 17th century.

The sheltered waters of the Baltic are ideal for yachting, while in the Mediterranean the age-old harbors of Venice and Alexandria have their yacht berths in the same way as do the more modern harbors of New York or Sydney. Motor yachting, which can be learned quickly, attracts as many people as does the sailing yacht. There are a great many standard craft on the market, and the outboard motor enables many hulls to be converted easily into power boats. Materials such as fibreglass make it possible for hulls to be mass-produced, and fabrics like Dacron prolong the life of sails. And the twin hulls of the catamaran have provided new thrills by letting small yachts sail very fast indeed with just a beam wind.

There may be something new coming out every month, but the conditions of wind and weather remain the same, and it is important that the many yacht clubs exercise some sort of control to insure that yachtsmen sail the seas in seaworthy craft. Seamanlike precautions are to be preferred to foolhardy risks. No doubt the general introduction of the auxiliary motor into most large sailing yachts has diminished the risk of shipwreck or collision, and it has also made it possible for yachts to cruise much farther in a given period.

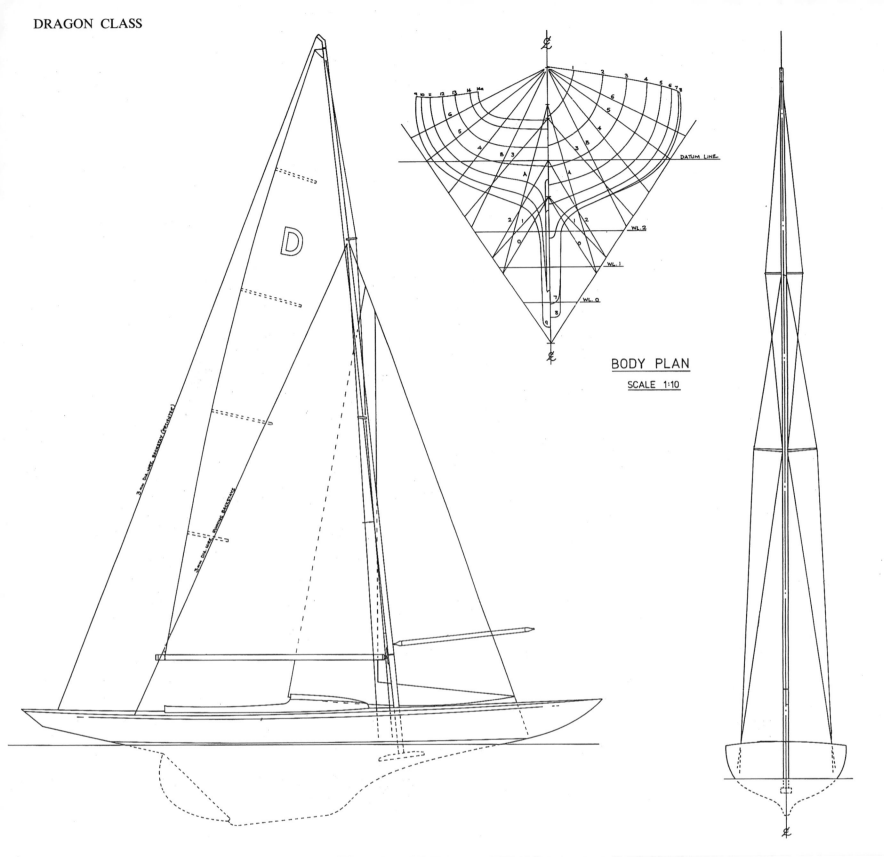

BODY PLAN

SCALE 1:10

THE INTERNATIONAL DRAGON CLASS

The Dragon is a very popular class of one-design, fixed-keel boat, and in Europe today the International Dragon class is probably the largest group of such boats. It was designed as early as 1929 by the Norwegian designer, Johan Anker, at the request of the Royal Yacht Club of Gothenburg. The class soon spread to all Scandinavia and Germany, and in 1935 it was introduced into Great Britain. The control of the class is administered by the International Yacht Racing Union.

The aim of the Dragon was to get a racing cruiser with a high speed and a cabin for two. At the same time, the boat is very seaworthy and able to carry her large sail, even in strong winds. The hull of the Dragon has not been altered, but the rigging was changed in 1946.

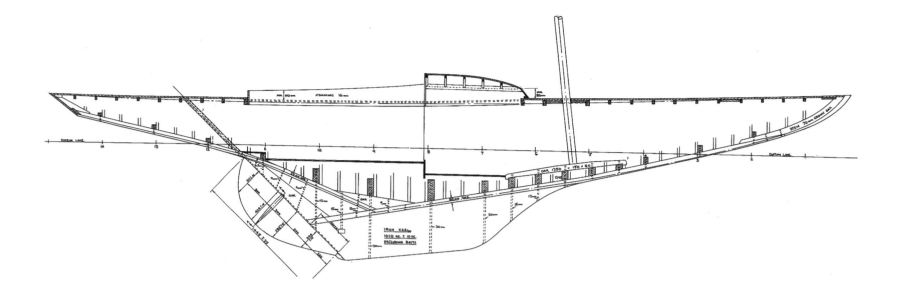

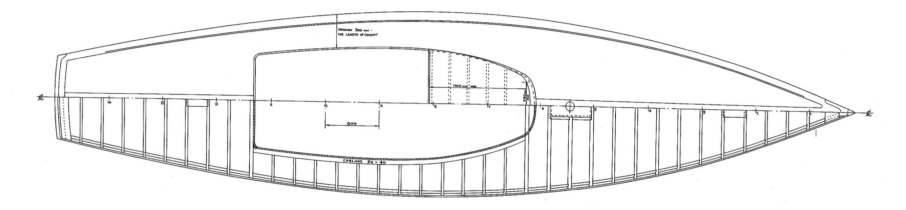

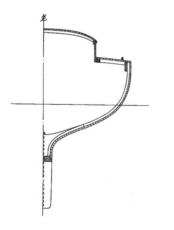

DRAGON RACES

The International Dragon Gold Cup was initiated in 1936, and is competed for annually in Britain, Norway, Sweden, or Denmark. Since 1948, the Dragon has been used at the Olympic Games, where the class now is the most popular.

The Edinburgh Cup was presented by the Duke of Edinburgh in 1949 for competition in Britain. The Herriot Cup was offered by the Yacht Club of France in 1948.

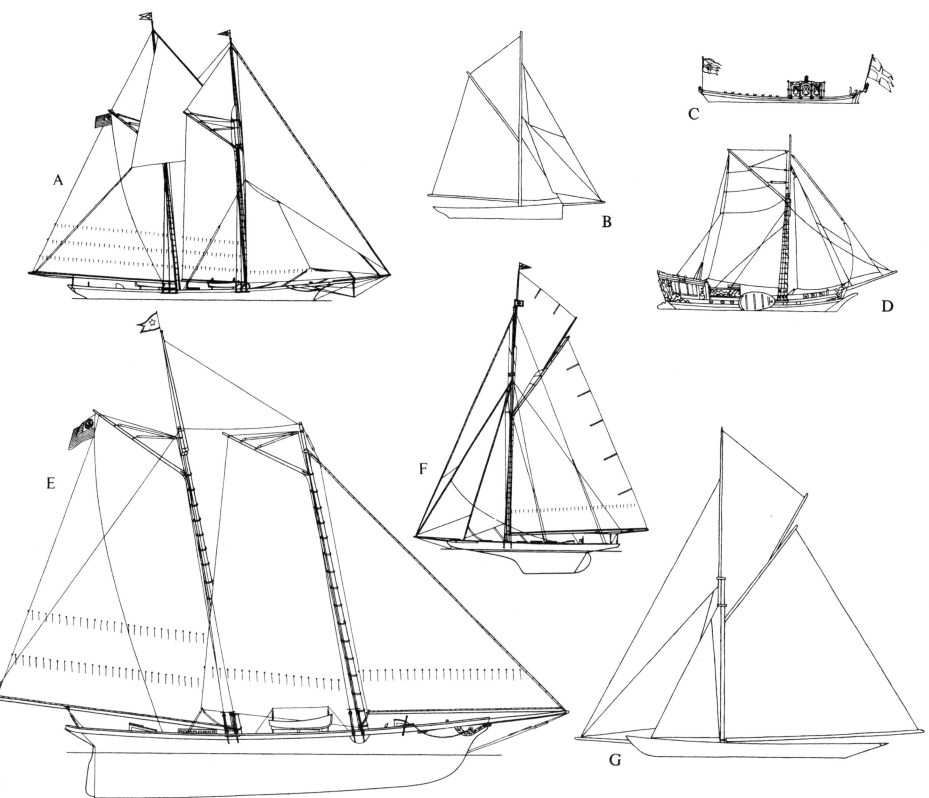

OLD YACHTS

A The American schooner, *Sappho,* defender of the America's Cup in 1871

B *Jolie Brise,* winner of the first Fastnet Race and founder of the R.O.R.C. Rule

C The Swedish state barge, *Vasaorden,* constructed in 1774 by af Chapman for King Gustavus III

D Dutch yacht, 1678

E The famous schooner yacht, *America,* which in 1851 won the Queen's Cup, later known as the America's Cup. The *America* was a development from the American East Coast pilot schooner.

F *Shamrock IV,* owned by Sir Thomas Lipton, the British challenger in the Cup race of 1920

G H.M. Yacht, *Britannia,* in her first rig; she was built in 1893 for the Prince of Wales, later Edward VII

OLD AND NEW LARGE YACHTS

1 The *Drott,* built in 1877 and rebuilt in 1883 for the Swedish king, Oscar II

2 The British Royal yacht, *Victoria and Albert,* built in 1899

3 The Royal Danish yacht, *Dannebrog,* built in 1931

4 The motor yacht, *Vedette,* built at Copenhagen in 1924 for Fred W. Vanderbilt, New York

5 The *Stella Polaris,* for tourist cruises

6 The British Royal yacht, *Britannia,* built in 1954

7 The three-masted fore-and-aft schooner, *Sunbeam II,* built in 1929 for Lord Runci-man; now a Swedish training ship under the name *Flying Clipper,* rigged as a topsail schooner

MODERN YACHTING

BY GÖRAN ROMARE

In the last chapter we have seen that yachting is not a new phenomenon, and have followed its historical development until around the beginning of our century, with a brief view of later events. Here the chief focus will be upon progress since about 1950.

Yachting is pursued either as a sport in racing, or as cruising for pleasure. Among the many forms of yacht racing, the most prominent is *course racing*. This is done along a special course with a starting and finishing line, between which a number of rounding markers have to be passed in a definite sequence. Different kinds of courses are used, according to the boats and competitions involved (see examples on page 194). Nowadays, the organizers try to make course racing more accessible for the public and the media: courses are laid closer to land, and are shortened, with greater emphasis on maneuvering and sail-changing.

The International Yacht Racing Union, which in 1996 became the International Sailing Federation (ISAF), was founded in 1906 and soon adopted international rules for yacht racing. It has remained the highest international body for this sport, although the United States joined it only in 1964. The ISAF decides which boats are given international status, adopts new racing rules, and selects – in consultation with the Olympic Committee – the boat classes that compete in the Olympic Games. During the 1996 Olympics, the competing classes were the *Finn-dinghy*, *E-dinghy*, *470-dinghy*, *Laser-dinghy*, the keeled boats *Soling* and *Star*, and the windsurfing class *Mistral*. Ocean racing is supervised by an independent body, the Offshore Racing Council.

The ISAF rules cover all aspects of a yachting race's organization and conduct, particularly regarding how the competitors should maneuver when near each other (see examples on page 195). The rules are revised every four years.

A variant of course racing is termed *match racing*. Two boats compete alone, sometimes in "three-set matches". If several boats participate, they are paired by drawing lots, and the winners continue until a final match. This is the procedure used in the America's Cup race, with boats until World War II in the so-called "J class" (the largest single-masted sailboats built, 40 metres long), during 1958-87 in the 12-metre class (whose boats are 20 metres long), and since 1992 in a special America's Cup class of boats about 22 metres long, which have some 300 square metres of sail area.

In course racing, the boats usually compete by class. They are either "one-design boats", identically constructed, or "type boats" that are built in accordance with a measuring-rule to fulfil a certain "rating". The International Rating (R-) Rule, established in 1906, created eight classes with different ratings, and has been revised several times. Today there are competitions only in the 6-, 8- and 12-metre classes. The Royal Swedish Sailing Society introduced its "skerry cruiser rule" in 1907, basing the class division on the sail area, with racing in classes between 22 and 150 square metres. This rule, too, has often been adjusted due to developments in material and design, but the smaller classes are still built.

Another form of yacht competition is the *distance race*. It normally takes place in coastal waters, and is also a test of skill in navigation. A famous example is the course around

the Isle of Wight, sailed by the schooner *America* already in 1851. But *ocean racing* has increased throughout the century. The first in modern times, across the Atlantic in 1905, was won by the three-masted schooner *Atlantic*. The Bermuda Race, starting in Newport, has been held every other year since 1906 except during the two World Wars. So has the Fastnet Race, which began in 1925 and goes from Portsmouth to Plymouth – around Fastnet Rock, south of Ireland. Major ocean races in Scandinavia include the annual Skaw Race (in Skagerrak) and Gotland Round (in the Baltic), and the biennial course from Helgoland to Skagen to Kiel.

An ocean yacht race around the world was first arranged in 1973. Since then, it has been held every fourth year, named after its sponsor, the Whitbread brewery. Several more ocean races are now organized, for instance with one- or two-person crews. Perhaps the most spectacular is the "Vendée Globe", a *single-handed* turn around the world – nonstop! It has been sailed every other year since 1989.

Distance and ocean races are also subject to measuring-rules. The ratings are used for handicap calculations, i.e. adjustments of the sailing duration to a time that determines the placing. The most popular rule today is the International Measurement System (IMS). In Scandinavia, the Danish Handicap rule (DH) is used as well, besides a very simple handicap rule called the Leading Yardstick (LYS). The latter does not require measurement of the boat, but takes account of the boat type's previous results, and is used for all kinds of yacht races.

When the lust to compete is absent, the motives for yachting are no less abundant. *Cruising* may range from long-distance and tourist voyages to family and hobby sailing. For families with a boat so big that everyone can sleep on board, it is natural to devote part of the holidays to long voyages. Sailing constantly in the same waters can be avoided by going as far as time allows in one direction, then laying up the boat there until the next season. Many people also share a boat with other relatives or families, so that one crew can sail it outward and another back home. Well-organized charter boat companies now exist too. Very long voyages – across oceans or round the world – are becoming ever more common among solo, family, and charter sailors alike.

Boats are acquired in numerous ways. Traditionally, a racing boat is ordered from a designer, in a particular size or class, with the aim that it should be faster than all other boats in that class. The designer's ability to create a fast, fine-sailing hull with a well-adapted rig, which makes optimal use of the revailing rule, is a combination of artistry and technical skill. Only a single boat, or "one-off", was formerly often built from each design. But a sailing club might order and promote a design for many boats. Such one-design boats were cheaper, and frequently more enjoyable for racing since they avoided handicaps; in addition, they could train young sailors. Long-distance and family boats were once also built in this manner. Today, however, most boats are produced industrially and are bought like cars, even at large second-hand markets.

While one-design boat classes have tended to remain local, some have spread to other countries and eventually gained

international status. Of those that emerged before the age of plastics, an example is the *Star* class, designed in 1911 by an American, Francis Sweisguth. This has been an Olympic class since 1932 (except in 1976), but will be replaced in the 2000 Games by the extreme dinghy *49-er*. The *Dragon*, designed by Johan Anker of Norway in 1929 after an order from the Gothenburg Royal Sailing Society, was an Olympic class during 1948-72 and is still built, occasionally in plastic.

Excellent boats were constructed for both racing and cruising in the era of wood and handicraft, giving ever greater importance to the designer. This trend has grown further in recent generations. Few firms in the United States can outshine Sparkman & Stephens, with its epoch-making ocean racer *Dorade* (1931), its *Goose* (1937) which won the finest prize in the 6-metre class four times (the Gold Cup), and its famous *Swan* boats (1968) which continue to be built in Finland. The British have proud traditionalists (W. Fife and Uffa Fox), followed by the multi-hull specialists Marsh and Prout. In ocean racing, the French have been highly successful with designers such as Dufour and Finot, while Bruce Farr of New Zealand and German Frers of Argentina are dominant designers in, for example, the Whitbread Race.

Scandinavian designers have included Jan Linge in Norway with the *Soling*, and Niels Jeppesen in Denmark with his fast series of *X-boats*. In Sweden, during the days of wooden boats, Tore Herlin was a pioneer of sound long-distance designs, as well as a founder of the Swedish Cruising Club. Knud H. Reimers has an international reputation ranging from skerry cruisers to big and little long-distance boats. Pelle Pettersson designed the *Maxi-boats* and the *12th Sweden*, and Pelle Norlin his *R-boats* and ocean racers such as *Scampi*. Among the small Swedish sailboats that have been built in extensive series and spread internationally, one can mention the *Nordic Folkboat* and its plastic successor the *IF-boat*, both by Tord Sundén, and Per Brohäll's extraordinary family boat *Vega*. Illustrations of modern sailboats are on pages 192-193.

Small boats come in countless classes, but sailing dinghies and canoes are the majority. The most popular are produced in very large series. Training and racing boats for the young also play a role, like the superb child-dinghy *Optimist* by Clark Mills. Two concepts with a wide following, mainly in America and Britain, are the multi-hull boats: *catamarans* and *trimarans*. These vary from toy-sized dinghies to seagoing competition machines. They have not yet caught on well in Scandinavia – and the same is true of *windsurfing*, whose explosive growth has levelled out lately.

If the boat hull's shape and construction have seen revolutionary changes, this applies equally to the rig and sail. In both cases, the new artificial fibre materials are a leading cause. Masts and other spars are built of fibreglass-strengthened plastic, with reinforcements made, for instance, of carbon fibre. The ropes are manufactured from synthetic fibres, sturdy as wire and smooth as silk. Sails are welded together from laminated materials that do not stretch and, per weight unit, are many times stronger than the sailcloths of only fifty years ago.

As a whole, yachting today can be said to satisfy all sorts of interests – from peaceful family life in protected waters, to the ultimate experiences of competition on inhospitable seas.

A

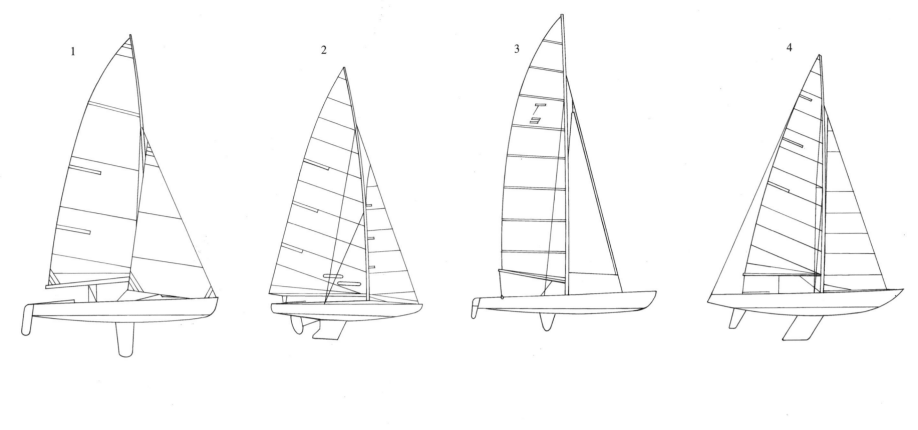

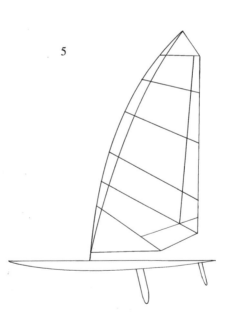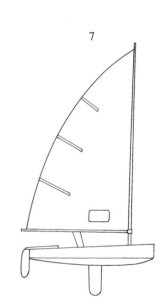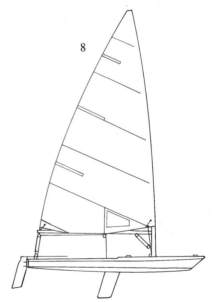

OLYMPIC CLASSES

A   *The Olympic classes*
    and their dates of
    recognition
1   470-dinghy (1976 –)
2   Star boat (1932 – 72,
    1980 –)

3   Tornado (1976 –)
4   Soling (1972 –)
5   Mistral (1996 –)
6   Finn-dinghy (1952 –)
7   E-dinghy (1992 –)
8   Laser (1996 –)

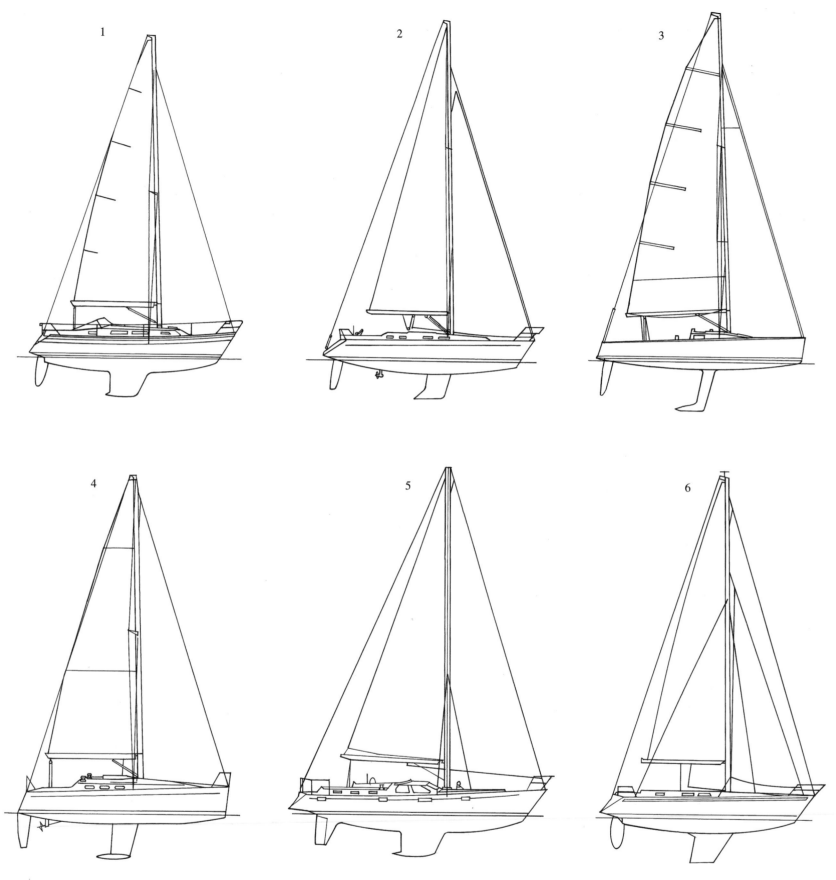

MODERN SAILING YACHTS

1 Hallberg Rassy 31
2 Bavaria 41
3 Mumm 30
4 Beneteau First 300
  Spirit
5 Oyster 485
6 Swedish Yachts 370

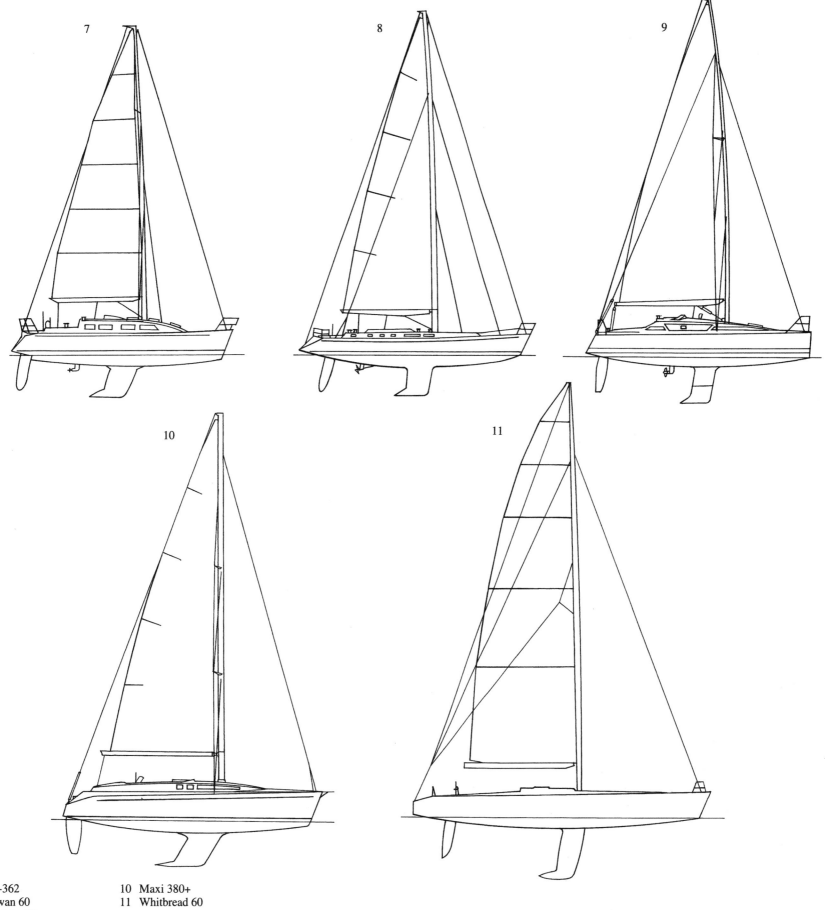

7 X-362
8 Swan 60
9 Dehler 33
10 Maxi 380+
11 Whitbread 60

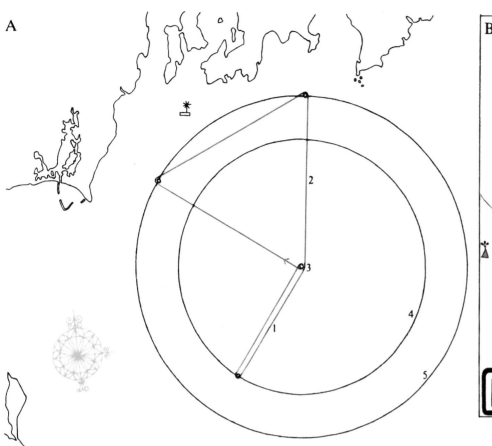

A

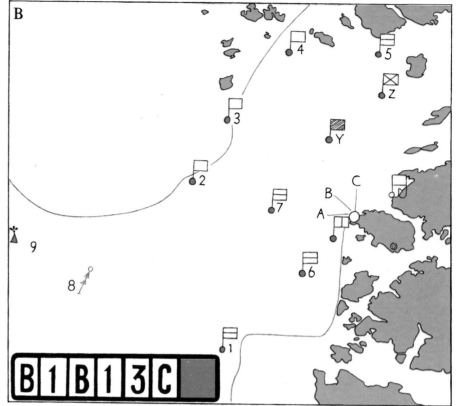

B

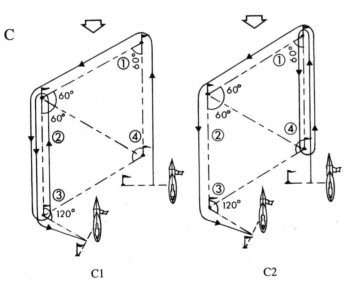

C1

C2

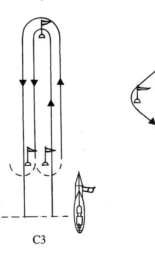

C3

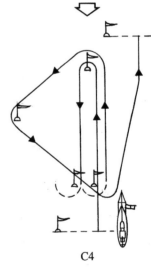

C4

YACHT RACING

A *The course of the America's Cup*
1 First, this course is sailed windward and leeward twice
2 Then, the triangular course is sailed once
3 Start and finish. Wind direction is assumed to be south-west
4 Circle of 6-mile radius
5 Circle of 8-mile radius

B *A common type of racing course. The start/finishing line is A, B or C. Rounding buoys are 1-9 and U, Y, Z. Red lines show course boundaries. The inset sign with letters and figures is the course-board, placed at the starting center. This board shows the follow-* *ing course: After the start over the B line, the following buoys must be rounded: 1, the buoy B of the starting line, 1 and 3, after which C is used for a finishing line. A red or blue field to the right indicates whether the buoys are to be taken on the port or on the starboard side* *of the boat. (This example shows the racing courses at Marstrand, Sweden.)*

C *Examples of Olympic courses (also laid by some sailing clubs): the arrows show wind direction*
1 Outer loop course
2 Inner loop course
3 Tack and run course
4 Tack, run and quarter course

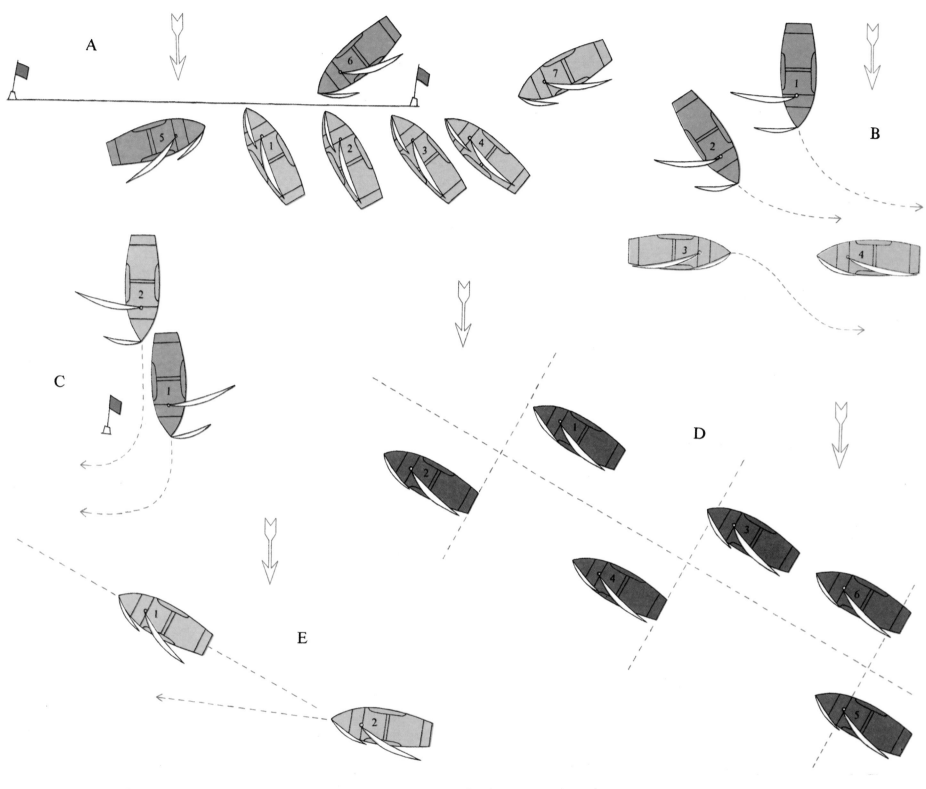

A Starting boat should lie on the wind or, when starting, in fair wind steering for the first buoy.
Here, 1, 2 and 3 are starting correctly. At the start, 3 is allowed to force 4 outside the buoy (see C). 5 is sailing on the port tack and has to give way to 1, 2, 3 and

4. 6 has to give way to the others. 7 is not a permitted course at the start.

B If two boats are sailing on different tacks, the one which has the wind on the port side has to give way to the other. 1, 2 and 3 should give way to 4.

C An exception from B is that, when rounding a buoy, the leading boat has to give way to the overtaking boat if the latter's stem has passed athwart of the leading boat's stern. (Exception: at start, see A.)

D Some definitions:
Boat 1 is astern of 2. The stem of 3 has passed the athwartship line of the stern of 4, and 3 should give way to 4 except when they are rounding a buoy (see C). By hauling her wind, 4 is allowed to block 3's hawse. When the mast of 5 is abeam the helms-

man of 6, 5 must not luff any more but should bear up (toward the buoy).

E If the distance between the boats is less than 3 boat lengths, 1 must not restrain 2 from trying to pass to leeward.

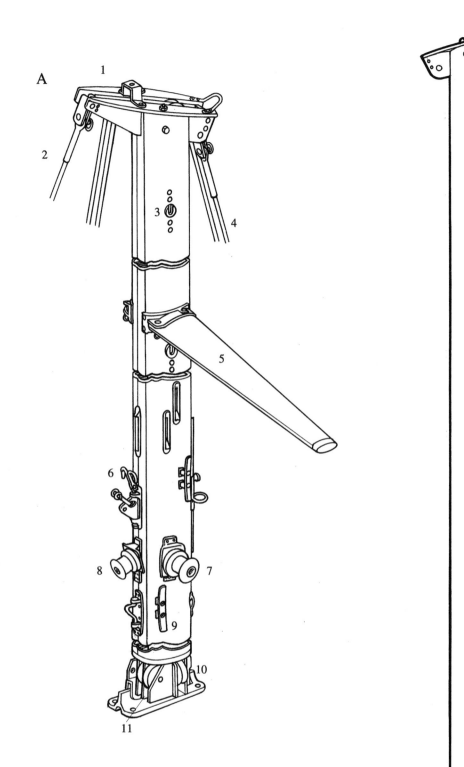

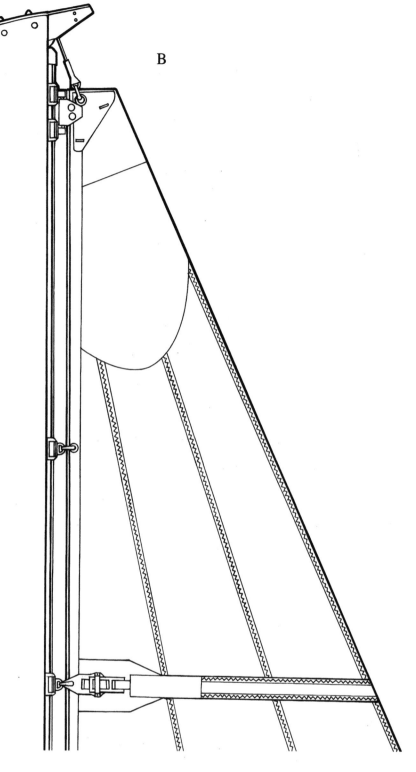

YACHT DETAILS

A	*Mast*	6	Reef hooks
1	Masthead	7	Halliard winch
2	Stern stay	8	Reef winch
3	Shroud lug	9	Cleat
4	Forestay	10	Mast shoe
5	Shroud spreader	11	Mast foot

B   *Top of a through-battened sail with mast track slide*

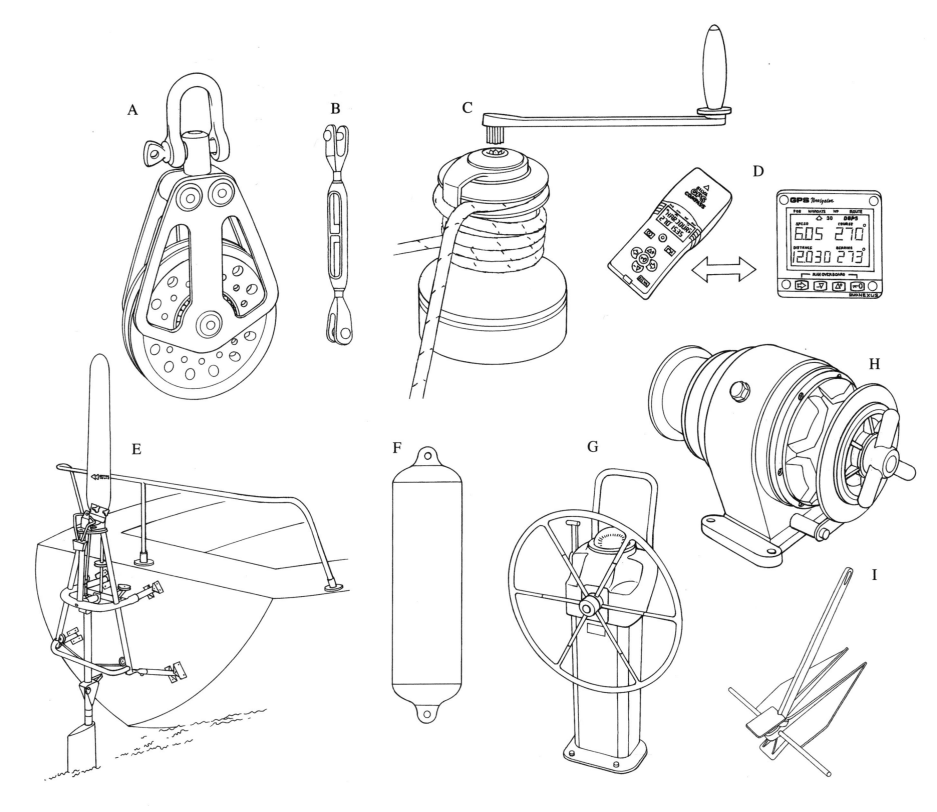

YACHT DETAILS AND FITTINGS

A   *Ball-bearing yacht block of stainless steel and aluminum*
B   *Forged turnbuckle*
C   *Deck winch with crank*
D   *Hand-held GPS compass and GPS navigation instrument*
E   *Steering vane*
F   *Fender*
G   *Steering-wheel pedestal*
H   *Windlass*
I   *Anchor*

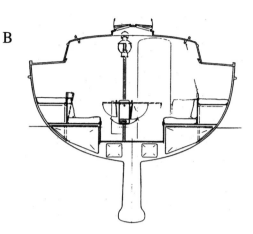

A

B

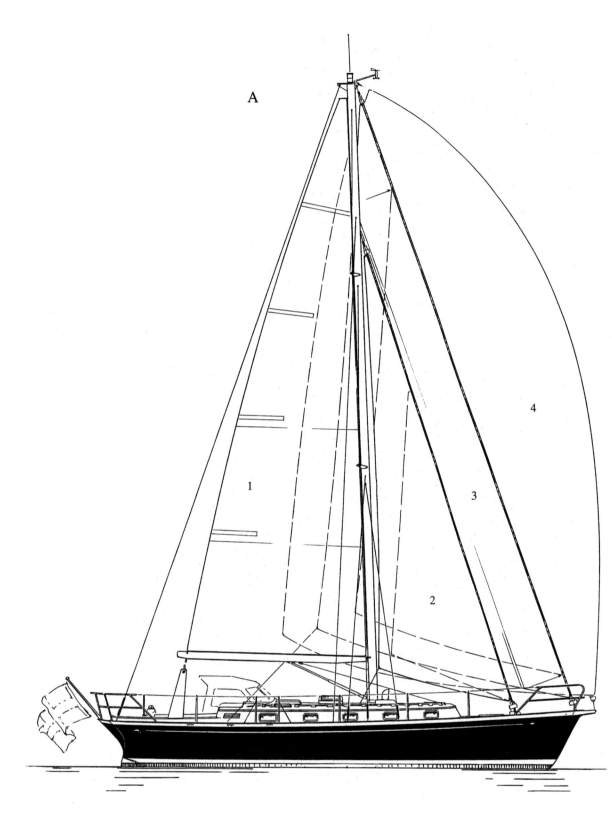

LONG-DISTANCE YACHT FOR OCEAN SAILING

Intended for two people to live on board during long periods, this boat was designed by Gabriel Heyman, of Heyman Yacht Design in Göteborg, for a competition in the English journal Yachting World.

The entry, named "Freja", won first prize in the professional category of the contest.
Total length: 13.18 m (43.2 ft)
Length at water line: 11.23 m
Maximum width: 3.96 m

Width at water line: 3.26 m
Draft: 1.78 m
Displacement: 9,440 kg
Lead keel: 3,500 kg

A *Sail design*
The boat has a cutter rig – with two foresails – for simple handling in all weather conditions. Both the mainsail and foresails on a roll system are constantly in place. The sail area can

be decreased continuously from the cockpit, from about 105 to 15 square metres. In light winds an asymmetric spinnaker is raised from the little platform in the stem, which also holds the main anchor.

Sail area (internationally measured): 81.1 m².
1 Mainsail 36.0 m².
2 Foresail 19.7 m².
3 High-cut genoa, "Yankee jib" type, 48.7 m².
4 Asymmetric spinnaker, 130 m².

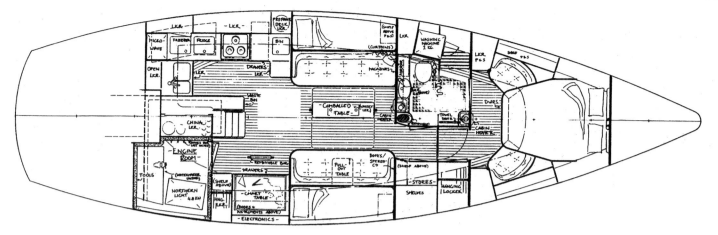

C

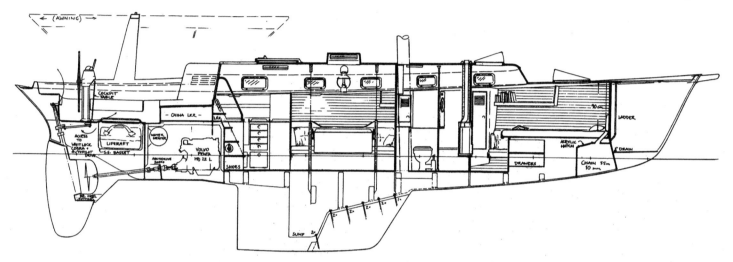

D

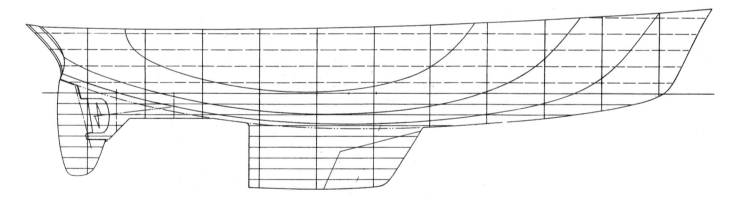

B *Cross-section of the boat through the salon. Under the sofas and flooring can be seen four of the tanks in cross-section. The keel has a lower bulb – a thicker part – to get the weight in the lead ballast as far down as possible.*

C *Interior design Astern on the port side is the pantry. The seats run longitudinally to provide support when the boat heels. Opposite is an isolated engine room with space for electric power plant and "water-maker". Forward of this is the* *navigation place. Amidships is the salon with sofas and, between them, a cardan-mounted dining table. Behind the sofas, in the part of the boat where least motion is felt, are two bunks. Forward is a bedroom for use while in harbor. The boat is warmed by* *two heaters and also has a refrigerator, freezer and washing machine.*

*Engine: 50 hp.
Electric power: 4.8 kW.
Fuel: 610 liters.
Water: 480 liters.
Battery capacity:
840 Ah.*

D *Line drawing with side view*

TYPES OF MOTORBOATS AND PLEASURE CRAFT

1 Motor gig (double-ender)
2 Half-decked utility boat, made of fibre-glass, with outboard engine
3 Small tender, of fibre-glass with outboard engine
4 Aluminum boat with outboard engine
5 Rubber boat with outboard engine
6 Long-distance boat, 11.40 m
7 Motor sailboat
8 Outboard cabin cruiser
9 Inboard motorboat, 6 m
10 Jet-ski
11 American motorboat for sportfishing
12 Formula 1 racing boat

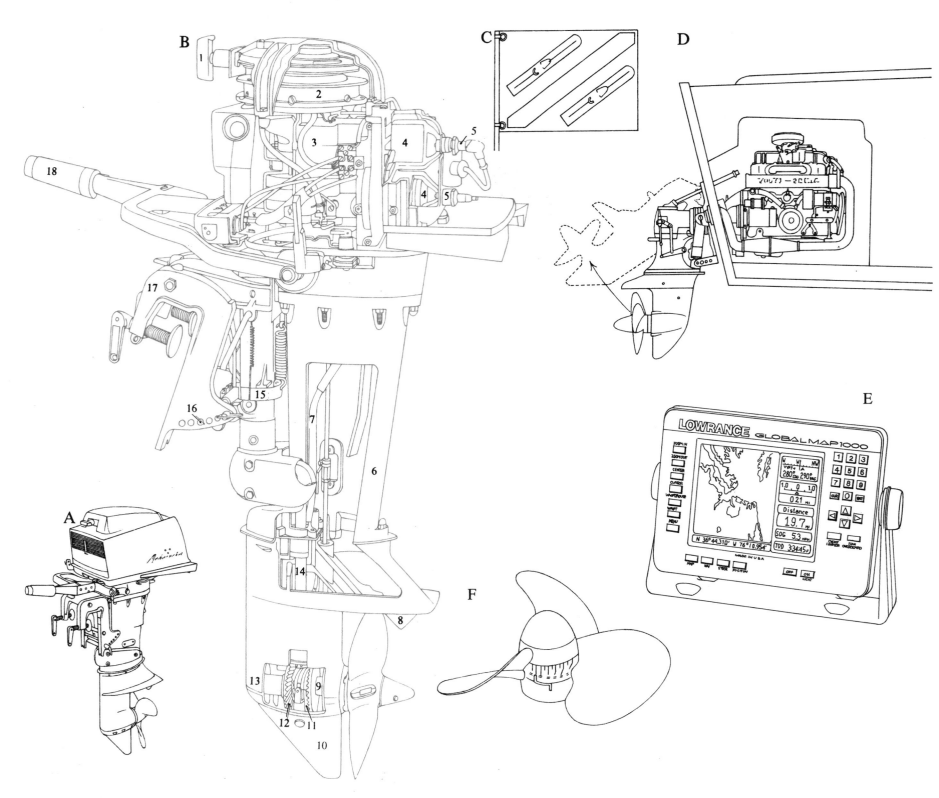

MOTORBOAT FITTINGS

A *Outboard engine*

B *Cross-section perspective of an outboard engine*
1 Starting handle
2 Flywheel
3 Crankcase

4 Cylinders
5 Spark plugs
6 Cooling-water pipe
7 Exhaust outlet
8 Propeller axle
9 Skeg
11 Forward gear
12 Reverse gear

13 Gearbox
14 Drive shaft
15 Back stop
16 Angle setting
17 Mounting brace
18 Tiller

C *Warning flag: "This boat is towing water-skiers." The flag is recommended by the American Ski Association*

D *Inboard-mounted "outboard" engine with a fold-up propeller section*

E *GPS with integrated navigation and map system*

F *Adjustable propeller*

A detail from an etching illustrating the battle on the Sound on October 29, 1658, appropriately introduces the chapter on gunnery. The etching was obtained from Histoire de Charles X by Pufendorf.

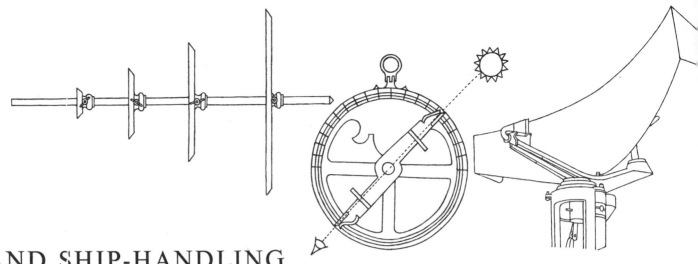

NAVIGATION AND SHIP-HANDLING

BY ROLF SCHEEN

The term navigation for this science is of comparatively recent date when compared with man's own hundreds-of-thousand-year history. Nobody knows when the first boat or the first ship was launched, but it is evident that the first man could not go very far from his original home without being stopped by water when he went out to look for something to eat. That water had to be spanned; the primitive craft is very, very old in the history of mankind. The first primitive navigation took place without an intended place of destination. The object was just to get over, to cross or pass a river, a bay, or a small lake. Of these first navigators, no man had ever been on the other side of a body of water. He only moved over the globe without knowing or thinking of a destination. Food was the only thing he thought of. He went in search of food; he crossed the water in order to get food. Only later, having left places where food was good and plentiful, he wanted to return, to find the same places once more. Then the question was to find one's way. Man learned to find out where he was. His primitive navigation must now be considered an art. The peoples of the Stone Age and of the Bronze Age might have been marvelously clever in many ways. But even if astronomy was considered a science in Babylon 3,800 years before our era and even if the Chinese were able to compute the advent of solar eclipses more than 4,000 years ago they were not able to transfer the results of astronomy to practical navigation at that time.

Rivers and coastal waters can be so turbid that even with a small boat it is impossible to see the bottom, if you have enough water to float the keel. Therefore, man from the oldest times has been forced to measure the depth of the water he was going to use. On ancient pictures of Egyptian riverboats a man can be seen in the fore part of the boat using a pole to determine depth and the advisability of continuing navigation. Very early, sailors or fishermen also learned to use lead and line to measure the depth when a pole could no longer be made use of. The lead was used on board the ship that was to take the Apostle Paul to Rome, the ship that foundered in the year 62. The lead was then so developed that it was already marked in fathoms. The main object of the lead was to save the ship from going aground. If the position of a shoal or bank had already been determined, other means were used to avoid it. Much used were (and are) the so-called landmarks. It is unnecessary to know all the ground, if you are to determine your position through landmarks and can follow a safe way through or past the dangerous places.

Very early, people who had learned to write were recording necessary information mostly, perhaps, for their own benefit. Greeks and Phoenicians collected what they could in so-called *peripli,* covering whole territories. Others misused this information. Herodotus (ca. 450 B.C.) relates that King Darius I of Persia about 490 B.C. hired Phoenician ships to spy upon the Greek coast in order to procure information about this country. Later on, sea charts became still more important than sailing directions. They could not be truly useful before the invention of the compass and they could never satisfy modern requirements until hydrographic offices had been established by the different nations to organize the work of surveying, sounding, etc.; but the chief of the famous library of Alexandria, Eratosthenes (276—196 B.C.) had already produced a map of the world with the first primitive framework of parallels and meridians.

A good chart should enable its user to draw the course (the compass direction) between two places. The charts on Mercator's projection were easily satisfactory in this respect. Gerard Mercator made the degrees of longitude parallel. As a result, he could draw a correct course line between two places on his chart, but the scale of the chart varied from the Equator toward the poles, so that at 60 degrees North, for instance, one nautical mile on the chart had twice the length of the mile at the Equator. In the neighborhood of the poles, the method could not be used at all.

As is well known, the distance from the Equator to the poles of the earth is divided in 90 degrees of latitude (north or south) for the purpose of ascertaining the position of a ship, for use on charts, for observations, etc. The Equator itself has been divided into 360 degrees of longitude, with verticals called meridians up to the poles. No 0-meridian being standard, different countries have used varius 0-meridians. At sea it was better to have a common 0-meridian for ships of all nations; consequently, many countries followed King Louis XIII's orders to place the 0-meridian through the Isle of Ferro. Ferro was thought to be the westernmost point of the Old World. From the year 1884, the 0-meridian through the Greenwich Observatory in England (founded 1675) may be considered international.

A great deal of courage was needed in ancient times to sail far out from the coast, losing all sight of land. No compass, no reliable charts existed. Good weather, the spirit of adventure, the feeling of having a good boat certainly tempted many to continue their explorations when prudence ought to have kept them back. As daring sea expeditions, the adventures of the old Norsemen through the mists of the North Atlantic to Iceland, Greenland, and North America must be said to rank high, but it must be presumed that they had quite a good knowledge of the celestial bodies and their movements in order to find their way to such distant countries and back again. Next to the sun, the Pole Star and perhaps still more the Little Dipper have helped navigators. For the Norsemen the brightest summer nights and also the Midnight Sun played a great part in their seamanship. Their ancient astronomical terms have been preserved, but their meaning has been difficult to explain, even in modern times. (For instance: *Eyktarstad)*

It has long been possible to determine latitude with a fair amount of certainty. But longitude was an almost insoluble problem so long as no instrument capable of measuring time with the necessary accuracy for use at sea had been invented. A chronometer was needed. Prizes were offered to anybody who could find the means of discovering the longitude. In 1714 the English Parliament granted 20,000 pounds for this purpose. Astronomers were able to determine the longitude by the help of lunar distances and other observations, but their methods were too impractical to be used at sea. At last, after working a whole lifetime, a Yorkshireman, John Harrison, in 1774, was given the prize for his invention. With Harrison, a revolution in the history of navigation had taken place; from now on the longitude of a ship's position at sea could be determined.

The most important innovation, however, was much older; this was the invention of the compass. No one knows who the inventor was. The Chinese Emperor Hoang-Ti is said to have used magnets on his chariot to find his way south as early as the third millennium B.C. But the earliest date for the use of a compass on board a ship occurs in Chinese literature in A.D. 1111, and it is possible that China had gotten the compass from India. According to Are Frode, the Norsemen are said to have used the *leidarstein* (loadstone or lodestone) for a primitive compass during a voyage to Iceland as early as in the year A.D. 868. Considering the huge quantities of magnetite to be found in Norway, it is not at all unreasonable to suppose that Norwegians very early conceived the idea of using magnetism on board their ships as they used it during their lives on shore. Their ability to find their way across the seas if they had no form of compass is almost incomprehensible.

Celestial navigation is based upon the measurement of the altitude of celestial bodies and the determination of their direction. All ships measuring the same celestial body at the same time and at the same altitude will be placed on the same astronomical position line. This can be determined according to principles first laid down by the American naval officer Thomas H. Summer in 1837, and further amplified by Marc St. Hilaire around 1875. Many different instruments have, in the course of time, been constructed for the measurement of the

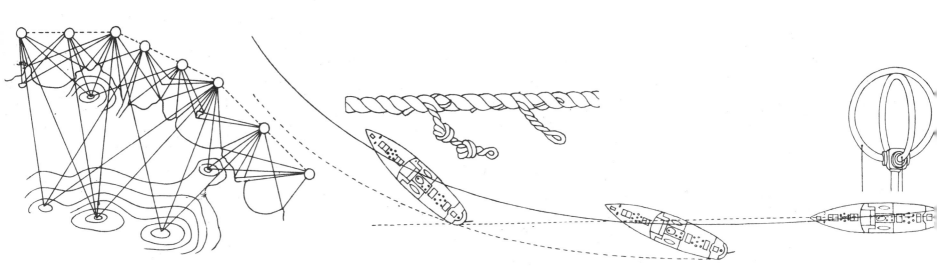

altitude of celestial bodies; the quadrant is set to have been invented by the Greek astronomer Hipparchos as early as the year 150 B.C. Levi ben Gerson from Catalonia discovered the Jacob's staff or the cross-staff in 1342; John Hadley constructed the Hadley quadrant in 1731; the British naval officer Campbell made the sextant in 1757.

To use celestial navigation it is necessary to have a number of tables computed in advance. Regimontanus published his *Ephemerides Astronomica* in 1475. Thomas Mayer at Göttingen edited the tables for using observations of lunar distances to find Greenwich time in 1755. The British Nautical Almanac, founded by the royal astronomer Nevil Maskeleyne and officially published since 1767, has proved its great value for the seafarer using celestial navigation.

The magnetic compass has been used for centuries to sail the right course at sea. In such navigation one must correct for magnetic variation, due for example to the different positions of the geographical and magnetic North Poles — as well as for magnetic deviation, caused by iron in the ship affecting the compass needle. Today large ships are equipped with gyrocompasses, which do not suffer these influences, although magnetic compasses are kept in reserve. The distance sailed was once measured on sailing ships by means of a hand log and hourglass. Later the patent log was developed, with a counter on which the distance could be read.

Numerous devices have been invented to improve safety at sea. Nautical charts enable the sailor to avoid shoals. Lighthouses have made it possible to navigate in darkness. International rules of the road help to prevent collisions, and ships are equipped with fixed lights for sailing by dark. Radar, which emerged during the Second World War, has greatly increased marine safety and allows ships to locate each other even in darkness and poor visibility.

Electronic navigation systems progressed rapidly during and after the War. Previously, only simple aids such as the direction-finder and gyrocompass had existed. But then Germany developed a system for long-distance radio navigation, called "Sonne" in German and "Consol" in English. The latter had a range of nearly 1,500 nautical miles. This system used navigation signals, transmitted at frequencies around 300 kilohertz. Seven Consol transmitters, placed along Europe's west coast, Europe, gave coverage of the whole stretch. Depending on the navigator's direction to a beacon, different numbers of dots and dashes could be heard, 60 in all. Using a table, these data were converted into the direction reading. The last Consol beacons stopped during the 1980s.

Instead, the Decca system was developed in England. Its concept came from an American engineer, but was bought by a record company whose name it acquired. Decca employs phase measurement of navigation signals. A complete Decca chain has three "slave" transmitters placed at the corners, and a "master" transmitter in the middle, of a triangle with sides 150 kilometres long. By comparing the phases of signals received from any slave and the master, a ship calculates the difference between its distances to them, which specifies its position as somewhere along a hyperbolic curve on the sea chart. This can be repeated for the other slaves, and the hyperbolas' intersection shows the actual position. Decca beacons transmit at frequencies of 70-130 kilohertz, which give a range of about 200-400 nautical miles, depending on the propagation conditions. The system determines positions with an inaccuracy between around 10 metres and several nautical miles; it is least exact during winter nights and at great distances from the transmitters. Decca is used chiefly on the western coasts of Europe, but also on coasts elsewhere in the world.

In the United States, the hyperbolic systems Loran and Omega were established. Loran differs from Decca mainly in calculating distances by measuring the travel times of radio pulses from Loran beacons. These transmit at a frequency of 100 kilohertz, and can reach 1,000-2,000 nautical miles. Loran is used to some extent outside the USA as well. Partly due to the development of the satellite navigation system GPS, the United States has turned over the operation of Loran chains abroad to the countries involved.

The Omega system serves primarily for navigation by American submarines. It obeys the same principles as Decca, but its beacons transmit on a much lower frequency, around 10 kilohertz. This enables navigation signals to be received down to 10-20 meters below the water surface. The transmitting antennas are very large, with wires several kilometres long, and the range is so great that almost the entire world can be covered by the eight Omega beacons. Therefore, Omega is sometimes called a Decca system "in seven-league boots". But the development of GPS has rendered the Omega system rather needless and it, too, is now being abolished.

A quite different system, created after World War II, is inertial navigation. Requiring no information or signals from the surroundings, it is used by airplanes and is especially suited to submarines. The principle is to measure the vessel's acceleration, starting from a known position. The measurements are integrated by a computer to obtain the vessel's speed data, which are integrated in turn to find the distance travelled. The computer keeps track of the course steered, and can thus also continuously calculate the vessel's position. Very accurate accelerometers and the gyrocompass are used for the measurements. Errors that accumulate in the calculations with time are due, for example, to drift in the gyro. Recently the mechanical gyroscope's spinning has been replaced by the laser gyroscope, with a beam that rotates in a triangular path. Any change of direction then causes a change in the beam's frequency. The low drift of this gyro has greatly improved the performance of inertial navigation.

With the help of a computer, several different systems of navigation, maneuvering, and surveillance can be combined into an "integrated" navigation system. The computer makes positional and navigational calculations, and sends guidance data to an autopilot which steers the ship. In this way the vessel's movement is being fully automated, and its navigators' work is increasingly reduced to supervising the system.

LEAD

20

17

15

13

10

7

5

3

2

HAND LEAD AND LINE

The lead is the sailor's oldest navigational instrument, known even in ancient Egypt. It consists of a lead weight and a measured line, which is used to determine the depth of water. For different depths, leads of different weights *were used, but today the deep-sea lead is replaced by sounding machines or echo sounders. The hand lead is still used occasionally in shallow water. The line used to be 20 fathoms long, and in the Royal British Navy it is marked in the following way:*

2 fathoms: two strips of leather

3 fathoms: three strips of leather

5 fathoms: a piece of white duck

7 fathoms: a piece of red bunting

10 fathoms: a piece of leather with a hole in it

13 fathoms: a piece of blue serge

15 fathoms: a piece of white duck

17 fathoms: a piece of red bunting

20 fathoms: a piece of house line with two knots

226

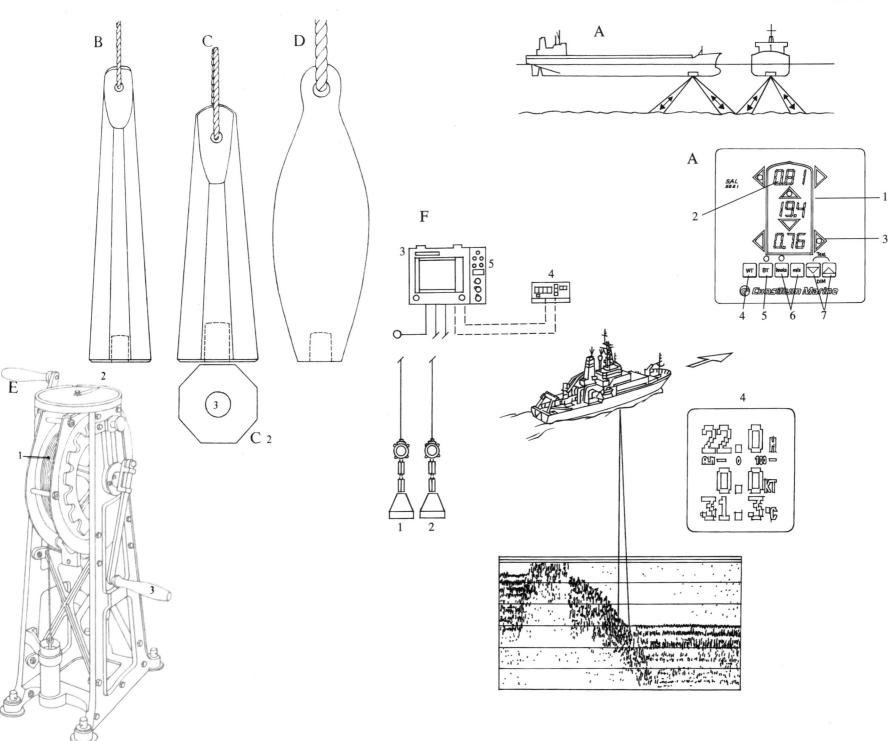

LOGS AND LEADS

A *Doppler log and corre-
lation log*
*These devices measure
the ship's speed both
longitudinally and
transversely, by sending
out sound pulses ahead,
astern and to the sides.
The Doppler log uses
the well-known principle
of measuring speed by
the frequency differences
between outgoing and
incoming (echo) pulses.
The correlation log
registers the bottom's
irregularities at two
times and measures the
interval between these.*

*The motion is presented
as forward or reverse
speed and side speed.*
1 Forward speed 19.4
knots
2 The stem is moving at
0.81 knots to port
3 The stern is moving at
0.76 knots to starboard
4 WT = Water Track,
measurement relative to
a water layer (at great
depth)
5 BT = Bottom Track,
measurement relative to
the bottom
6 Choice of speed data in
knots or in metres per
second

7 Choice of suitable
lighting strength

B *Deep-sea lead, 8 kg*
This was used with
measured hemp line, so
the ship had to be stop-
ped. A hollow in the
lead's lower end was
filled with tallow, to
pick up samples of the
sea bed for examination

C *Deep-sea lead, 10 kg*
2 End view
3 Hole for tallow

D *Deep-sea lead of cast
iron*

E *Sounding machine for
measuring depth while
under way, with a thin
wire lead-line*
1 Wire drum
2 Indicator showing how
much wire has run out
3 Handle, to wind in the
lead and act as a brake
on the drum

F *Echo sounder
Here the depth is found
by measuring the time it
takes for a sound pulse
to travel from the trans-
mitter (1) beneath the
ship, reflect from the
bottom, and return to*

*the receiver (2). The
depth is registered on a
printer (3) or presented
in figures on a separate
indicator (4).*
4 Depth 22 m, speed 0
knots (from logbook)
Temperature 31.3° C
(from temperature
sensor)
5 Setting of measurement
ranges, e.g. 0-10, 0-20,
0-50, 0-100, 0-200, 0-
500 and 0-1000 metres
in density degree, with
an audio-visual alarm if
the depth becomes less
than the set depth

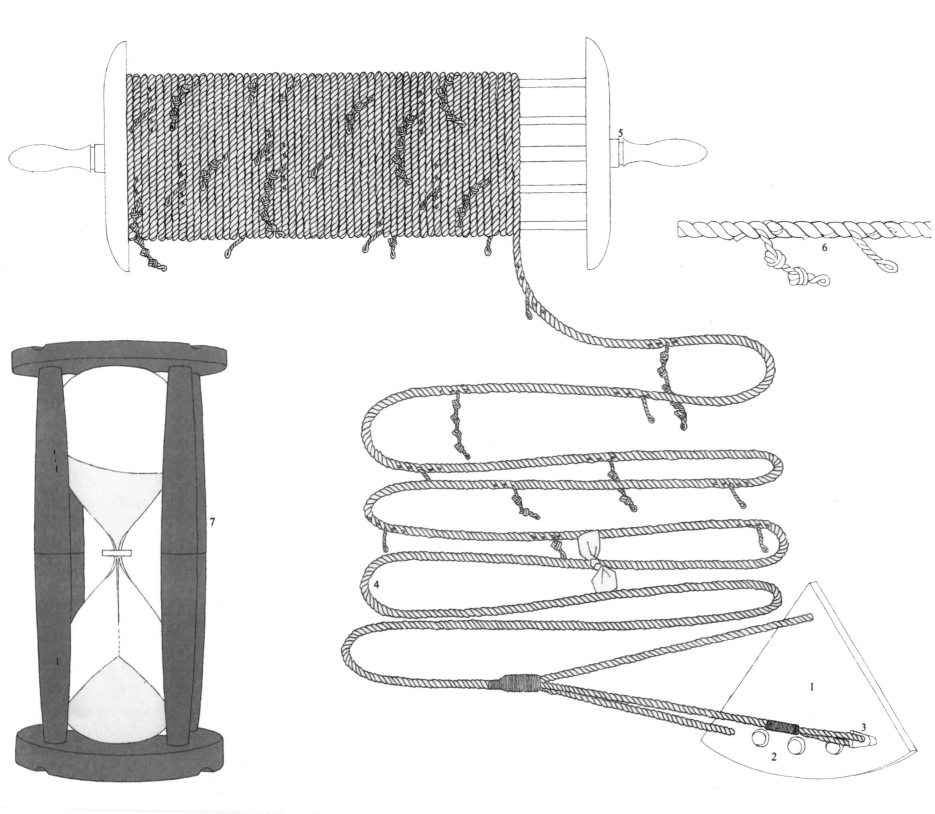

THE OLD LOG WITH A LINE AND GLASS

The chip log is an old instrument for measuring the speed of a ship. It consists of a flat piece of wood formed as a sector of a circle and weighted to enable it to float upright, secured to a line so as to make it float square. When thrown overboard it will remain stationary in the water and, as the ship sails away, the measured line will reel off at a corresponding rate. An hourglass determines *the fixed interval of time, and the length of line run out will measure the speed of the ship. A quick pull on the line will detach the peg in the log chip, making it float flat so it can be hauled in.*

1 The log, known as the wood float or chip
2 Lead pellets holding the chip vertically in the water

3 Wooden peg, which allows the chip to float flat when it is pulled out
4 Log-line measured off in "knots," having a similar relation to a nautical mile as the trickle of sand in the hourglass has to one hour

5 Log reel
6 Mark for two knots and a plain mark for half a knot
7 Hourglass, log glass, running for 28 seconds. A 14-second glass is used for speeds over 8 knots

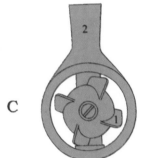

A

B

C

LOGS

A *Patent or taffrail log*
1 Rotator
2 Governor
3 Log line
4 Fastenings
5 Register (1, 10, 100, 1000 nautical miles)
6 Base plate, located sternmost on railing

B *Pitometer log*
   This device measures water pressure and converts it to speed
1 Distance indicator
2 Speedometer in knots
3 Distance counter in nautical miles
4 Connection to log in engine room

5 Height-adjustable pitot tube
6 Static pressure tube
7 Bottom plating
8 Log instrument in engine room

C *Chernikeff log (details)*
   This is similar to the pitometer log, but has a tube beneath the ship, with a small impeller fan whose rotation is registered electrically and converted to speed
1 Impeller
2 Height-adjustable tube

A
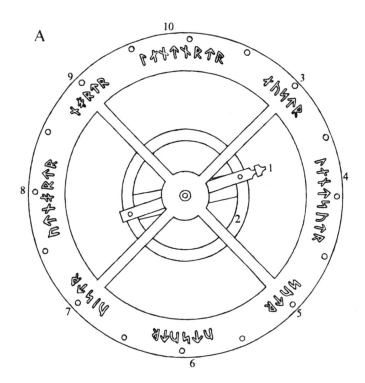

B
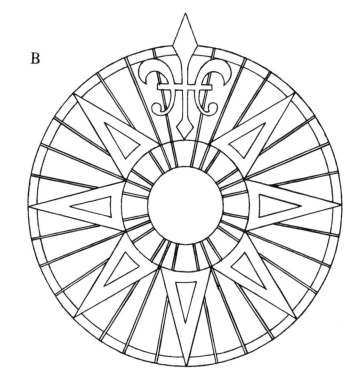

C
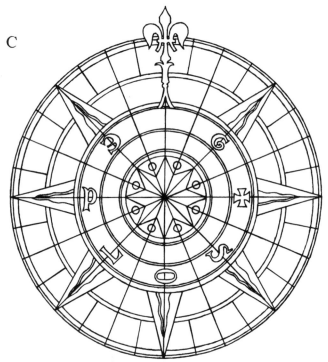

D

OLD COMPASS CARDS

A   Compass, 13th century.
    Reconstruction of a
    Scandinavian compass
    (leidarstein) with a
    bronze bowl and a
    wooden float, guided
    through a central cross
    in the lid
1   North point over float
2   Float with lodestone
3   AUSTR, east (in old
    Norwegian)
4   LANDSUDR, southeast
5   SUDR, south

6   UTSUDR, southwest
7   VESTR, west
8   UTNORDR, northwest
9   NORDR, north
10 LANDNORDR, north-
    east

B   Compass card, 1345

C   Compass card, 1545

D   Compass card, end of
    the 18th century

COMPASSES (PAGE 231)

A   *Gyrocompass*
    The heart of a gyro is a
    rotor spinning very fast
    (ca. 12-20,000 rpm),
    with a pendulum hung
    under the axle, inside a
    case mounted on two
    cardan joints. The pen-
    dulum influences the
    axle to keep the gyro
    pointing north.
1   Cardan rings
2   Gyro housing
3   Rotor with pendulum

B   *Compensating binnacle*
    A magnetic compass is
    placed in a binnacle,
    which has magnetic
    devices to shield the
    compass from influence
    by the metal ship's own
    magnetism
1   Protective hood over
    the compass, with a
    bearing plate (pelorus)
    on top. The compass is
    cardan-mounted to keep
    its orientation despite

    motion of the ship
2   Soft iron balls which
    cancel influence by the
    ship's soft iron
3   Clinometer
4   Emergency-lamp
    holders
5   Locker for permanent
    magnets. These are
    oriented along, across,
    and vertical to the ship,
    compensating for its
    permanent magnetism

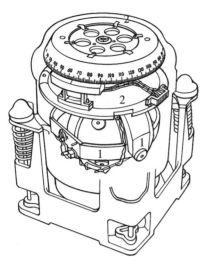

1   A

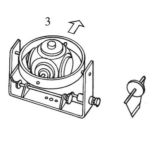

3

E

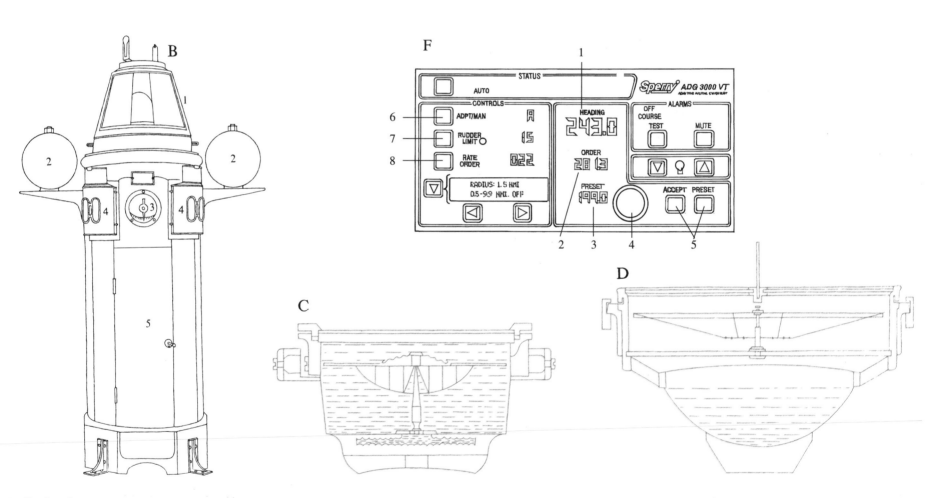

Continued

C   *Liquid compass (cross-section)*
1   Liquid, e.g. alcohol, to damp the magnetic needle's movements
2   Expansion box for the liquid
3   Pin
4   Stone
5   Compass card
6   Magnets hung parallel under the compass card

7   Float with damping wire (regulates surface of liquid in container)

D   *Dry compass (cross-section), predecessor of the liquid compass*
1   Pin
2   Stone
3   Compass card
4   Magnetic needles hung

parallel under the compass card

E   *Digital repeater instrument for the gyrocompass course. It shows the ship's course numerically. Direction and speed of the ship's yaw are read off with the five rotating points*

F   *Autopilot*
Course data from the ship's gyro are sent to the autopilot, which controls the rudder to hold the set course
1   Present course of ship
2   Ordered course
3   Pre-set next course
4   Execution button for next course
5   Buttons used by the

operator to accept or reject proposals for when to change course, which are made by the navigation system once it has been coupled to automatic steering
6   Choice of adaptive steering (with gradual commitment to the next course) or manual rudder selection

7   Setting of maximum rudder angle
8   Setting of yaw speed

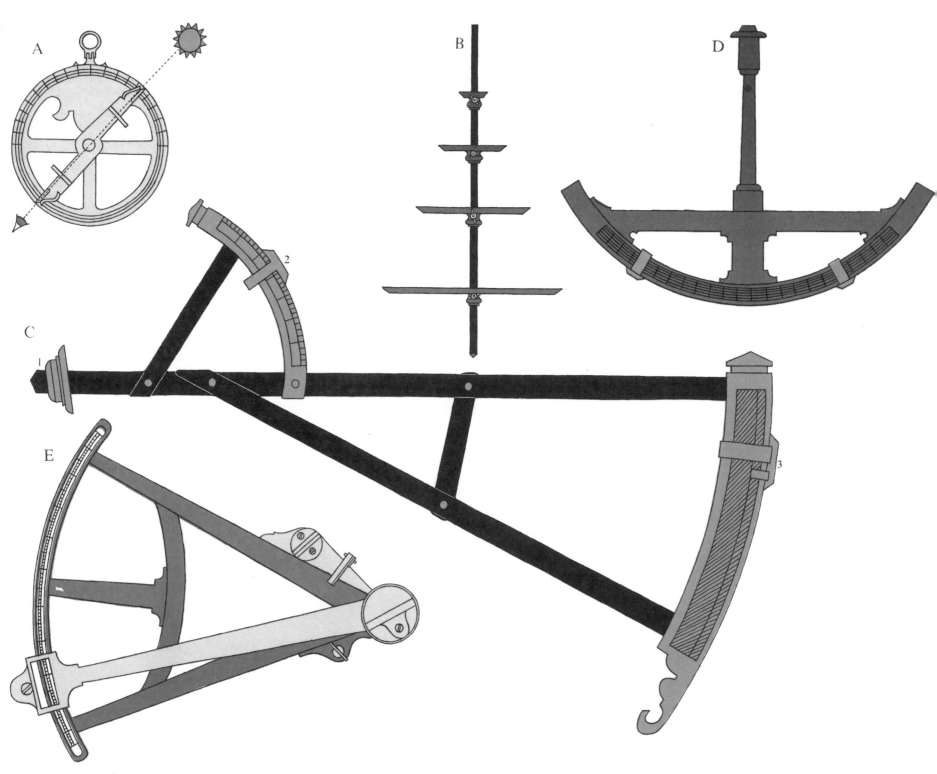

OLD NAVIGATIONAL INSTRUMENTS

A Astrolabe, constructed by the Arabs in the 10th century, and used, mostly by the Spaniards and Portuguese, up to the 17th century. It consists of a freely suspended graduated ring with a diametrical ruler holding two sight vanes through which the sun or a star may be observed, the altitude being read off on the circle.

B The fore staff is composed of a square staff and three vanes of different lengths. The sides of the staff have different scales, each corresponding to one of the vanes. When observing the altitude of the sun (star) only one vane is used. Holding one end of the staff to his eye, the observer moves the vane until he sees its lower end level with the horizon and the upper end in one with the sun. The altitude is read off where the vane cuts the staff.

C Davis' quadrant is composed of two arcs of a circle having the same center and three vanes: the horizon vane (1) with a slot, the shade vane (2), and the sight vane (3) with a sight hole. The horizon vane is fixed at the center, the other two vanes run upon the arcs. The quadrant is used with the observer's back to the sun. The shade vane is set at a suitable number of degrees, and the observer moves the sight vane until he observes the sun's shadow in one with the horizon, as seen through the slot in the horizon vane.

D Gunter's quadrant is made on the same principles as the Davis' quadrant, and it is used with the observer's back to the sun.

E Hadley's octant, invented in 1731, and a forerunner of the sextant. The octant brought the art of measuring altitudes at sea to theoretical perfection, and later improvements are due to better methods of manufacturing only.

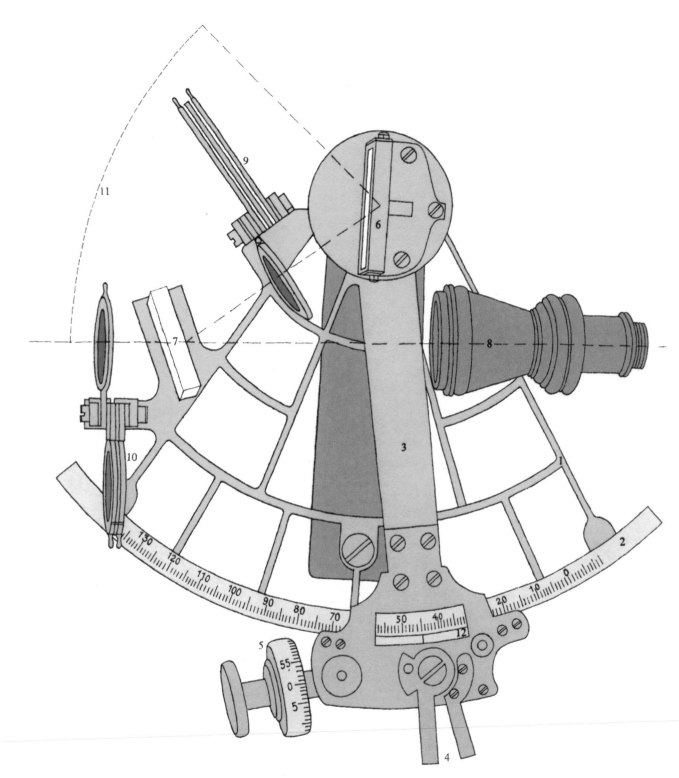

A MODERN SEXTANT

The sextant is an improvement on Hadley's octant, which is said to have been invented in 1731. The sextant is a portable, reflecting astronomical instrument for measuring angles. When used, it can be held in the hand without a stand, which is essential on board ships at sea. The instrument consists of a sector-shaped frame with a graduated arc of a circle. Pivoted at the center of the arc is a radius bar, which swings across the surface of the graduated arc. The principal parts of a sextant are:

1 The frame
2 The arc, known as the limb
3 The index bar
4 Clamping mechanism
5 Micrometer screw
6 Index mirror
7 Horizon glass
8 Telescope
9 Index shades
10 Horizon shades
11 Measured angle
12 Reading of measured angle, here 45° 0'

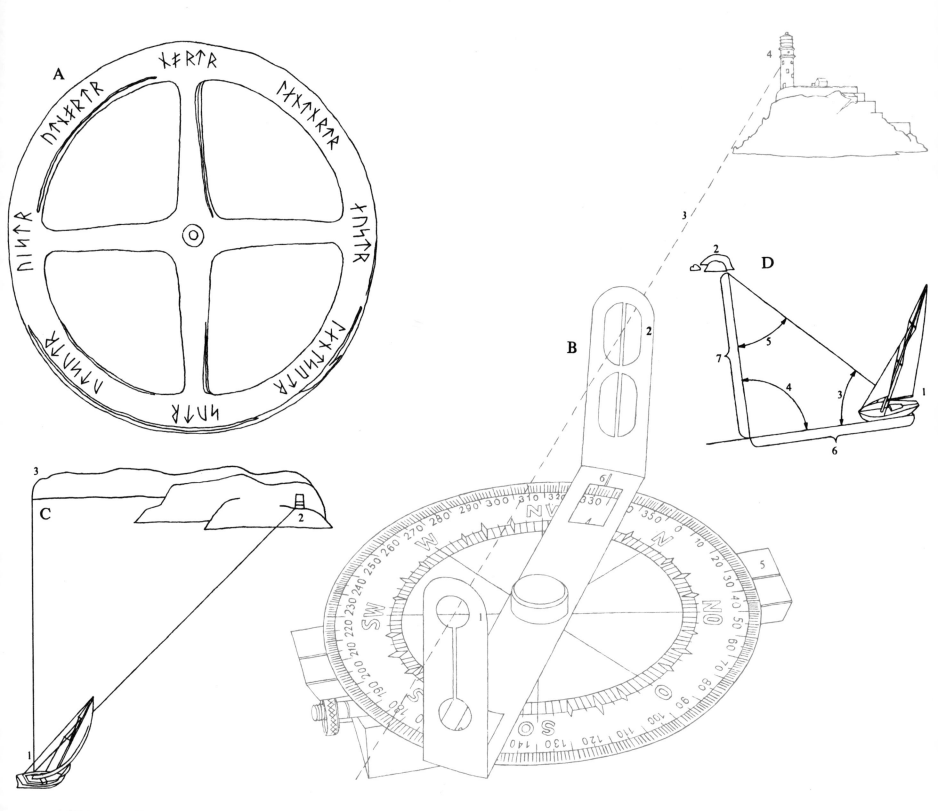

A *Reconstruction of a compass card from the Viking Age*

B *Pelorus*
1, 2 Sight vanes
3 Position line
4 Object
5 Fore-and-aft mark to which the ship's course on the pelorus is clamped
6 Compass bearing

C *Cross bearing*
The exact position of the ship (1) will be known if bearings of two objects (2 and 3) are taken at the same time

D *Distance by four-point bearing*
When a fixed object (2) is bearing 45 degrees on the bow (3) note the time or log. Then the same course is steered until the object bears on the beam, or 90 degrees from the course (4). The distance (6) run by the ship (1) in the interval is the distance (7) of the object when abeam. This is clear from the fact that the ship's course and the two bearings form an isosceles triangle (3, 4, 5), where the two sides (6, 7) are equal.

234

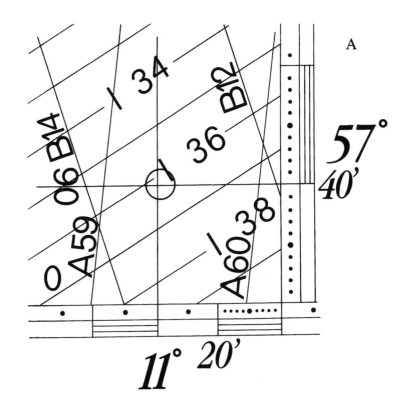

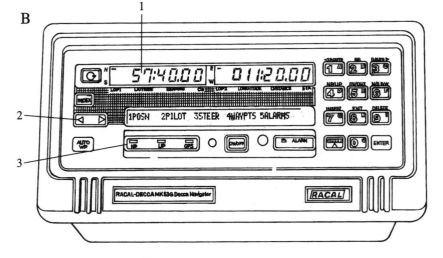

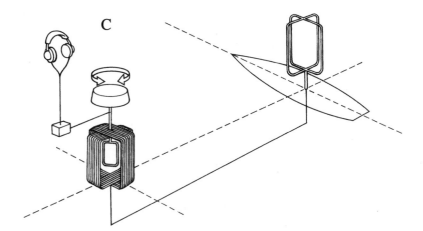

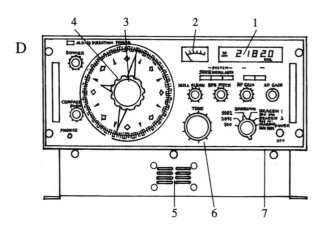

A *Decca nautical charts*
Decca uses a chain of radio stations whose signals enable a ship's receiver to calculate its position on a sea chart. At first, this method of navigation required special charts showing its systems of hyperbolic lines, or "lanes". Every Decca chain has at least 2-3 such systems, colored red, green and purple on the chart. The lanes are numbered in groups that are designated by letters.

Illustrated here is part of a chart with groups B (red), I (green) and A (purple). The receiver gives the lane values B 13.2, I 36.1 and A 59.3, which can be converted to the corresponding position N57° 40' E011° 20'. Today, a receiver can do the conversion directly, reducing the need for special Decca charts.

B *Decca and GPS receiver*
This apparatus combines Decca with the

Global Positioning System
1 Calculated position N57° 40.00' E011° 20.00'. Alternatively, lane values can be shown
2 Selection of functions
3 Receiver selection, with latitude and longitude calculated from the Decca receiver (NP) or from the GPS receiver (GPS), or with the position's lane values shown (LIP)
4 Option of programming different routes and their waypoints (WP)

C *Taking radio bearings*
Bearings are taken on the radio beacons along coasts with a direction finder. Most beacons transmit at frequencies of 285-315 kHz. Radio waves, picked up by a double loop antenna, induce an AC voltage in it, which is fed to the cross-laid coils in the receiver. These hold a small directional loop, which is thus induced with a voltage that depends on the loop's orientation

relative to the radio beacon. This voltage is converted to an audible tone. The weakest signal strength is used to determine the beacon's direction.

D *Direction finder*
The need for bearings on radio beacons to fix one's position has been decreased by the development of better navigation systems. Still, international marine safety rules (IMO) require that all ships

larger than 1,600 tons carry a direction finder, because it can be used to locate ships in distress.
1 Set frequency. The international emergency frequency is 2,182 kHz
2 Signal strength meter
3 Reading of direction to radio beacon
4 Manual control to turn the directional loop
5 Loudspeaker
6 Frequency selector
7 Frequency range setter

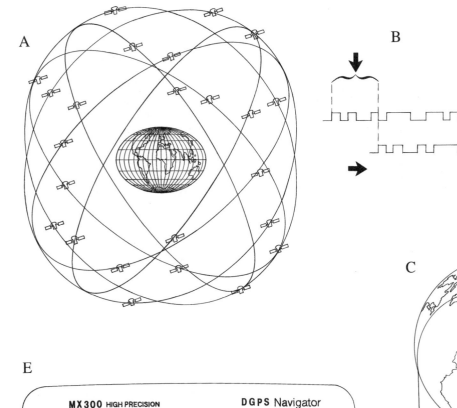

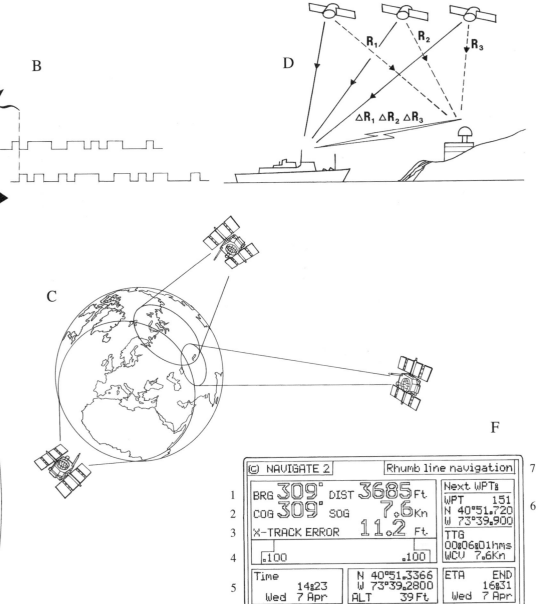

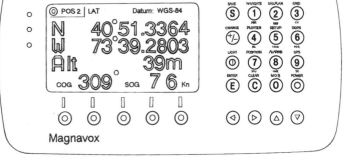

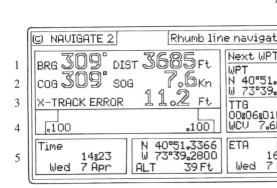

NAVIGATION BY GLOBAL POSITIONING

A *The GPS system*
This navigation system, developed by the USA for defense, uses 24 satellites (and several reserve ones), which circle the earth every 12 hours in six orbits at altitude 20,200 km. Position is found by calculating distances to the satellites. This is done by measuring the travel times of radio signals from them. These signals contain very exact data on time and on the satellite orbits. A similar satellite navigation system, GLONAS, has been developed in Russia. Now being planned is a common international system, the Global Navigation Satellite System (GNSS).

B *Determining distances*
The satellite signals are coded, and the GPS receiver generates a similar code. It can thus compare the codes to measure the time delay in arrival of a satellite's signals. This delay allows it to calculate how far away the satellite is.

C *Determining position*
With signals from at least four satellites, the receiver can find its position at an exact time. The data on position include latitude, longitude and altitude. Since a ship is known to be at sea level, i.e. zero altitude, its receiver need only have contact with three satellites.

D *The DGPS system*
Each satellite sends out both a generally accessible signal, the C/A code (Clear Access or Coarse Acquisition), and a signal that only an authorized receiver can use, the P code (Precise), which is also encrypted and termed the Y code. In the C/A code, a disturbance has been added (SA = Selective Availability), which worsens the position accuracy to ca. 50-100 metres. In order to improve the accuracy, different national and international systems are designed to send correction messages. A "reference station" with a GPS receiver and transmitter is set up, and its exactly known position is com-pared to the position found by the GPS receiver. The difference is sent to other receivers in the same area, as a correction to their calculated satellite distances. Positions can thus be determined within ca. 2-10 metres, and within centimetres if more advanced input methods are used. Such a system with special correction signals is called "Differential GPS" (DGPS). In the future, corrections will be sent out via special communications satellites to reach receivers all over the world, a system termed Wide Area Augmentation System (WAAS).

E *GPS receiver for ships and automobiles*
The display shows the ship's position, course and speed over ground. The buttons at right allow one to select different functions and to create waypoints (WP) and travel routes. Date: WGS 84 = reference system.

F *Route navigation with GPS receiver*
1 Bearing and distance to next WP
2 Course and speed over ground
3 Navigation error on the beam, relative to the programmed route
4 A ship symbol (not drawn) shows, at chosen scale, the ship's position relative to the programmed route
5 Time, position, and calculated arrival time at destination
6 Data on next WP, number 151 (TTG = Time to Go)
7 Calculations for rhumb-line navigation

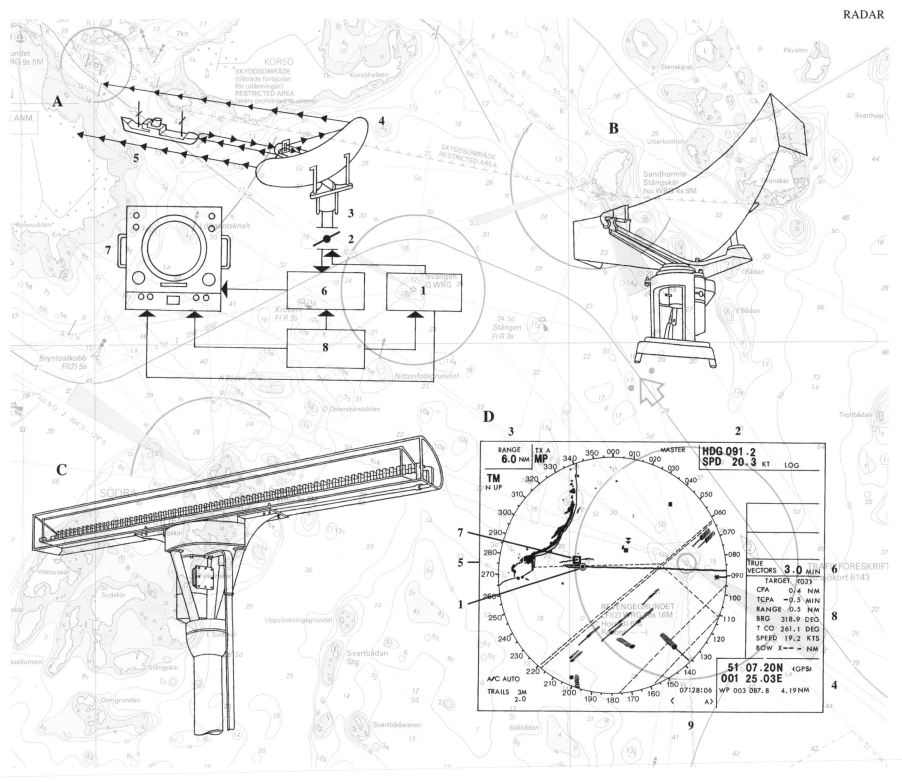

The illustrated sea chart shows the approach to Stockholm via the skerry route from Sandhamn

A *Principles of radar
High-frequency radio pulses are sent out by the transmitter (1) via a shunter (2) and wave guide (3) to the rotating antenna (4). The pulses form a thin directional lobe. If they hit ships (5), land or other objects, some of their energy is reflected back to the antenna and, via*

the shunter, reaches the receiver (6). This echo pulse is fed to the PPI (7) which presents it as a point of light. The process is regulated by the control unit (8). To see the PPI images in daylight, screening is needed. However, the presentation has been improved by video technology, replacing the old PPI with the Day Light Indicator (DLI), which can show either a daylight or a night image.

B *Parabolic radar antenna with radiation horn*

C *Slot radar antenna*

D *Radar indicator
This instrument shows the radar lobe as a "sweep" line, rotating in synchronization with the antenna. When the radar lobe hits an object, the echo pulse is shown as a bright point, strengthened every time the sweep passes it. The picture that results is formed*

partly by the object's own reflections, and partly by the echoes' movements (called a "relative" picture). Most radar equipment can now present a true picture of the course and speed of a ship's echoes. Radar having such a capability of calculation is termed ARPA radar, Automatic Radar Plotting Aid.

1 Own ship
2 Own course (as shown here, 091.2°, speed 20.3 knots)

3 Distance scale, 6 nautical miles from the center
4 Ship's position (from GPS receiver). The planned travel route is programmed in, and the distance is given to the next waypoint (WP 003)
5 Land echoes
6 For the ship echoes, a vector length has been chosen which shows the echoes' position in three minutes' time
7 Marker symbol (square) laid over one of the ship echoes. Data on

this echo can be read under "TARGET"
8 Target information: CPA = Closest Point of Approach, TCPA = Time to CPA, and Distance = -0.5 nautical miles (the ship has already passed) on a bearing of 318.9 degrees
9 Time

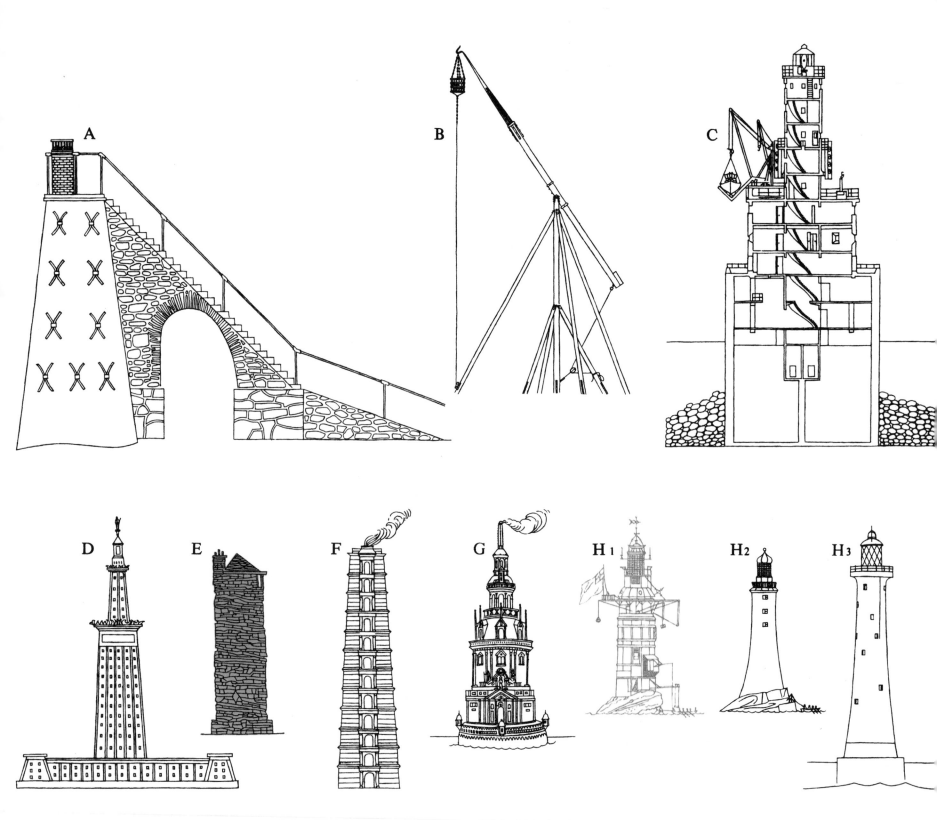

LIGHTHOUSES

A Open coal fire at Djur-
sten, Sweden, 1765

B Fire on tilting spar,
1635

C Modern caisson light-
house, built of concrete
on shore, launched, and
towed to its station and
there sunk

D Pharos at Alexandria,
300 B.C.

E Torre de Herculum at
Coruna, at the time of
Christ

F Tour d'Ordre at Bou-
logne, A.D. 40

G Cordouan at the mouth
of Girande estuary in
France, 1610

H Eddystone light in the
Channel
1 1698 (at low water)
2 1759 (at low water)
3 1882 (at high water)

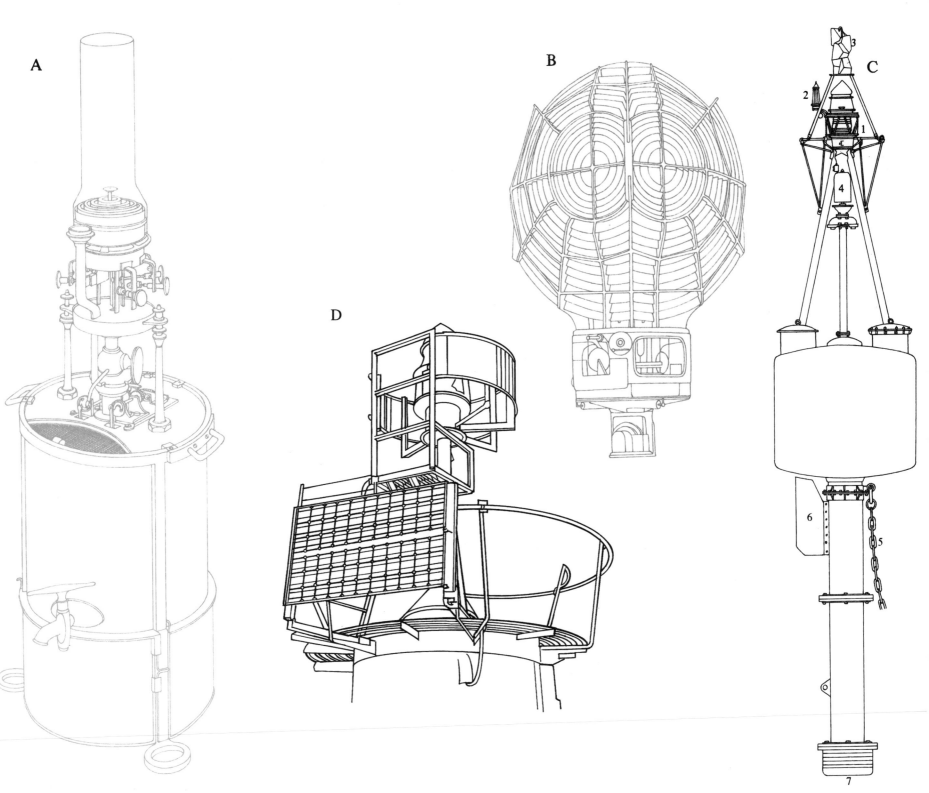

LIGHTHOUSE LAMPS

A   Lighthouse lamp for
    paraffin oil with four
    wicks, 1880s

B   Lens arrangement for
    large coastal light.
    The lens may be up to
    2 metres wide, with
    light strength 500,000
    candelas

C   Light buoy
1   Lamp burning acetylene
    gas
2   Sun valve, which puts
    out the light in daytime
    and thus reduces the gas
    consumption by 50%
3   Radar reflector
4   Whistle
5   Mooring chain
6   Anti-rotating fin
7   Ballast to keep the buoy
    vertical

D   Solar-powered light
    Ever more and bigger
    lights are now being
    powered with solar
    panels. The panel re-
    charges batteries so
    that the system is self-
    supplying

COASTAL LIGHTHOUSES

Indicated here are some of the world's largest coastal lighthouses. Their ranges of visibility are given in parentheses. More than *1,000 have visibility over 20 nautical miles. Such lights are used for determining position when approaching coasts. Many are pro-* *vided with mist-signal senders that can be heard in fog. Some also have a radar beacon, or "Racon", which activates when hit by the* *ship's radar emission. Then the beacon is identified on a radar screen by a Morse sign issuing from its place in the picture.*

1 Makapuu Point, Oahu (27)
2 Molokai (28)
3 Cape Hinchinbrook (22)
4 Cape St. James, Queen Charlotte Islands (24)
5 Main Channel (22)
6 Cape Blanco (22)
7 Cape Mendocino (28)
8 Farallon, San Francisco (26)
9 Point Sur (23)
10 Anacapa Island (23)
11 West Benito Island (28)
12 Natividad Island (26)
13 Cape Tosco (23)
14 Guaymas, Cape Haro (24)
15 Cerro Partido (24)
16 Mazatlán (30)
17 Punta de Campos (26)
18 Acapulco, Grifo Island (26)
19 Golfito (24)

20 Santa Elena Point (25)
21 Callao (25)
22 Atico Point (21)
23 Curaumilla Point (24)
24 Guafo Island (28)
25 New Year's Islands, Staten Island (20)
26 Cape Virgins (21)
27 Leones Isle (23)
28 Montevideo (29)
29 Arvoredo Islet (24)
30 Castelhanos Point (27)
31 Cape Frio (28)
32 Cape Agostinho (24)
33 Olinda Point (24)
34 Mel Point (24)
35 Chacachacare Islet, Trinidad (30)
36 El Roque (23)
37 Cartagena (26)
38 Manzanillo Point (24)
39 Bocas del Toro (23)
40 Port Cortez (23)

41 Roca Partida (23)
42 Cape Moul à Chique, St. Lucia (35)
43 La Trinité Bay, Martinique (27)
44 Hams Bluff, St. Croix (27)
45 Cape Borinquén (24)
46 Guantánamo (26)
47 Pensacola (20)
48 St. Augustine (20)
49 Gibb's Hill, Bermuda (26)
50 Cape Hatteras (20)
51 Cape Charles (20)
52 Chapel Hill Beacon (21)
53 Staten Island (21)
54 Cape Cod (20)
55 Seguin Island (20)
56 Cape Gaspé (26)
57 Cape Pine (40)
58 Belle Isle (28)
59 Dyrholaey (27)
60 Myggenaes (22)

61 Sumburgh Head, Shetland Islands (24)
62 Dunnet Head (24)
63 Whitby (22)
64 South Foreland (26)
65 Lizard (21)
66 Great Ormes Head (24)
67 St. Bees (25)
68 Mull of Galloway (25)
69 Barra Head (33)
70 Flannan Islands, Hebrides (24)
71 Cape Wrath (27)
72 Clare Islands (25)
73 Bull Rock (23)
74 Mine Head (23)
75 Cape Stolbiovo (20)
76 Kharlov Island (27)
77 Vardöy (22)
78 Udsire (22)
79 Kullen (24)
80 Hogland (26)
81 Dager Ort, Kopu (25)
82 Dornbusch (24)

83 Stevns Klint (21)
84 Hirtshals (20)
85 Helgoland (24)
86 Hook of Schouwen (41)
87 Cape Gris-Nez (21)
88 Cape La Heve (27)
89 Ouessant (20)
90 Biarritz (22)
91 Hercules Tower, Coruña (25)
92 Cape Finisterre (29)
93 Cape Roca (30)
94 Cape St. Vincent (22)
95 Mesa de Roldán (31)

96 Cape Nao (27)
97 Cape Formentor, Mallorca (30)
98 Cape San Sebastián (31)
99 Cape Camarat (28)
100 Punta del Faro (27)
101 Cape Pertusato (25)
102 Cape Sandalo (28)
103 Imperatore Point, Ischia (31)
104 Milazzo (24)
105 Cape Santa Maria di Leuca (25)
106 Sapientza (25)

107 Parapola (26)	119 Cape Anaga, Tenerife (30)	128 Basaruto Island (26)	141 Table Island (20)	155 Nugget Point (22)	169 Pulo Pisang (30)
108 Cape Armenisti (32)	120 Isleta Point, Grand Canary (30)	129 Shangani River (24)	142 Breueh (30)	156 Tasman Island (36)	170 Cape Rachado (27)
109 Cape Meganom (25)	121 Cape Verde (26)	130 Katsepe Head (27)	143 Batu Mandi (30)	157 Cape Naturaliste (29)	171 Koh Pai (30)
110 Mount Carmel (30)	122 Fontes Pereira de Melo, Cape Verde Islands (27)	131 Taperina Point (24)	144 Chilachap (30)	158 Cape Borda (30)	172 Cape Padaran (30)
111 Cape Carthage (29)		132 Flat Island, Mauritius (25)	145 Kelapa Islet (30)	159 Deal Island (40)	173 False Tinhosa (30)
112 Cape de Garde (30)		133 Cape Guardafui (Ras Asir) (35)	146 Wangi Wangi (29)	160 Cape Byron (26)	174 Agincourt Island, Hoka sho (30)
113 Cape Carbon (29)	123 Ponta Quicombo (28)	134 Ras-al-Bir (22)	147 Ambon Island (24)	161 Sandy Cape (27)	
114 Ceuta (29)	124 Ilha das Cabras, Sao Thome (25)	135 Jebel Teir (30)	148 Batanta (22)	162 Fitzroy Island (29)	175 Gyoku San (41)
115 Cape Spartel (24)	125 Cape of Good Hope (23)	136 Jaziat Halul (21)	149 Port Moresby (24)	163 Cape Bolinao (24)	176 Shashi To (24)
116 Ribeirinha Point, Fayal (28)		137 Drigh Road (23)	150 Guadalcanal Island (20)	164 Suluan Island (28)	177 Toi Misaki (38)
117 Ferraria Point, San Miguel (25)	126 Copper (28)	138 Aguada, Goa (23)	151 Port Noumea (22)	165 Sandakan (33)	178 Okino-Shima (32)
118 Pargo Point, Madeira (35)	127 Barra Falsa (27)	139 Kadalur Point (20)	152 Cape Reinga (31)	166 Great Sambas River (53)	179 Ko Shima (75)
		140 Madras (20)	153 East Cape (30)	167 Serutu Island (30)	180 Awo Shima (39)
			154 Cape Palliser (23)	168 Anamba Islands (33)	181 Motsuta Misaki (40)
					182 Cape Lazareva (38)

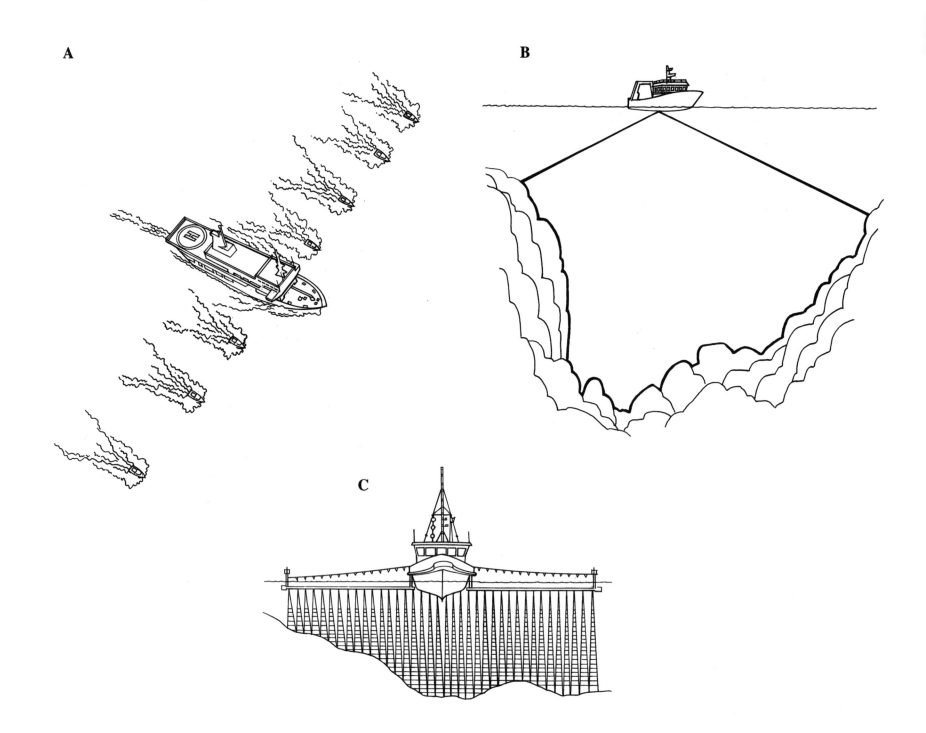

A

B

C

SURVEYING METHODS

A *Parallel sounding
Hydrographic survey
work has long since
replaced the old
hand-plumb with echo
sounders of various
types. To increase the
search width, a method
of parallel sounding
has been developed in
Sweden, using a larger
ship for measurements*
*and up to 8 smaller
boats with echo soun-
ders. The ship continu-
ally registers positions
of all vessels and the
depths detected by the
boats.*

B *Multibeam surveying
Surveying is also done
with a multibeam echo
sounder. This emits*
*sound pulses in about
30 narrow lobes (ca. 2
x 4°) covering a sector
of around 60° on each
side. The strake width
is then ca. 3.5-7 times
the depth. Such a sur-
vey is faster than the
usual method and its
depth information is
more dense.*

C *Framing
In harbors and along
important sections of
fairway, where more
exact depth data are
needed, a measurement
frame is used. About 30
metres long, it may
have several echo
sounders, as in the
illustration (Atlas
Bomasweep), or the*
*depth may be measured
only mechanically by
sinking the frame
column ever deeper.
The mechanical frame
is divided into 6 sec-
tions, each of 5 metres.
Impact of any section
on the bottom is regis-
tered. Depth can be
measured down to
25-30 metres. Both*
*kinds of frame also
carry underwater TV
cameras for optical
inspection of the bot-
tom. The echo frame's
depth data are shown in
the small picture.*

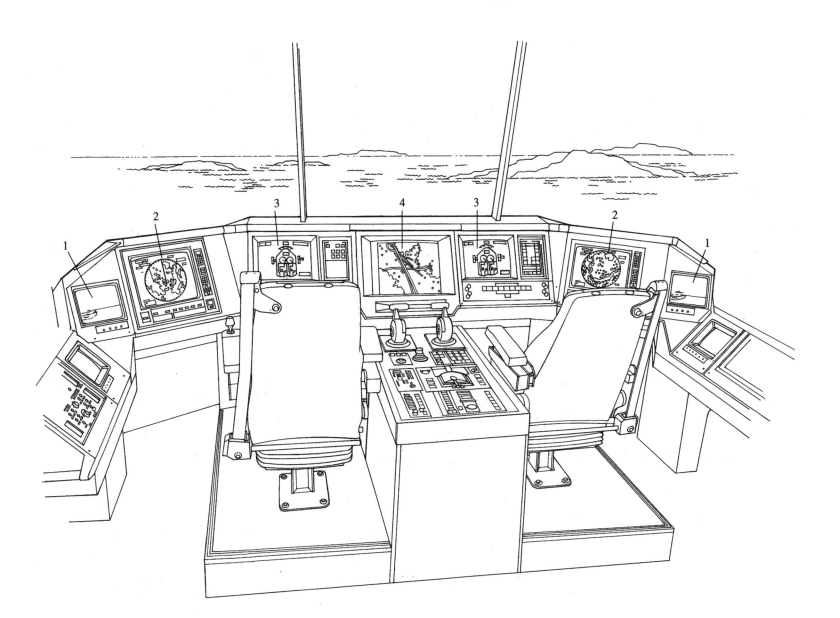

INTEGRATED COMMAND BRIDGE

Computerization has made it possible to combine several systems as an integrated bridge, to control both the ship's navigation and steering as well as its technical systems for propulsion etc. Such bridges have been built mainly for "high-speed vessels". Two navigators operate the bridge illustrated here.

1 Video picture of the nearby surroundings, supplied by either day or night sighting in the mast
2 Radar picture, from either short- or long-range reconnaissance (respectively called X and S radar, with wavelength 3 and 10 cm). Planned travel routes can be fed from a navi-gation computer to the radar picture
3 Control display for the ship's principal instruments. It shows pictures of data from different sensors and systems, such as: Navigation (course, speed, engine speed, rudder angle, depth, position, current, wind, air pressure); Engine equipment (the working temperatures, oil pressure, options of operation, electric connections etc.); Fire system; Door-closing system; Ship drawings
4 Digital sea chart for ECDIS, Electronic Chart Digital Information System. Here the navigator can retrieve the desired chart at the suitable scale. The chart is composed of different layers so that he can remove information of no interest, such as depth curves over 100 metres. Ship echoes can be retrieved from the radar and placed in the chart picture
5 Engine and propeller controls

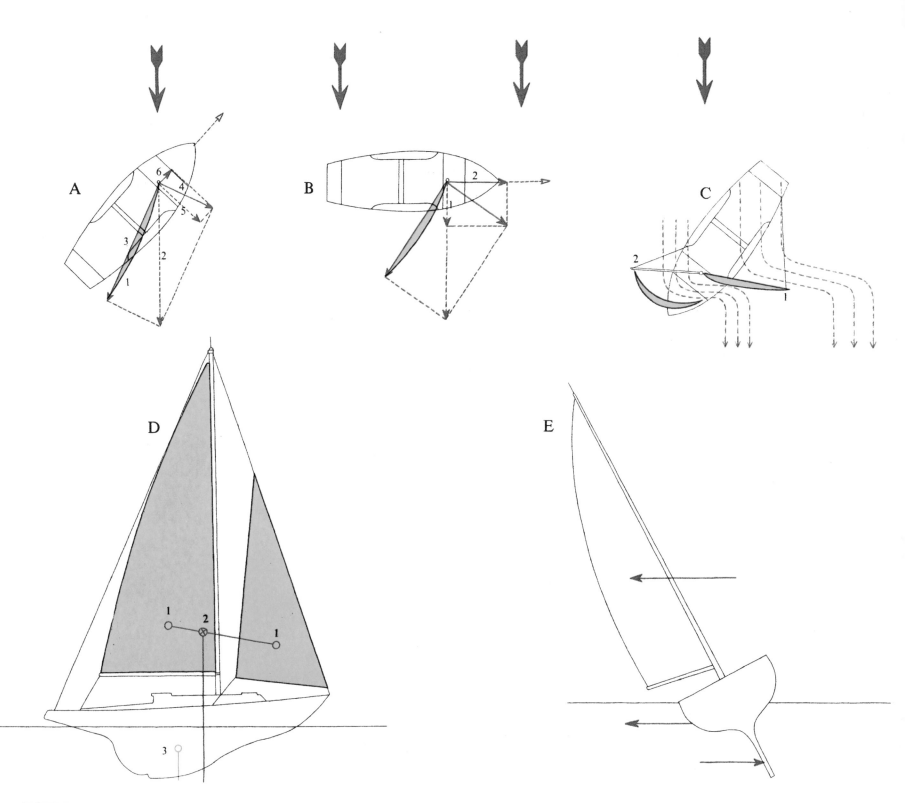

A *A boat beating to windward*
1 Sail
2 The force and direction of the wind, which can be resolved into the two components, 3 and 4
3 This force blowing parallel to the sail may be disregarded
4 This force can be resolved into two components, 5 and 6

5 This force works abeam and tends to heel the boat and to drive it to leeward. This tendency, however, is largely overcome by the lateral resistance of the water on the boat's hull and keel.
6 Of the original wind force, it is this component only that carries the boat ahead

B *Reaching; the wind abeam*
1 When the wind is abeam the lateral component (1) is reduced and the fore and aft component (2) is increased. The boat moves faster than when beating to windward (A).

C *Running*
When running, the sails must not be at right angles to the direction of the wind
1 Mainsail
2 Spinnaker
D *Center of effort*
Every sail has a center of effort (1). The center of effort of the total sail area (2) is obtained by combining the centers of each sail. Theoretically, if the center

of effort is ahead of the center of lateral resistance (3), the boat will tend to pay off from the wind. If 2 is abaft 3, the boat will tend to come up into the wind.
In reality, the boat, when sailing, is heeling to leeward and the force of the wind will be applied at the center of effort on the lee side of the boat and cause her

to luff. To counteract this, the center of effort of the sails is always placed forward of the center of lateral resistance, as shown above.
E *A fact which is not familiar to everyone is that a drop keel under special circumstances may have a dangerous capsizing effect, for instance, if the boat when running suddenly broaches to.*

A

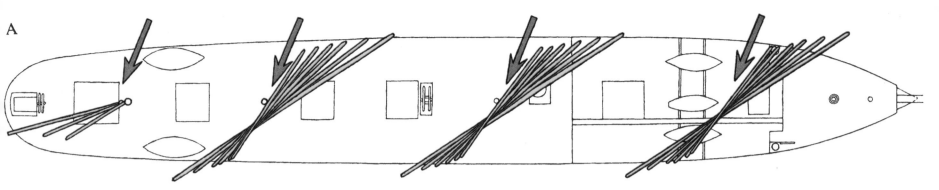

B

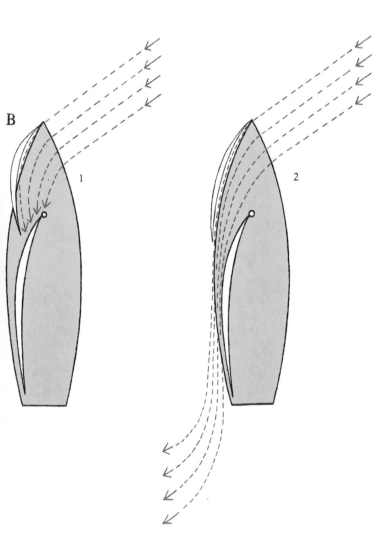

1

2

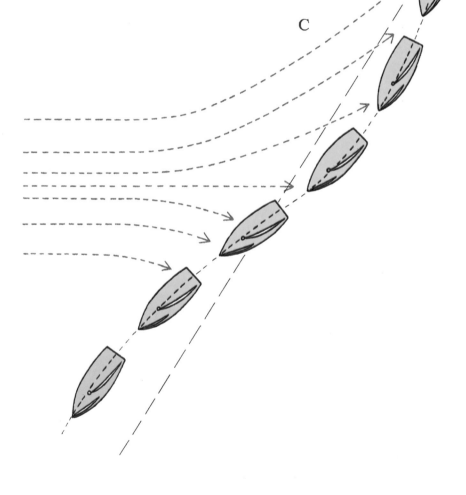

C

THE SET OF SAILS

A   A square-rigged vessel
    beating to windward.
    In a square-rigger
    sailing on the wind, the
    lower yards are always
    braced up more than
    the upper yards. The
    reason for this is that
    the lower sails cannot
    be set as flat as the

upper sails, and thus
require a broader wind
to fill them than the
small sails. Again,
should the wind shift
and the ship be caught
aback, the upper sails
will back first and warn
the ship in time, so that
she can be paid off.

B   The lead of the fore
    staysail sheet
1   There must be suffici-
    ent gap between the
    fore staysail and the
    mainsail; otherwise (as
    in the figure) the driving
    force of the mainsail
    will be reduced.

2   A fore staysail which is
    correctly sheeted incre-
    ases the suction on the
    lee side of the mainsail,
    and thus increases its
    power.

C   Unsteady wind.
    A squall generally
    blows in a fan-shaped
    pattern. In spite of pay-
    ing-off at the beginning
    and then luffing, the
    squall may be used to
    bring the boat to wind-
    ward of her first track.

245

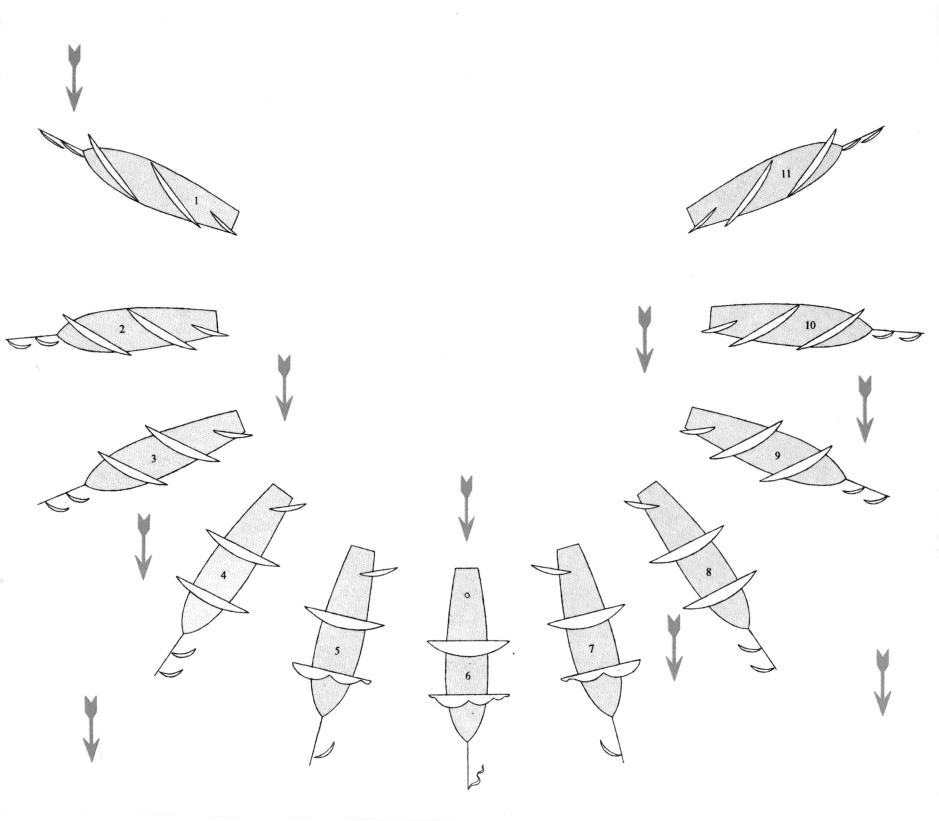

A BARK SAILING ON DIFFERENT COURSES

1 Bark sailing on the wind on the starboard tack
2 Sailing, reaching with wind abeam on the starboard side
3 Going large with the wind abaft the beam on the starboard side
4 Running free with the wind on the starboard quarter
5 Running before the wind; the wind is on the starboard side; headsails are partly blanketed, some staysails are furled
6 Running dead before the wind, scudding in a gale; spanker is furled, staysails not drawing, the headsails are blanketed
7 Running before the wind; wind is on the port side. Headsails are partly blanketed, some staysails are furled
8 Running free with the wind on the port quarter
9 Going large, sailing with a fair wind, with the wind abaft the beam on the port side
10 Sailing, reaching with the wind abeam on the port side
11 Sailing on the wind on the port tack

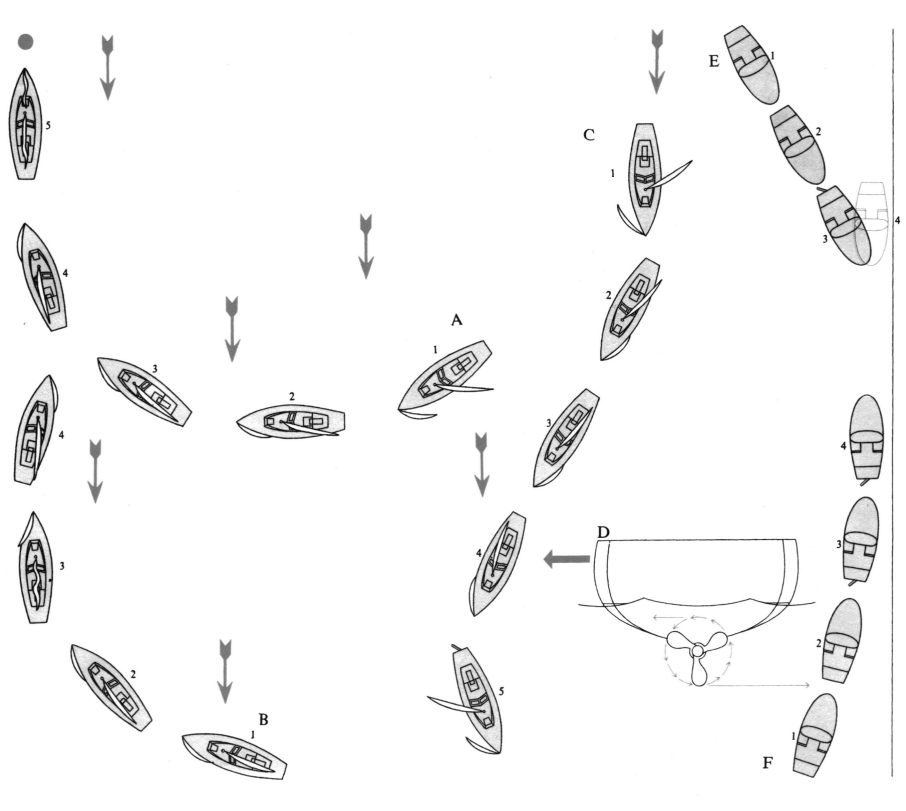

SMALL BOAT HANDLING

A *To fetch a buoy*
1 Sails set to the wind
2 Luff and trim sails to the wind
3 Luff and flatten in the sails
4 Luff as much as possible and spill the wind from the foresail and mainsail
5 Steer close to windward of the buoy and carefully judge the speed of approach

B *Going about*
1 Keep her full and by
2 "Helm's alee"
3 Flatten the foresail (applicable to dull-turning boats only)
4 Haul the foresail over and trim sheets by the wind on the new tack

C *Jibing*
1 Boat steering before the wind; you want to take the wind on the port quarter
2 Luff a little and shorten your sheets
3 By ready to jibe
4 Up helm; jibe easily and let the sheets run
5 Meet her and trim yaw sails

D *Yawing influence of right-hand propeller going astern;*
the blades of the screw have a better grip in the water at the deepest part of the rotation, and work the stern to port

E *Going alongside, port side to the quay*
1 Approach the quay at a broad angle
2 Stop
3 Full astern
4 Stop

F *Starboard side to the quay*
1 Small angle to pier; stop
2 Slow astern
3 Port helm
4 Stop

WEARING

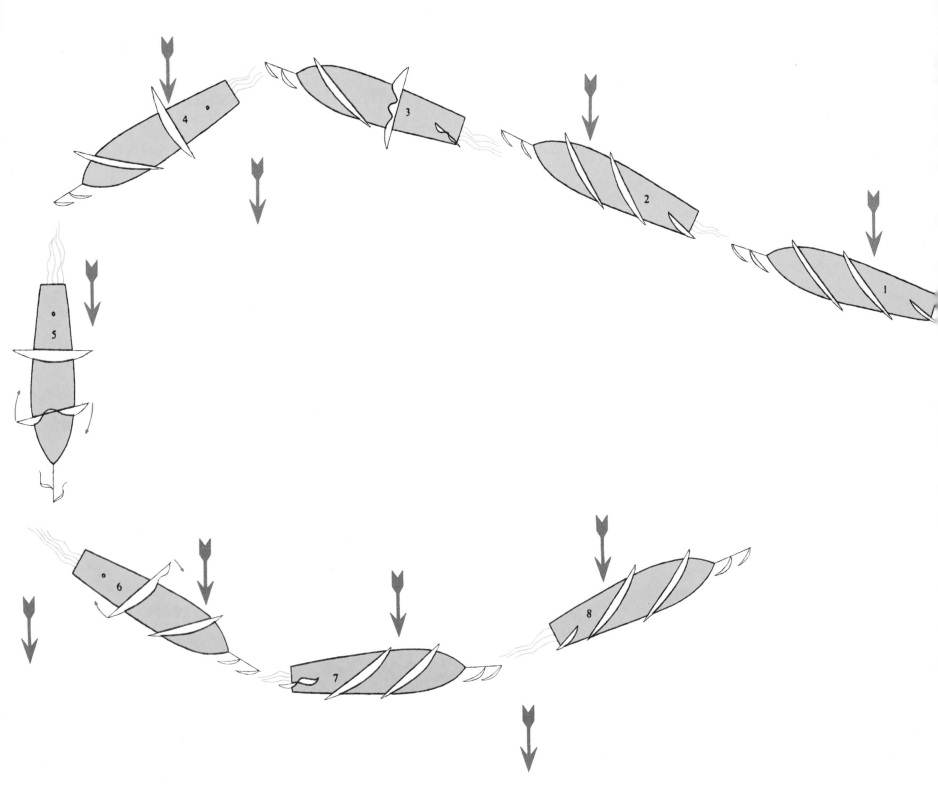

A SQUARE-RIGGED VESSEL, A THREE-MASTED BARK, WEARING

1 The bark is sailing on the wind on the starboard tack.

2 "Ready to wear ship!" The mainsail is clewed up and the braces are coiled down for running.

3 The spanker is furled. "Up helm!" "Square in the mainyard!" The wheel is put to port and the mainyard is squared.

4 Without sail aft the vessel is paying off.

5 The bark is before the wind. "Round forward!" The headsails are braced around and the jibs sheeted over to starboard.

6 When she is coming up on the new tack the headsails will meet her. The after yards are braced up.

7 The spanker is set and all sails are trimmed by the wind.

8 The bark is kept on the wind on the port tack. The main sail is set and the deck cleared up.

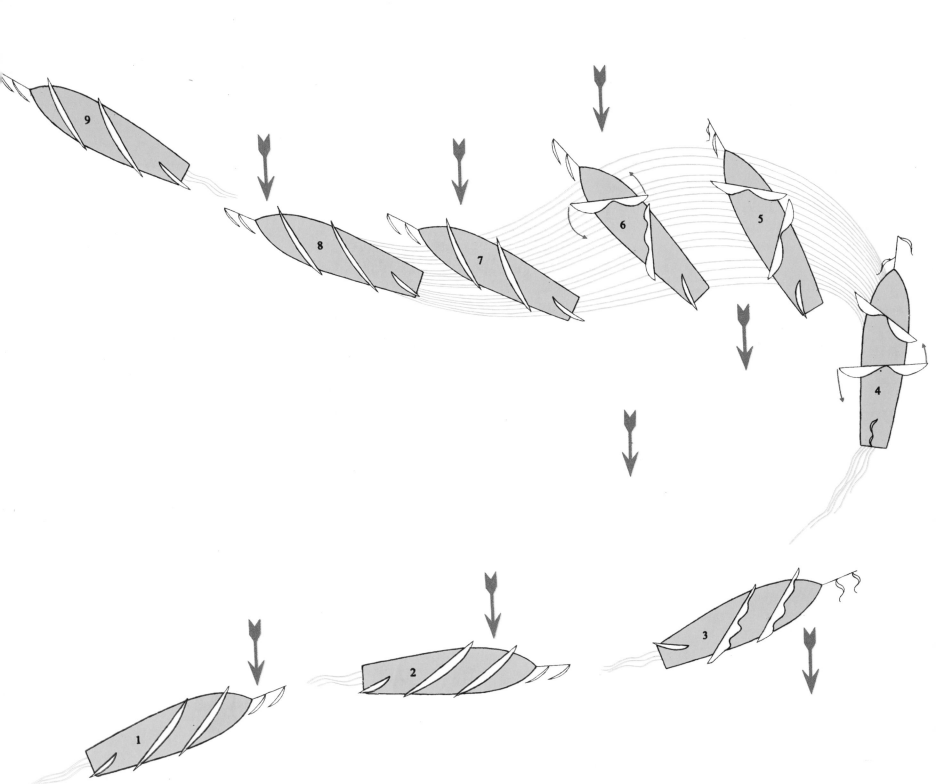

A SQUARE-RIGGED VESSEL, A THREE-MASTED BARK, TACKING

1 The bark is sailing on the wind on the port tack. "Ready about!"

2 She is kept off a little to make all sails draw better to increase the speed.

3 "Helm's alee!" The wheel is put down, the headsheets are let go to make the jibs spill the wind; the spanker is hauled aweather to assist the luffing.

4 The bark is nearly into the wind. Now "Mainsail haul!" The mainyards are braced around, the jibs are hauled over and sheeted home, while the vessel is head in the wind.

5 The movement ahead is decreasing. With the headsails aback the bark is forced over to port.

6 When the sails of the mainmast begin to fill, the order is, "Let go and haul!" and the headsails are hauled around.

7 The vessel is paying off until the sails are filling. All sails are trimmed by the wind.

8 The bark is going ahead, the wake is becoming normal.

9 She is kept on the wind on the starboard tack; the running gear is coiled down.

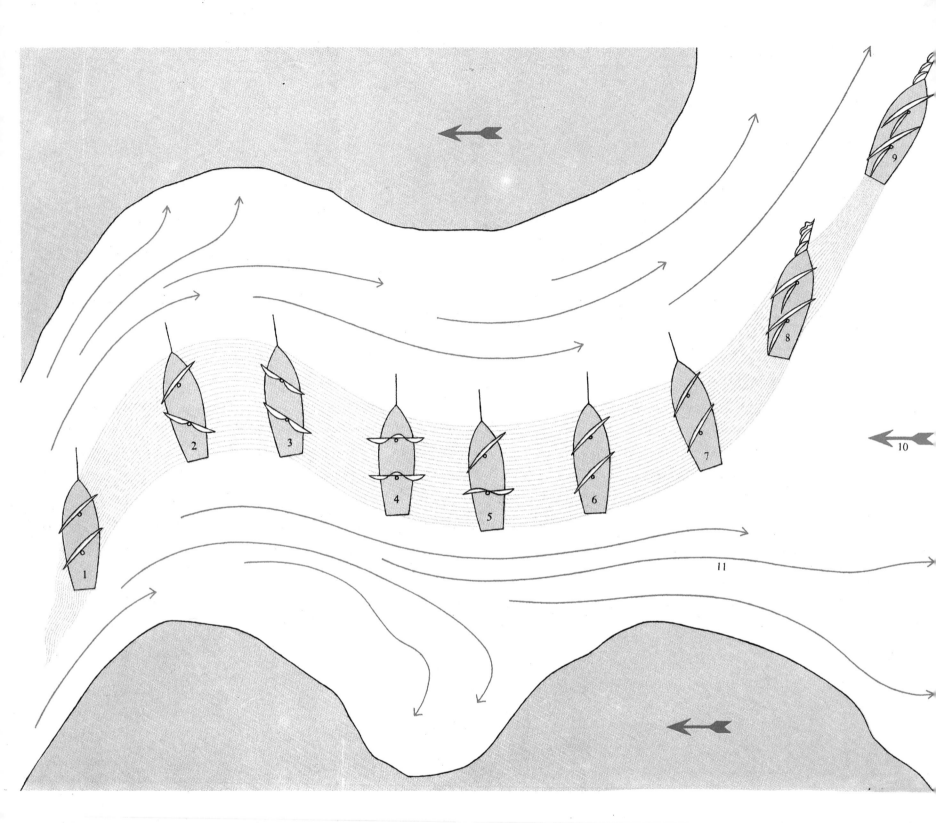

A SAILING VESSEL, A BRIG, BACKING AND FILLING DOWN A RIVER WITH THE EBB TIDE, AGAINST A HEADWIND. SHE HAS ONLY THE TOPSAILS SET.

1 The brig is filling both topsails to make her move ahead to keep her in the fairway

2 Backing the mainyard stops her progress and makes her drift broadside downriver

3 Backing all makes her take a stern board

4 By pointing the yards into the wind she is made to stand still and drift with the ebb tide

5 Filling the fore topsail makes her draw ahead

6 Filling all makes her go ahead more

7 She is kept off a little to increase her movement through the water

8 She is making sail, and trims them by the wind

9 She is clear of the river and stands to sea under all sail on the starboard tack

10 Wind direction

11 The ebb tide

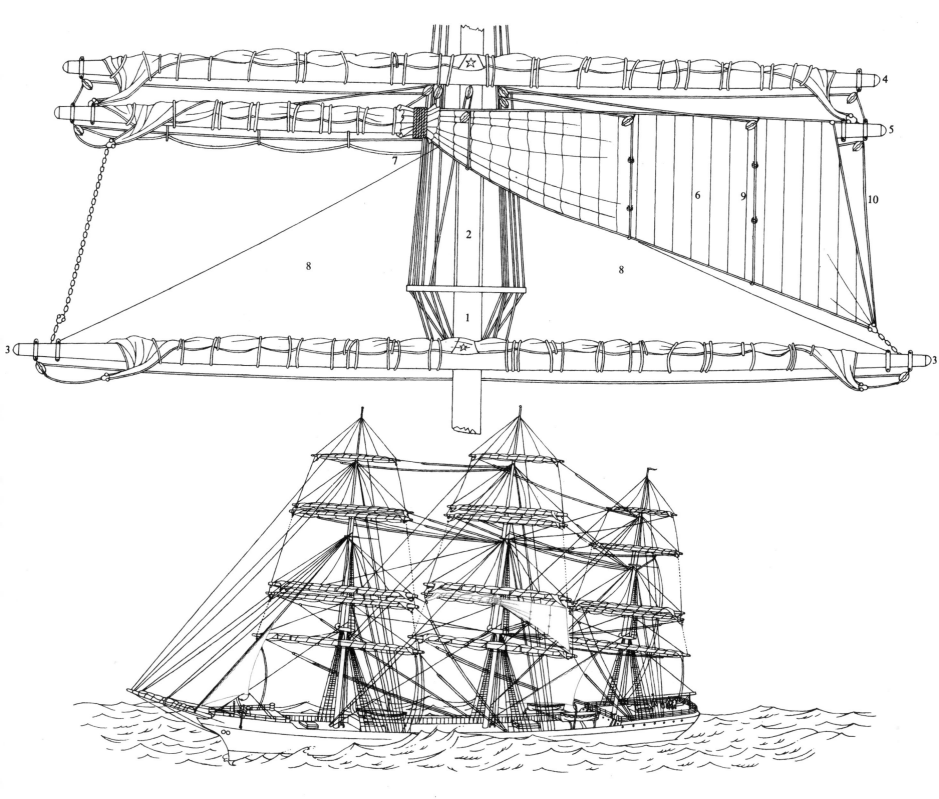

TO HEAVE TO AND TO GOOSE-WING A SAIL

When a sailing ship was in a contrary gale of wind the order to heave to meant that most of the sails were taken in and the helm was put down. This kept the ship's head to the wind, and, with the sea on the bow, she would ride well enough as long as some sail could be carried. This full-rigged ship has the fore topmast staysail, the mizzen staysail and the goose-winged main lower topsail set. To furl the weather half of a lower topsail was the last re-source to shorten sail without having to furl all and drift under bare poles. The large scale drawing shows a part of the main mast with the goose-winged lower topsail. The numbers indicate:

1 Main mast
2 Heel of topmast
3 Mainyard with main-sail furled
4 Upper topsail yard with topsail furled
5 Lower topsail yard
6 Goose-winged lower topsail
7 Heavy lashing on sail, parceled to protect sail from chafe
8 Size of lower topsail when set
9 Lower topsail bunt-lines
10 Lower topsail clew-lines

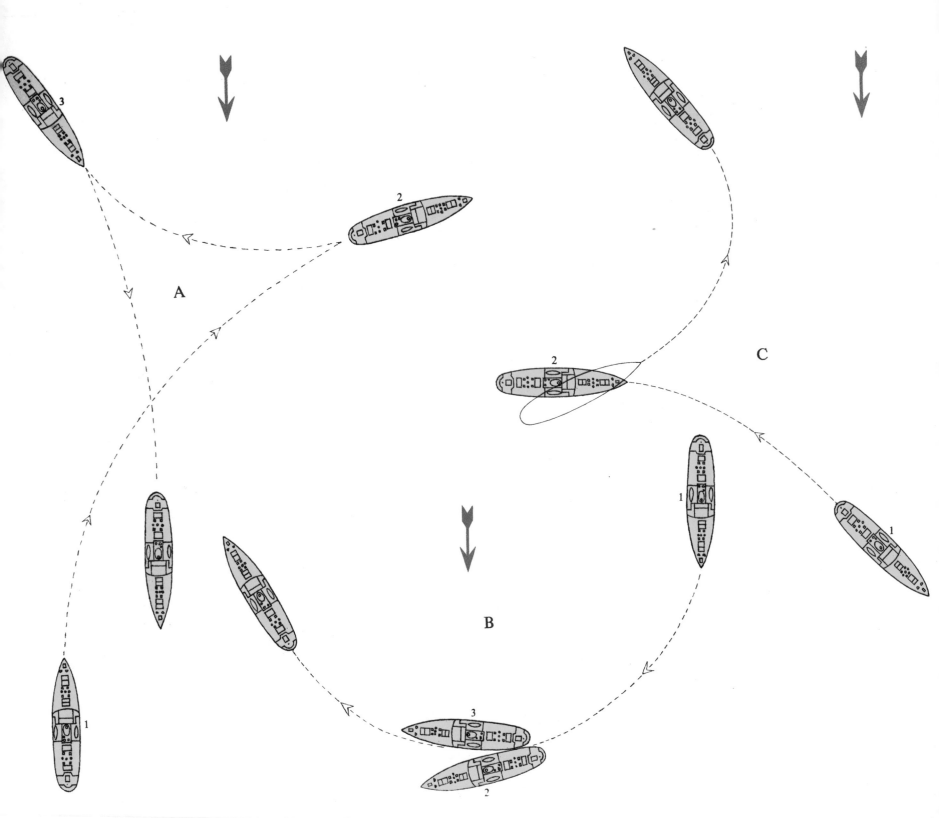

MANEUVERING A POWERED SHIP WITH A RIGHT-HANDED SINGLE SCREW

(Page 253)

A *Turning with the wind ahead*
1 Ahead with the rudder hard astarboard
2 Full astern with the rudder hard aport
3 Ahead with starboard rudder
4 Steady the helm on the new course

B *Turning with the wind astern*
1 Ahead with the rudder astarboard
2 Full astern with starboard rudder
3 Before getting stern-way: Full ahead with starboard rudder and the screw effect will help swing the ship
4 Steady on the new course

C *Turning with the wind on the quarter*
1 Astern with the rudder hard astarboard
2 Full ahead with port rudder; steady the helm on the new course

A *The effect of the rudder*
1 When turning, the power of the rudder may be dissolved into two components: one braking the ship and one forcing the stern aside

2 When the ship starts turning, a resistance arises on the bow which co-operates with the rudder
3 Only after several ship's lengths will the stern pass the original track

B *Heeling during a turn*
1 At first, the ship is heeled inward. This depends upon the fact that the rudder component and the lateral resistance work on different levels. Then, the centrifugal power applied at the center of gravity makes the ship list outward.

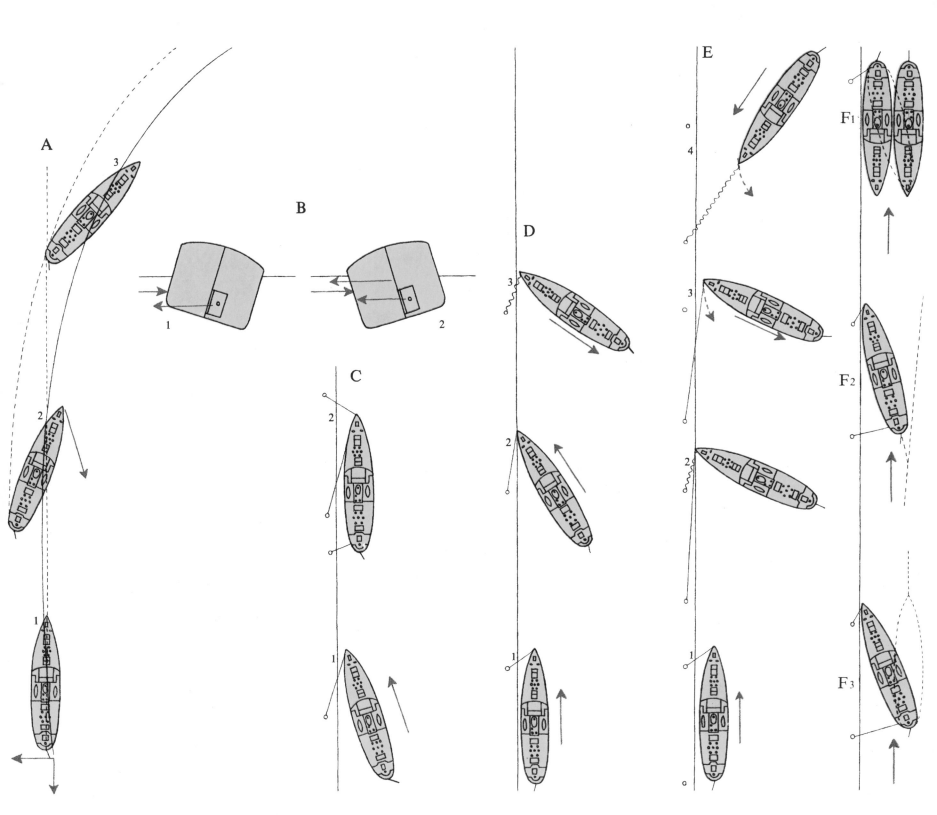

A

B

C

D

E

F₁

F₂

F₃

MANEUVERING A POWERED SHIP

C *Going alongside*
1 Put a spring ashore, slow ahead, starboard the rudder
2 When in position, tie her up, finish with engines

D *Leaving the quay*
1, 2 Keep a spring a-shore, go slow ahead, and port your rudder
3 Let go the spring, slow astern, rudder amidships

E *Leaving the quay turning*
1 Keep a spring ashore, go slow ahead, and port your rudder
2 Stop engine, rudder amidships, shift the spring, further astern
3 Heave away the spring, go slow astern, starboard rudder
4 Let go the spring, go slow ahead, port your rudder

F *Leaving the quay under different current circumstances*
1 The ship has the current from ahead and the starboard side to the quay. Hold on to the spring aft and ease off the forward breast rope. The vessel is held parallel with the quay by engine and rudder.

2 The ship has the port side to the quay and the tidal stream aft (right-handed screw), the forward spring is held on and she is eased off by the breast rope aft. When all clear, slow astern and let go the shore lines.

3 If the ship has the current aft port side to quay, and left-handed propeller (or starboard side to quay, right-handed propeller), the forward spring is held on, and the aft breast rope is eased off. Then the breast rope is held on while the engine is put slow astern, with the rudder to port (starboard).

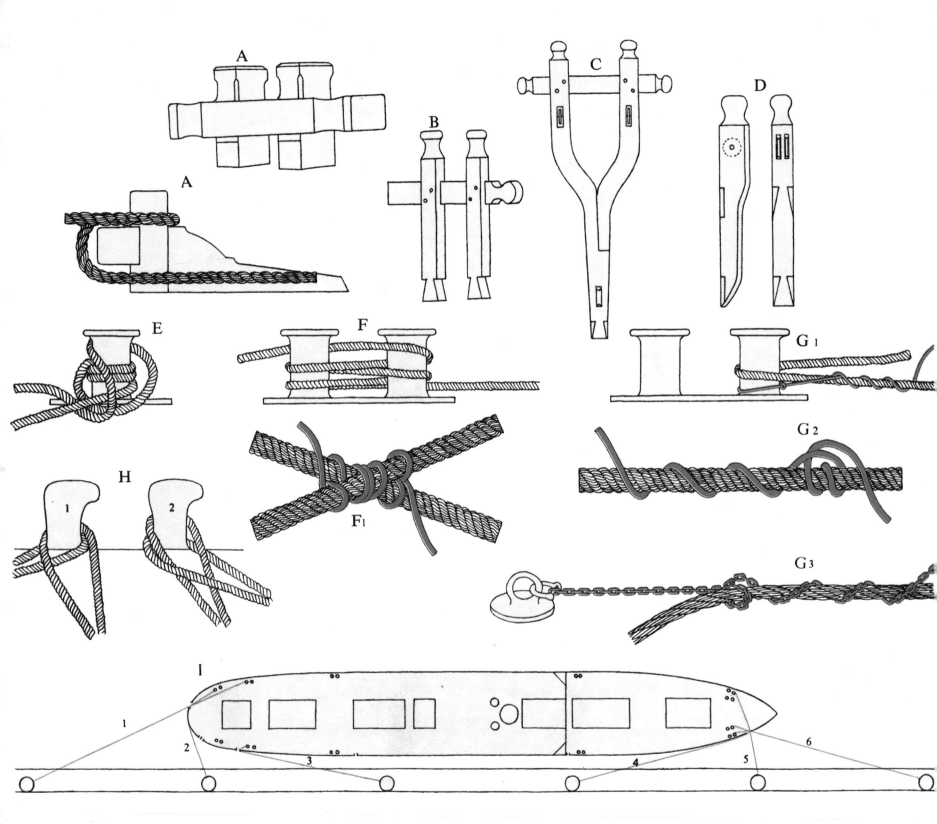

MOORING AND BELAYING

A *Bitts*

B *Knightheads*

C *Bitts on the forecastle head*

D *Knighthead*
A-D are from a book on ship building by Å.C. Rålamb (1691)

E *Belaying to a single bollard*

F *Belaying to twin bollards*
  1 Racked turns

G *Stoppering a rope*
Stoppers are used when hawsers are to be moved from the winch to the bollards, chain stoppers are used on wires

H *Two berthing hawsers on the same bollard on shore*
  1 Wrong way, the second hawser will block the first one
  2 Right way, either of the hawsers can be removed from the bollard independently of the other

I *Berthing hawsers*
  1 Stern rope
  2 After breast rope
  3 After back spring
  4 Fore back spring
  5 Fore breast rope
  6 Head rope

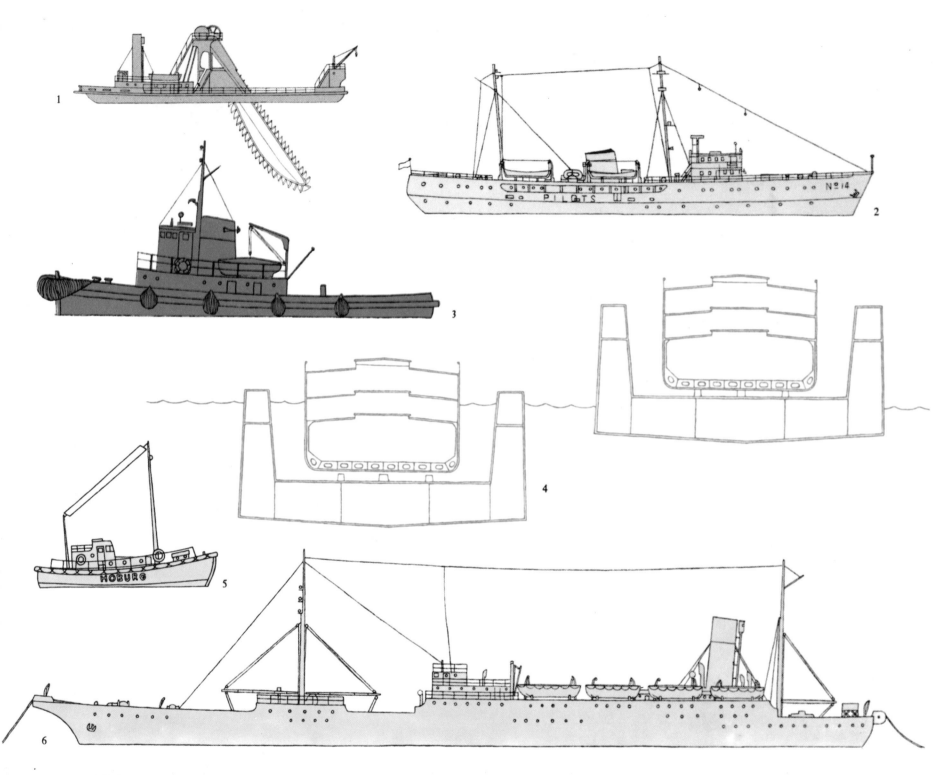

AUXILIARY VESSELS

1 Bucket dredger
2 Pilot vessel
3 Harbor tug
4 Floating drydock
5 Swedish cruising lifeboat
6 **Cable ship**

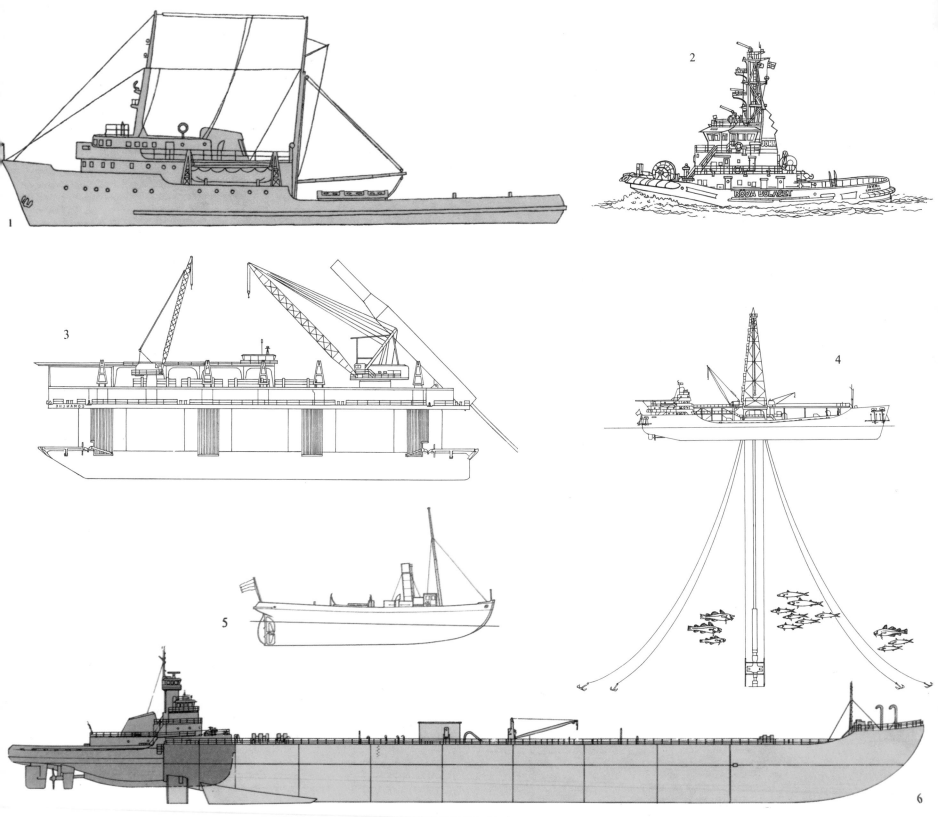

1   Ocean-going tug
2   Tugboat *John* from
    Röda Bolaget, built
    1990. L 32.89 m, B
    10.23 m, D 3.89 m,
    344 tons, 14.5 knots

3   Pipe-laying ship. The
    pipe lengths are welded
    together on the ramp,
    then fed over the stern
    as one conduit.
    Working depth max.
    500 m.

4   Oil-drilling vessel
    Grand Isle, with tower-
    mooring that allows it
    to hold position over a
    source in rough seas
    and strong currents

5   *Eisbrecher*, the first
    true ice-breaker, built in
    Hamburg 1871.
    L 40.5 m, B 9.75 m,
    570 tons. Its main
    power was a 600-hp
    steam engine, coupled
    directly to a propeller.

6   Tugboat *Exxon
    Sunshine State* and
    barge *Exxon Port
    Everglades* (31,000
    tons), specially built to
    be coupled together
    during transport. The
    tug's stem fits into the

barge's stern and locks
there. Such a design
enables the same power
unit (tug) to be used
with several barges.
Similar systems include
Catug, Seebeck,
Sealink and
Mitsui-TBS.

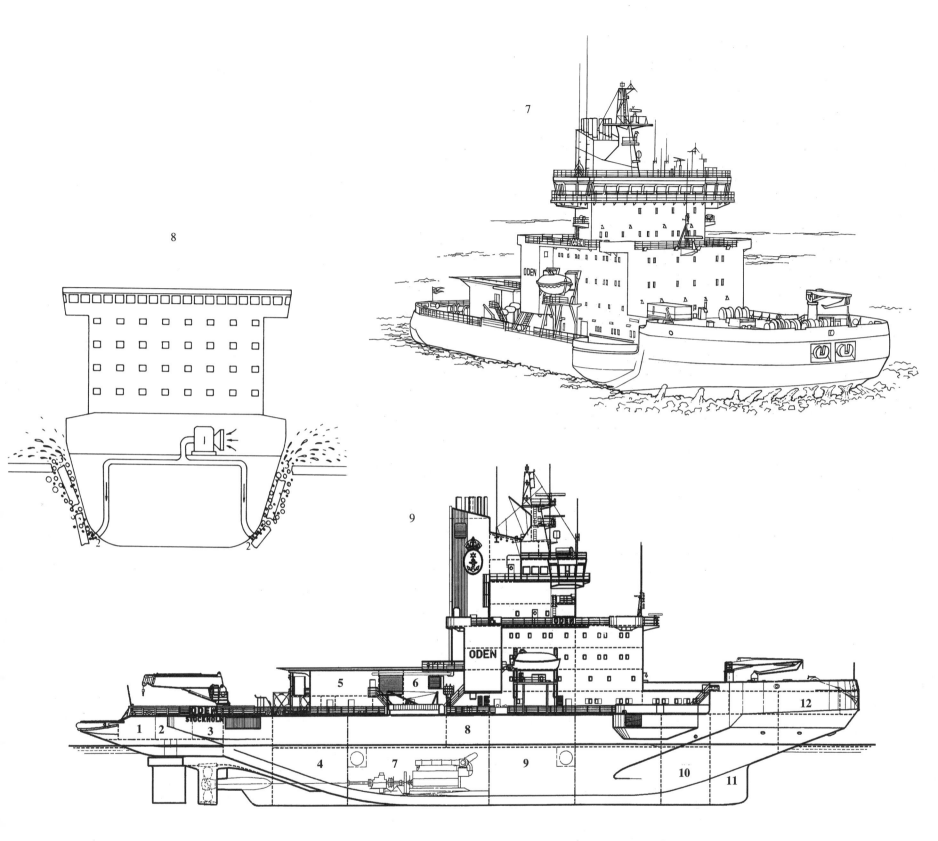

7

8

9

ODEN

STOCKHOLM

ODEN

5   6

1 2   3

8

12

4   7   9   10   11

7 Swedish ice-breaker
Oden, delivered 1988.
L 107.8 m, B 31.5 m,
D 8.0 m, dead weight
4,900 tons, 17 knots,
crew 25. Ice-breaking
capacity 1.8 m at 3
knots. Engine 24,500
hp. This is one of the
world's strongest ice-
breakers, and among

the first conventionally
powered ships to have
reached the North Pole.
8 Diagram of the
Wärtsilä air-bubbling
system for ice-breakers
and icegoing ships. The
system blows out high-
pressure air through a
row of holes in the ship's
sides. This effective

flushing reduces the
friction when under
way in snow-covered
ice and ice-barrages. It
also has the same effect
as a bow propeller, but
lacks protruding parts
and thus works well
even in polar regions.

1 *Air compressor*
2 *Nozzles*
3 *Air stream that lifts
water along the ship
sides and decreases
friction against ice*

9   The ice-breaker *Oden*
(cross-section)
1 *Stowage for reserve
towlines, center*
2 *Steering room*
3 *Dry tank side*
4 *Heavy-oil tanks,
center*
5 *Emergency generator
room*

6 *Auxiliary engine room*
7 *Main engine room*
8 *Feed-water tank*
9 *Pump room*
10 *Dry tank side, diesel
oil tank center*
11 *Dry tank*
12 *Fresh-water tanks*

SAILOR'S OUTFIT

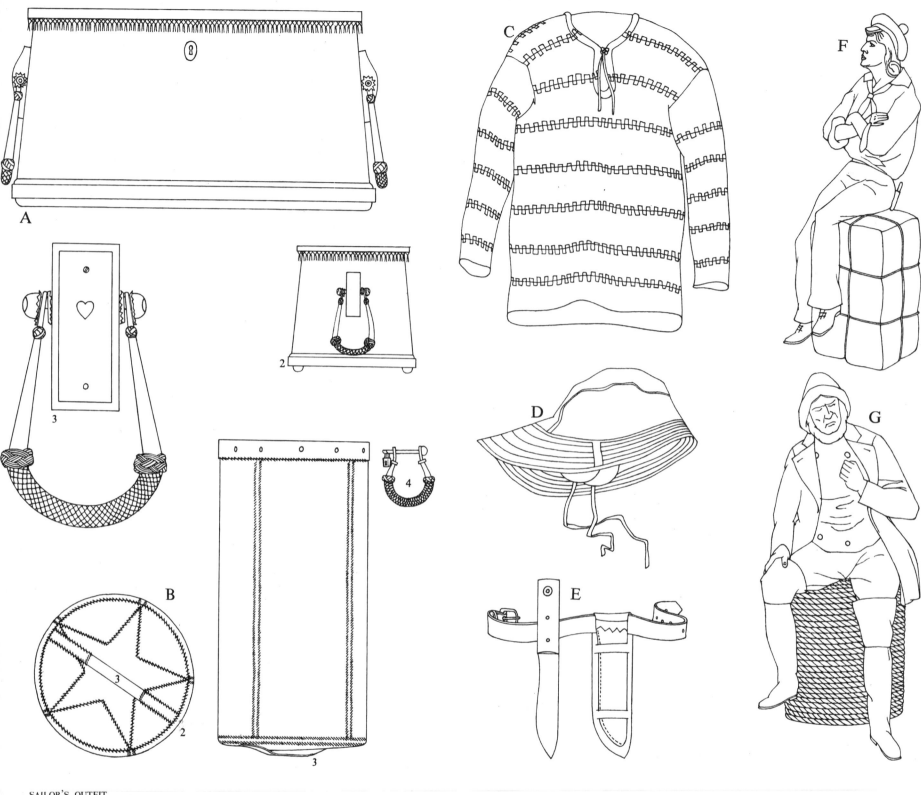

SAILOR'S OUTFIT

A *Seaman's chest with tassel work on its canvas-covered lid*
2 *End view of chest*
3 *Fancy handle*

B *Sailor's canvas bag (3 ft. high), made of five half cloths*
2 *The bottom of the bag with its canvas handle, 3*
4 *The shackle of the bag with bolt and lock*

C *Shetland wool jersey*
D *Sou'wester*

E *Sailor's sheath knife, carried in the middle of the back where it was available to both hands*

F *A young sailor from the 1860's*

G *An old sailor from the 1860's*

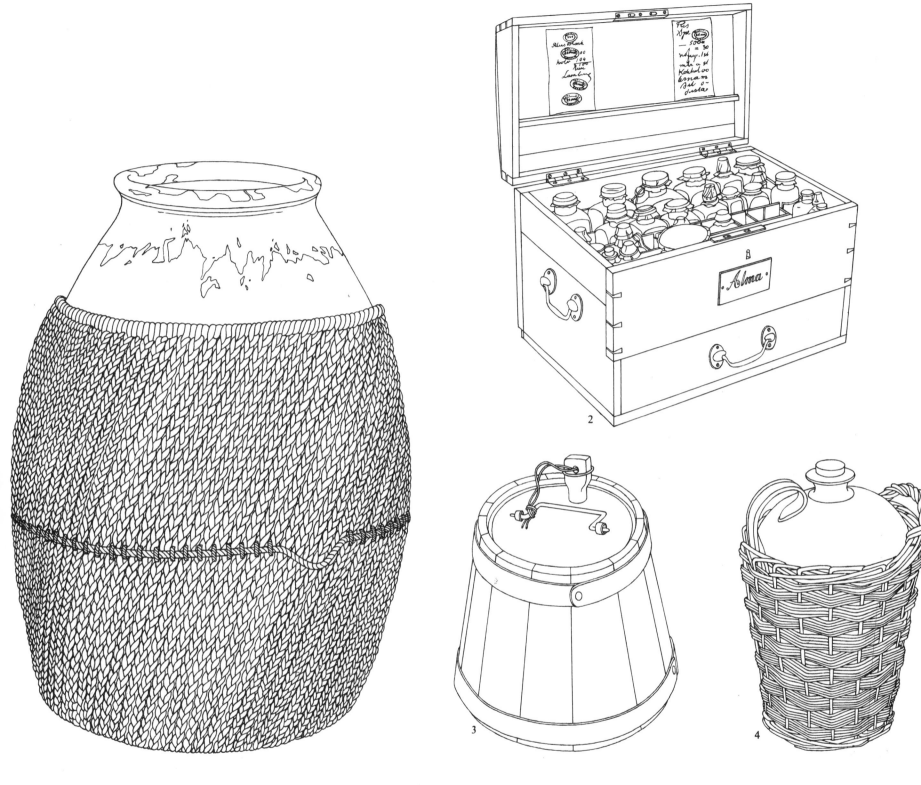

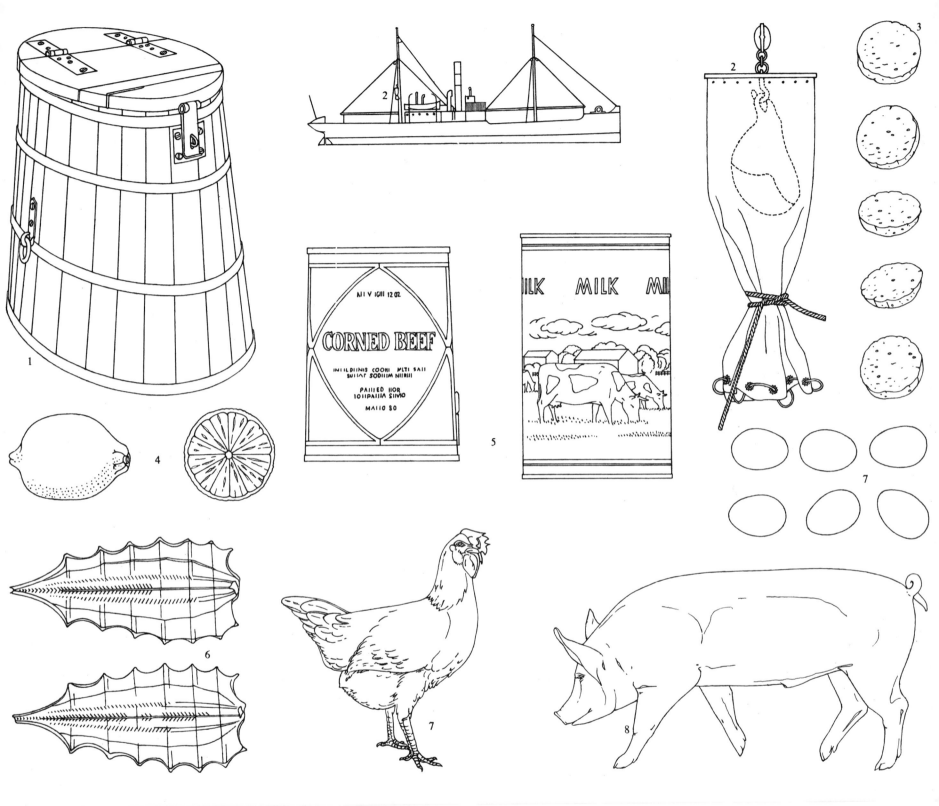

CORNED BEEF

MILK MILK MIL

PROVISIONS

Today, food on board ships is the same as that on shore. By freezing and other methods of preservation it is possible to keep fresh food even on long voyages. Formerly, however, things were different. Preserved food was scarce and voyages took a longer time.

1 Harness cask for salted beef and pork
2 A canvas bag used to hang meat in the rigging may be seen even in our day

3 Ship biscuits
4 To prevent scurvy, lime juice was used

5 When the Frenchman F. Appert invented the canning method in 1804 the problem of food supply on board ships began to be solved. The most common canned products on board were corned beef and condensed milk.

6 Dried fish, a common food on board

7, 8 On long voyages sailing ships carried some livestock for fresh provisions. In good weather, chickens would thrive and lay eggs for the cabin table. Pigs could stand all kinds of weather at sea, and a few were always carried on deep-water voyages.

SAILOR'S HOBBIES

1 Ship model in bottle
2 Circular mat, plaited of three parts
3 Three-stranded Turk's head
4 Cross made on board, and used as cabin-altar during W.W. II
5 Bottle engraved with a nail by two Danish sailors on board the sloop *3 Bröder* *(3 Brothers)*
6 Carved wooden box
7 Tool bag of canvas with strap of sennit
8 Plaited cot strap

This picture of a rope-yard is taken from the classic nautical volume Allgemeines Wörterbuch der Marine by J.H. Röding, published in 1798.

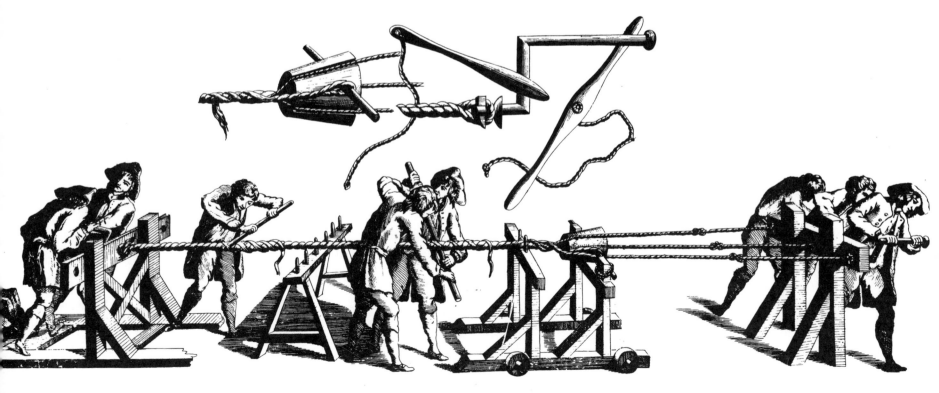